Weaving Backstory Into Your Novel

R.C. MATTHEWS

Dedication

This book is dedicated to all of the authors
aspiring to be published!

Table of Contents

CHAPTER ONE

What Is Backstory?

Let's face it. Writing a novel is hard work. Authors have to develop an intriguing goal, motivation and conflict (i.e. GMC) for their main character(s), as well as a fascinating plot that includes external forces working against the hero/heroine on his/her journey.

The good news is that there are numerous books, blogposts, news articles, YouTube videos, webcasts and in-person training resources available to aspiring authors on the topics of GMC and plot. And, quite frankly, the underlying concepts of GMC and plot are relatively easy to explain and grasp.

So why is it that 97 percent of all writers who set out to write a novel quit before they type The End?

Personally, I think it's because the mechanics of writing a novel are difficult. There are so many writing skills one must master to get from the first word to the last. Things like:

- Weaving in backstory
- Show, don't tell
- Character development
- Proper pacing
- Grabbing reader attention from page one
- Dialogue tags and stilted dialogue
- Scene /sequel
- Passive voice vs. active voice
- Varying sentence length and structure
- Points-of-view (first, second, third person)
- Tense (past, present)

Every author has been told that they must weave backstory into a novel to avoid "info dumping" on the reader. That's great advice in theory. But what exactly is backstory, and how do you "weave" it into your novel?

Backstory refers to the characters' history and other story elements that underlie the situation at the start of the book. These elements help establish the setting and make the reader care about what happens to the characters.

Every single fictional character in your book has a past that shaped their lives: the hero, the heroine, the villain, and all secondary and tertiary cast members. Even the town where your story takes place has a history that might impact your current storyline. Your main characters may be fully aware of certain pieces of history (i.e. "known history"), or critical past events are revealed to them in the course of the story, so the character and reader are discovering the history together (i.e. "discovered" history"). In addition, sometimes the backstory comes to light but the main character doesn't recognize its importance until a later chapter. As an author, these little nuggets of hidden past are the most fun to write.

Backstory includes, but is not limited to:

- The town and country where your characters grew up and their socioeconomic class.
- Nationality, ethnicity, religion, sexual orientation, political views, etc.
- Family members (huge family or small family), whether they're an only child, one of many, or adopted.
- Where they went to grade school or if they were home schooled.
- Whether they're college educated or not.
- Work experiences or lack thereof.
- Likes and dislikes with respect to everything from food to colors to books and more.
- Major events that shaped their personality, whether that was an earthquake or fire, being bullied in school, car accidents,

or traveling from town to town with a parent who changed job locations often, just to name a few examples.

- Who they have dated or the fact that they've never dated.
- Whether they're an introvert or extrovert.

Think of the past (backstory) and present (novel) like an iceberg. Everything above the surface of the water is the novel you're currently writing, and everything below the surface of the water is the backstory that formed the foundation for your novel's characters and plot. The key thing to note here is that everything under the surface is hidden! Only limited and relevant portions of the backstory should be revealed to the reader.

That doesn't mean backstory isn't important. In many ways, backstory makes a story richer and more fascinating because it explains why characters behave the way they do and the factors influencing their decisions. A character's history makes him/her multi-dimensional. When delivered in the correct doses and at the right times, backstory strengthens the reader's emotional connection to your characters and fosters empathy and understanding. Consider examples from your favorite novels.

My all-time favorite Jane Austen novel is *Pride and Prejudice*. For the first half of the book, I shared Elizabeth's viewpoint that Mr. Darcy was a pompous ass, and he could not have made me an offer of marriage in any possible way that would have caused me to accept him. But then I read his letter to Elizabeth. I dare you to tell me you didn't empathize with poor Mr. Darcy after reading about what happened to his sister Georgiana at the hands of the wicked Mr. Wickham. That letter was a major turning point in the storyline! Until that point, the reader viewed Mr. Darcy as a villain and Mr. Wickham as a hero.

Or take *John Wick,* for example. An ex-hitman goes on a rampage and murders the gangsters responsible for killing his dog. And we root for him 100 percent of the way. Or at least I did. Why? Because that dog was the last gift John received from his dying wife. I could understand the root cause of his anger and devastation. John Wick had also walked in the shoes of the men who killed his dog, so there is a certain element of "you reap what you sow" that allows us to forgive him for killing the bad guys.

Are you a *Harry Potter* fan? I despised Severus Snape along with the rest of the world. That is, until the author revealed his double agent status in *The Deathly Hallows* and how much he loved Harry's mother. The flashback scene where Severus finds Lily dead in Harry's bedroom gives me chills every time I read it. Again, the author blew the reader's world apart with this revelation. One of the most despicable villains in the series was actually a good guy. Say what? I never understood why Dumbledore relied so heavily on Severus throughout the series until this backstory came out.

So what is the common thread in all of these examples? These snippets of backstory are vital to understanding the main characters in the context of the novel's current storyline.

Now that we understand the concept, let's take a look at some of the common pitfalls authors encounter when incorporating backstory.

CHAPTER TWO

Common Pitfalls

Before we dive into ways to effectively incorporate backstory into a novel, let's first tackle what to avoid. Authors face several common pitfalls with respect to backstory. A telltale sign of an inexperienced author is too much, too soon, which has the unintended consequence of slowing the story's pace. In addition, new authors often include backstory that's either irrelevant in the context of the novel's storyline or is inconsistent with the character's personality traits.

Let's examine each of these common pitfalls:

Pitfall #1: Backstory destroys your novel's pacing.

I find the biggest offenders of this pitfall are authors who write paranormal, urban fantasy, or science fiction where world-building is paramount to understanding the story. However, authors from every genre can trip up on this issue. A reader doesn't need upfront knowledge of all the details of the world your characters live in or the characters' pasts in order to understand the storyline. The key is to reveal pieces of their world and past at the last possible moment before the reader would become hopelessly lost if they didn't know the facts. You can also reveal the past in the current storyline naturally. More on that later!

Let's go back to the story of *Harry Potter and the Sorcerer's Stone*. The story begins with Mr. Dursley leaving his house for work and noticing strange happenings: owls flying during the day, a black cat seemingly reading a map, and people dressed in odd cloaks. One of them calls him a Muggle, whatever that is. These cloaked strangers remind him of his wife's sister and brother-in-law, the Potters.

People Mr. Dursley and his wife prefer to forget exist because if their friends knew what the Potters were…

The day passes and he ignores all the signs of odd happenings. Once Mr. Dursley is in bed that night, the scene shifts to the street outside the house where an old man dressed in a cloak appears, Dumbledore. He uses a device (Put-Outer) to take the light out of the street lamps. And where the black cat used to be, there is now a woman, Professor McGonagall. She asks if the rumors that You-Know-Who is truly dead are true, and Dumbledore insists on calling You-Know-Who by his name, Voldemort. Professor McGonagall is shocked that both Lily and James Potter died and yet their son Harry lived. She remarks that the child would someday become famous as "the boy who lived," which is why Dumbledore insists Harry should grow up with his aunt and uncle, Mrs. and Mr. Dursley.

Notice that nowhere in chapter one does the author come out and tell the reader that the world Mr. Dursley lives in is magical or that the Potters are a witch and a wizard. The inciting event that killed the Potters and caused Voldemort to "go away" isn't described in any detail whatsoever. All the reader knows is that the child Harry was the sole survivor. We don't know why. The author doesn't reveal that Dumbledore and Professor McGonagall work at Hogwarts or that they'll someday invite Harry to attend the magical school. We don't even know what a Muggle is for sure.

Trying to explain all of these details would be tedious and information overload for the reader. At this point in the story, those tidbits simply aren't necessary and would slow down the pace. The reader can infer that this is a world where magic exists from the Put-Outer and a cat transforming into a woman. Further, the fact that Dumbledore and Professor McGonagall knew the Potters and were delivering their surviving son to the Dursleys' house implies that the Potters were magical, too.

> **Hint:** When revealing bits and pieces of the backstory at the beginning of your novel, be as vague as possible. Make them want to turn to the next page to discover more!

I made the mistake of including too much backstory in the draft of my very first book, *Little White Lies,* and ended up deleting the first three chapters. Ouch! Let's explore where I went wrong so you won't make the same mistake. The story teaser goes like this:

Madalyn Russell leaves her fiancé at the altar—and embarks on a solo voyage aboard their would-be honeymoon cruise! She enlists a devilishly handsome stranger to act as her new husband, but how far can they take the lie? A sexy, sidesplitting romance!

The story originally started in the middle of the wedding ceremony when Madalyn realized she was making the biggest mistake of her life, so she dumped her fiancé at the altar. She drove home to her apartment...changed into her PJs...cried a lot...and thought about all the reasons why she and her fiancé weren't a good match. Her sister showed up at the apartment soon after and convinced her to go on the honeymoon cruise alone.

Snoozefest... That beginning was slower than a snail climbing uphill!

All three chapters were backstory. Remember the teaser? The novel is about a woman who goes solo on her honeymoon cruise and meets a sexy stranger. That's what the back cover promises. So I deleted the first three chapters and started the story with Madalyn at the bon voyage party on the deck as the cruise ship is leaving port. Then I introduced the reasons why she dumped her fiancé in a matter of a few paragraphs interspersed in chapter one. The books starts like this:

I'm going to hell!

The thought crossed Madalyn Russell's mind for the umpteenth time since reading the article plastered over the front page of the society section in the morning paper: "Dumped at the Alter—Chicago's Hottest Bachelor Back on the Market!"

Had she really abandoned a church with nearly a thousand family and guests yesterday? Her stomach felt slightly nauseated just thinking about it. Poor Charles! He didn't deserve to be humiliated that way. What had she been thinking?

Madalyn stood at the ship's railing, staring out at the deep blue water, as *The Cleopatra* slowly made its way out of Port Miami and into the Atlantic Ocean. How in the world had Jeanine convinced her at the last minute to go on the honeymoon cruise alone? It felt so wrong. What would people think of her? But, difficult as it may be, Madalyn was going to try to take Jeanine's advice and learn to live a little, not be so black and white in her thinking, and find the shades of gray in life. There would be plenty of time next week to worry over what others thought of her. An opportunity for a new beginning lay before her and she planned to take advantage of it.

In few sentences, the reader knows Madalyn dumped her fiancé at the altar as well as the fact that she feels horrible about what she did. Also, notice I introduced this tidbit through a news article, not just her "thinking" about it. Find interesting ways to bring out the backstory. In addition, this is a natural part of the current storyline where she'd think about her ex-fiancé because she is embarking alone on their would-be honeymoon cruise.

I also reveal that Madalyn decided to go on her honeymoon cruise alone at the urging of her sister even though she had reservations about doing so. This is a tough trope to sell to readers. A woman who dumps her fiancé at the altar has "potential psychotic bitch" written on her forehead. So it was imperative that the reader immediately sense the heroine's remorse for her actions.

The next several pages of chapter one focus on Madalyn meeting two single women on the cruise, who she'll end up spending a lot of time with. After her newfound friends leave, Madalyn lays in the sun near the pool to relax before dinner. Check out how I integrated the last piece of the critical history, which is the reason why Madalyn didn't go through with the wedding:

Madalyn settled down in a lounge chair by the pool and closed her eyes while listening to the children laughing and playing. A couple sitting next to her were whispering back and forth. She couldn't quite make out their words, but the woman giggled, and Madalyn could hear her playful slap on his arm. She and Charlie used to be playful, but those playful times had been short-lived. They were both so driven to become successful in their careers as lawyers that there was little time for having fun. And as soon as they had moved to Chicago, his mother had dictated their social calendar in her continual effort to propel Charles into Chicago society. Madalyn felt a sense of regret and wished she could relive those days. Perhaps she would have seized the day more and pushed back harder for what she wanted out of life. It had been so long since she had made her own decisions that she wasn't certain she even knew what she wanted out of life anymore.

So was this execution good or bad? Let me give you a hint. This was my first book ever. Unfortunately, this last passage is rather lengthy and definitely qualifies as "info dumping." At this point in the story, the reader doesn't need to know why Madalyn dumped her fiancé. The "why" comes out much more naturally in chapter two when Madalyn meets her new love interest.

Shockingly, I replaced three chapters (or 6,000 words) with less than 500 words, but I could've accomplished my goal with only 209 words if I had deleted the third paragraph above. I might have cried when I deleted those three chapters, but my story was so much better after the changes because the heroine met her hero in chapter one.

> **Hint:** In a romance novel, get the hero and heroine on the page together as soon as possible! If they haven't met by the end of chapter three, the editor is getting very squirmy. In a thriller or mystery, start in the middle of an action scene. But no matter what you choose, the first chapter must be the story you promised the reader, not the history leading up to the story.

Pitfall #2: Character history revealed too soon kills the thrill factor.

Imagine how anti-climactic *Harry Potter and the Sorcerer's Stone* would've been if J.K. Rowling had revealed the existence of Hogwarts in that first chapter when she introduced Dumbledore and Professor McGonagall. Do you remember the thrill of the owls delivering thousands of letters to Mr. H. Potter at The Cupboard Under the Stairs? I wanted to know what was in those letters so bad! Withholding information about Hogwarts until chapter four was brilliant.

Treat your story like *The Bourne Identity*. The author couldn't info-dump because his main character had lost his memory Jason Bourne learns bits and pieces about his past as the story progresses. Employ the same type of mindset when writing your novel. Bit by bit, over the course of the whole story, flesh out pieces of the past.

This is the tactic I took with my hero's past in *Little White Lies*. While it was important to reveal Madalyn's backstory early on to make her likeable, I slowly teased out the hero's history.

- In chapter two, the reader learns that he works for his "family business" in the pharmaceutical industry, and he divulges that his father passed away.
- In chapter eleven, Royce reveals how he is driven to achieve his father's dying wish of taking the family business public through an initial public offering (IPO).
- In chapter fifteen, Madalyn discovers that Royce is under investigation for bribing an official at the FDA to get his

patent passed early, in time for the IPO. The kicker is, Madalyn witnessed Royce having a conversation with the FDA official on the cruise and passing the man an envelope.

Wow! Did Royce bribe the FDA official and use Madalyn as his alibi while on the cruise? All of the facts about Royce's father and family business could've been dumped on the reader in chapter two when Royce initially talked about his father passing away. But having him behave closed-lipped at the onset and revealing the importance of going public closer to when the allegations occurred really enhanced the suspense.

> **Hint:** Wait until the absolute last possible moment to reveal critical or thrilling bits of history. Think Severus Snape and his double-agent status, which wasn't revealed until the last book of the series.

Pitfall #3: Irrelevant facts are boring.

This one is important. Everything you include in your novel about the characters' pasts should be germane to the current storyline of your book. Otherwise, toss it out! Your heroine's uncle Bob might be the funniest guy on earth, but if his humor didn't have a profound impact on the main character's personality traits or it doesn't impact his/her goal, motivation, or conflict, the reader doesn't care. We don't need to know that the hero moved from Boston to San Jose when he was five years old unless that move somehow shaped his life. By all means, write a super detailed history for each of your characters so you understand what makes them tick. But only write in the details that impact the novel.

Let me give you an example from *The Secrets of Chateau Swansea*. The heroine, Maribeth Sommerset, was sold into slavery at the age of five, but she was ultimately rescued by a pirate who had been sold into slavery himself as a child. Dominick Sommerset took pity on Maribeth and became her legal guardian. He raised her for several years on his pirate ship before he reclaimed his title as Lord Covington and moved into Devil's Cove Manor. Two of his most trusted crew members, Victor and Charles, became like foster fathers to Maribeth as well. All four of these characters are in my Tortured Souls series. Maribeth is, arguably, as close to Victor and Charles as she is to Dominick.

However, when it came time to write *The Secrets of Chateau Swansea,* I never mentioned Victor or Charles in her story. Why leave them out?

I'm marketing *The Secrets of Chateau Swansea* as a standalone book. Readers who never touch my Tortured Souls series don't know about Maribeth's upbringing. Including Victor and Charles would only have confused the readers and slowed the pace. Leaving them out of the novel did not detract from the storyline in any discernable way. The only important aspect of Maribeth's upbringing was that she was the ward of Dominick Sommerset, a pirate who eventually reclaimed his title as a marquess.

Why was this information vital to the story?

The main conflict between the heroine and hero is the difference in their social class. Maribeth is the ward of a Lord and her guardian plans to bestow a dowry upon her, while the hero, Arthur, is the steward of the haunted mansion where Maribeth is conducting a psychic investigation. The year is 1889. Heiresses did not marry working-class men in the late nineteenth century. However, one might actually believe Maribeth would consider marrying below her social class because of the fact her guardian was a former pirate and she had been a captive on a slave ship.

Hint: Just because an event, person, or place seems vital to a character's background, you don't necessarily have to reveal it to the readers. Before you add any bits of history, ask yourself why it matters in the context of your plot or characters' GMC.

Pitfall #4: Inconsistent character behavior is annoying.

Giving your character an interesting background is great. I love reading about fascinating heroes and heroines. But I hate when they act in a way that makes absolutely no sense based on their history. You know what I'm talking about, right? The kid who was picked on by his classmates incessantly throughout grade school who is suddenly super confident in college. Or the girl who was the captain of the cheerleader squad and class president but is portrayed as super shy. Conflicting backgrounds and character traits ruin the credibility of the story and the reader experience.

Let me give you an example from *Devil's Cove*. The hero, Dominick Sommerset, was sold by his mother to a notorious pirate, the Butcher, because she believed that Dominick showed violent tendencies similar to his deceased father. My hero was sexually abused and mutilated by the Butcher while serving on his ship. So when Dominick arrives in the small town of Devil's Cove, he is bitter, brooding, and set on getting revenge against his mother. He is snarly for the first half of the book and doesn't give into fits of laughter. This is a man on a mission. Nothing and nobody is going to stop him.

Now imagine if I had given him a teasing personality and made him prone to goofing around. The thought is like nails scraping against a chalkboard. The reader would be taken out of the story entirely and shaking her head at such nonsense. Yes, I admit that I'm prone to fits of outrage and cursing at the characters on the pages of my iPad, and it's usually because the character is behaving in a way that makes absolutely no sense given their backstory.

On the flip side, when an author aligns the backstory and character traits, it is poetry in motion. In *Blackburn Castle,* the hero, Victor, was kidnapped when he was a ten-year-old boy. That sense of helplessness and loss of control shaped him in many ways, but it manifested in the fact that he was extremely tidy. His bedroom was immaculate and his chest of clothes and belongings was neat. Everything had a place. Why? Because his personal space was something he could control even while under captivity.

Hint: Write the outline for a story and then work backward to figure out what kind of a backstory would've shaped your characters into who they are today.

Remember, the reader bought your book based on the blurb. That's the story they want to read, not the history of how the characters came to be in their current position.

CHAPTER THREE

When Should I Incorporate Backstory?

Using backstory effectively means using it for a purpose. This can include bringing to light past events that drive your character's current behavior, using backstory for plot development, showing past events that increase the suspense in your current storyline, and giving historical details that will foster empathy for your characters.

This may seem harsh, but if you cannot draw a connection between the backstory and the relevance to the current story—*delete, delete, delete.*

Let's explore each of these ideas.

#1: To explain character behavior and the forces influencing their decisions.

This is arguably the easiest concept of backstory to understand and implement without a lot of effort. When done effectively, the correlation between the character's past and their present is self-evident.

In *Harry Potter and the Sorcerer's Stone*, Harry Potter grew up in the cupboard under the stairs, with his aunt, uncle, and cousin treating him like a second-rate citizen his whole life. Once he entered the magical world at the age of eleven and became infamous as "the boy who lived," Harry avoided the limelight and played down his importance. He was a humble guy who just wanted out of the cupboard.

You can easily analyze all of your favorite stories and pick up on the backstory that influenced the characters' behaviors.

In *Emma* by Jane Austin, the heroine was raised by her governess, who indulged the heroine's every whim. The Woodhouse family was one of the most prominent and wealthy families in the neighborhood. This gave the heroine a sense of self-importance, so she often meddled in the lives of her neighbors without any serious thought about the consequences.

It's fun to think up backstories that would influence a character's behavior:

- The hero's brother drowned at a young age after falling out of a rowboat because the brothers often snuck out on together on the lake. But on the fateful night of his death, the hero was chasing skirts instead of meeting his brother as planned. So in the current storyline, the hero is a serious chap who doesn't believe he deserves to have fun or be loved.

- The heroine was chubby throughout grade school and finally lost weight in college. Still, she can't quite get past the years of her classmates' teasing and heckling, so she hides beneath clothes that are far too big for her beautiful new body.

You get the idea. The hard part is homing in on the truly important people, places, or events in a character's background that shaped who they are today and why they behave the way they do within the context of the current storyline.

> **Hint:** If you reveal all of your characters' backstory within the first 25 percent of your book, you're missing out on a fabulous opportunity to keep the reader turning the pages.

#2: For plot developments.

Use backstory for developing the plot. However, any incident that occurs before the main narrative events of your story must be relevant to the current storyline. The correlation of backstory to plot development is readily seen in the cozy mystery genre. Cozy mysteries are based on a small-town sleuth who gathers evidence by questioning suspects related to the gruesome murder victim in order to figure out "who done it." Since cozy mysteries usually begin with the discovery of the murder victim's body in chapter one, all of the alibis of the suspects interviewed are backstory that influence the current plot.

However, sometimes backstory for plot development isn't so obvious or drastic. In fact, an author can sneak in backstory to develop the plot without the reader actually realizing it until much later in the story. In my erotic romance, *Breaking His Rules,* the black moment is shocking because most readers don't catch on to the backstory I planted in chapter one. Let's read the book teaser first to get our bearings:

> As a bartender at the best nightclub in town, Samantha knows she shouldn't sleep with her billionaire boss. But Damon's seductive ways are hard to resist—and he has no problem bending his own rules…but is she ready to break her own?

My heroine has one rule she never breaks: she doesn't date men who are rich and powerful, because her father is wealthy and controlling. Samantha moved from New York to Chicago to escape his clutches and build a life of her own. In chapter one, while Samantha is bartending during her first week on the job at Midnight Blue, she reveals in her deep point of view:

> Bartending was the one useful skill my father taught me. He was proud of our family business, and encouraged me to learn all aspects of the business from washing dishes to bartending to scheduling staff and balancing the books. I did it all without complaint on weekends and during summers while I attended college to earn a degree in hotel/restaurant management. But when I accepted an entry-level position with another company to get out from under my father's control for a while, the job offer was "regrettably" rescinded two days later. I chalked it up to bad luck. Until it happened a second, and then a third, time. By then it became painfully

obvious my father exerted his considerable influence in the business community in an effort to force me to work for the family business. Maybe he feared I would abandon him entirely for a career when all I really wanted was to spread my wings for a while. In the end, I left home anyway to escape his control, using the skills he had taught me to support myself. Life was strange that way.

So when Samantha lands the bartender job at Midnight Blue after six months of waiting for a response to her application, she is ecstatic. The high-end nightclub attracts the kind of clientele that tip generously and she is one of the youngest bartenders they've ever hired. Finally, she has landed the job that can pay her bills and keep her out of her father's control. But the nightclub owner has fifteen rules that the staff must follow. *Rule #1: Don't sleep with the patrons. Offenders will be terminated immediately. No exceptions.*

On her first weekend working on the VIP floor, Samantha locks gazes with a hunky patron. Sparks fly between them. He sits at the bar, orders a drink, and comes on strong. She tries to avoid his advances nicely, but he isn't taking the hint. She can't risk losing this job by breaking the owner's rules, so when the patron won't take no for an answer, she tells him in no uncertain terms that they wouldn't suit:

> I leaned in close, because my words were meant for his ears only. "If there's one thing I've learned about men who wear expensive suits, it's that they suck in bed. You're probably no different than every other self-absorbed millionaire of my acquaintance."
>
> His eyes narrowed on me, and he couldn't quite control his growing irritation as his nostrils flared for an instant. "Billionaire," he corrected with the tiniest inflection on the "B."
>
> *Oh shit.* He was an honored guest, and I had overstepped the boundaries. But despite his anger, the sparks between us were flying, and my resolve was growing weak. So, I did the

one thing that would kill all hope of a rendezvous at his place after hours.

I asked his name. "Pardon the offense, Mr.—?"

"Baxter," he said with triumph glowing in his eyes. "Damon Baxter."

And now the heroine of my story is in major trouble. She has insulted the owner of Midnight Blue, even though it was in an attempt to follow his blasted rules. He asks to speak with her in his private quarters on the VIP floor after her shift ends. She figures he's going to fire her anyway so why not end the night pleasurably? They get hot and heavy and then fall asleep in his private quarters. When she wakes the next morning, Damon doesn't fire her. They can't seem to get enough of each other over the course of the next two weeks. And when Samantha's ex-fiancé comes to Chicago and starts pursuing her again, Damon protects his territory.

So what does all of this have to do with backstory being used to develop the plot?

In the black moment, the reader learns that Damon hired Samantha with the express purpose of firing her and using his considerable influence in the bartending business to ruin her reputation, thus forcing her to return to New York and her daddy. All of this was at the urging of Samantha's father so he and Damon could close on a mutually agreeable business deal.

Whoa. What just happened? Readers flew over the paragraph in chapter one where Samantha revealed that her father often used his powerful influence to get her fired from her jobs as a means of controlling her and forcing her to work for the family business. And her father did it again with Damon.

Damon hired Samantha six months after first receiving her application because of the deal he struck with her father. She was the youngest bartender ever hired at Midnight Blue because Damon had other plans for her. He knew exactly who Samantha was the night they first met at Midnight Blue. He came on strong on purpose, betting she would have sex with him so he could fire her for breaking the nightclub's rules. In doing so, he would conclude the business deal with Samantha's father.

Do you see how I tied Samantha's backstory to the plot of the current storyline?

And the best part? No one saw this freight train coming despite the backstory planted in chapter one and the heroine's repeated comments that wealthy men put business before people.

> **Hint:** Even one tiny nugget of backstory delivered seamlessly in a scene can have a profound impact on the current storyline's plot. However, if you bury it too deeply, the reader feels tricked rather than enjoying the twist.

#3: To increase suspense.

Events that precede and influence your narrative can create expectations of future developments. An example of this can be found in the prologue of *Devil's Cove*. Before we get to the backstory, let's first read a shortened version of the book blurb.

> Feared as "The Devil" on the high seas, Captain Devlin Limmerick is lured to the haunted Devil's Cove Manor by an unquenchable thirst for revenge. It is a thirst matched only by his hunger for the blind, powerful medium he has coerced to aid him. Though Grace finds herself wickedly drawn to the Devil's darkness, she refuses to sacrifice her soul to set Devlin's unspeakable plan in motion. An evil lurks within Devil Cove Manor's walls. Grace's presence spurs inexplicable happenings, forcing Devlin to believe nothing is as dead as it seems, not even his heart. Plunged into the throes of passion and danger, they discover the only way out is to search deep within and summon the courage to believe in love.

Devil's Cove is a gothic romance story. From the blurb, we know Devlin wants revenge for something and the heroine, Grace, doesn't want to help him. Also, the haunted manor plays a role in Devlin attaining his revenge, and Grace's presence at the haunted manor spurs inexplicable happenings. So let's analyze the prologue, which is 100 percent backstory in the form of a scene (i.e. show, don't tell). I have shortened the excerpt for purposes of this exercise.

1865, Devil's Cove Manor, England

As Josephine slithered between the humans **littering the ballroom floor**, a wicked grin curled up her lips. Their anguished cries vibrated like sweet music through her scales. Sliding her long tail back and forth, rhythmically, she bumped against their mangled forms, enhancing their pain. The waning taste of her dark magic slipped over her forked tongue as she lapped at the air, and she knew its effects would soon wear off, **finally allowing her victims to succumb to the darkness of death**.

All but one.

Lord Marcus Deveraux would not fall peacefully into oblivion. He would feel the weight of her body as it wrapped about him, crushing him. He would hear his bones snap and stare into her red eyes as she squeezed his throat with her hands, taking his life. **He deserved nothing less for his heinous deeds.**

She raised herself high on her tail, above the carnage, swaying in each direction, allowing her tongue to guide her to her prey. Ebony hair fell in a waterfall of waves over her shoulders to the middle of her back, and she knew she must make a frightening sight, **half-woman, half-serpent**.

Marcus lay in a puddle of his own excrement and blood, a sonorous wheeze emitting from his chest. She coiled her tail around his body and lifted him toward her. His eyes flew open, and the terror encapsulated in his stare filled Josephine with a euphoric high.

"Before I escort you through the gates of Hell," she said, leaning closer to ensure he heard every word, "know thissssss: **Your dirty little secrets aren't safe from me.** Beatrice Mitchell warned you of the evil lurking on this land. You chose to ignore her, and now you'll pay a dear price. Your friends and family are dead, save one helpless child. But fear not, Marcussssss, **the day will come when Eveline is old enough to understand your crimes, and then I will collect the last of your debt**."

Revenge the second time around would be oh so sweet.

The reader learns that sixteen years before the current story starts, a lot of people were killed in the ballroom of Devil's Cove Manor by Josephine, a half-woman, half-serpent, who is a gatekeeper to Hell. She killed everyone because she wanted revenge against Lord Marcus Deveraux for "his heinous crime," but she plans to collect the remainder of his debt when the last of his family and friends (Eveline) is old enough to understand his crimes.

However, the reader doesn't know

- Who Eveline is and how she's connected to Devlin or Grace,
- What heinous crime Marcus committed and how that might be connected to the story's plot, and
- How Josephine plans to get her revenge.

Do you see how this backstory immediately increases the suspense for the current storyline? Right off the bat, the reader knows there is a badass villain lurking in Devil's Cove Manor, intent on revenge. So imagine the reader's reaction in chapter five when she reads this scene with the blind heroine, Grace:

> The crackling fire soothed her tattered nerves, and she drifted into sleep.
>
> A moment later, an elongated hiss echoed in her eardrum, jolting her into an upright position. Fear ran cold in her blood, sending rippling waves of angst throughout her body.
>
> She could face every manner of evil spirit known to man, but she shriveled under the threat of snakes and spiders. Was she in that awkward state between wakefulness and sleep? She mustn't allow her imagination to get away from her. "Who's

there?" she cried out into the stillness. "Please. Is someone there?"

Oh my god! Is that Josephine in the bedroom hissing in Grace's ear? Readers don't know for sure because the heroine is blind and can't see who or what is in the room with her. But we read that prologue, and horrible thoughts are careening through our heads in that moment. Without the backstory in the prologue, this scene in the current storyline wouldn't have been nearly as scary or suspenseful.

But at this point, the reader still doesn't know what Josephine is up to or how her revenge is connected to the hero and heroine of the book.

> **Hint:** Bring out the connection to backstory naturally through a scene that is relevant to the current storyline.

Let me show you how. Devlin hired Grace to rid his newly acquired mansion, Devil's Cove Manor, of evil spirits. Or at least that's what he told her at the onset. Secretly, he really wants Grace to negotiate a deal with the gatekeeper to Hell for him. So while Devlin and Grace are searching the attic for evil spirits in chapter eight, they stumble upon family portraits of the former owner of the estate. The reader finally learns of a potential connection between Lord Marcus Deveraux and Grace in the following scene:

> Devlin stared at the portrait in awe, almost unable to believe his eyes. A man stood erect, staring down his patrician nose at all onlookers. But it was his chestnut colored hair with burnished gold streaks that captivated Devlin. And the man's eyes. Blue as a cloudless sky.
>
> **"Who shares your hair color, Grace?"** Devlin asked, never taking his gaze off the portrait, so mesmerized was he. "Your mother or your father?"
>
> "Neither," she said, cocking her brow. "I once heard my father jest that I shared the coloring of our milkman. But

mother only slapped him on the shoulder and insisted I had the same hair as her grandfather. Why do you ask?"

"And your eyes?" he whispered. "Sky-blue eyes."

She grabbed his arm. "What is the matter with you, Devlin? Why are you asking? What do you see?"

He glanced at the portrait once more. She deserved to know the truth, though he had no idea how she might react. It would most likely come as a shock.

"I think it must be a portrait of the patriarch, the original owner of the mansion." He braced her by the shoulders and said, "And you're the mirror image of him."

Armed with the knowledge that Grace looks like Lord Marcus Deveraux, she pieces together worrisome memories from her youth and confronts her mentor, Brother Anselm, demanding to know if she is the bastard daughter of the former owner of the haunted mansion. Brother Anselm finally tells her the truth of her parentage and the fact that Eveline was renamed Grace in order to try to "hide" her from Josephine. Brother Anselm knows that Grace's life is in danger if Josephine should discover who she is, but he doesn't know why.

Oh boy! Now the reader knows that the heroine is Eveline, the last surviving relative of Lord Marcus Deveraux, and she is all grown up—old enough now to understand her father's heinous crimes!

> **Hint:** The prologue can give the reader knowledge that the protagonist doesn't have, which amps up the suspense of the current storyline for the reader.

At this point in *Devil's Cove*, the reader still doesn't know how Josephine will collect the last of the debt owed her and exact her revenge. In chapter twenty, the reader learns that Marcus killed Josephine's soul mate, Rosalie, when he excavated the ground to build the ballroom. Josephine plans to revive Rosalie's soul within Grace's body using black magic. On the first night Grace came to the mansion, her tea was spiked with alcohol that contained Rosalie's essence. So the soul of Josephine's dead lover resides within Grace.

Other than heightening the suspense, why is all of this relevant in the context of the current storyline?

Our villains, too, need a goal, motivation, and conflict in order to make them shine. Otherwise, the villain is cookie-cutter and boring. The prologue shows Josephine's goal (take revenge on Marcus through Grace) and motivation (because Marcus's heinous crime, e.g. he killed the villain's soul mate). Later, the reader learns the villain's conflict (i.e. what's keeping her from getting her revenge) is that the black magic needed to revive Rosalie's soul can only be invoked if Josephine can find someone willing to betray a loved one in exchange for her help.

Enter our hero, Devlin. He wants his own revenge on his enemies but needs Josephine's help. So he will strike a deal with her. Can you guess what deal he strikes? You got it! He will betray a loved one (i.e. the heroine) in exchange for Josephine's help.

And now you know the secret to how this very short prologue heightens the suspense while creating curiosity in the reader and serves a purpose in the context of the current storyline.

> **Hint:** Our villains need robust backstories, too, if we want them to shine.

Check out this Amazon reviewer's comment: Josephine seemed to be a character straight out of a horror film, and as seductive and evil as she was presented, I couldn't help but love her as well. She wasn't a cardboard villain in a black hat—and I loved that about her. She was a real person with real motivations, and she was both dangerously evil and sweet at the same time.

So be sure to invest time in the development of your villain's backstory.

#4: To strengthen the reader's emotional connection to your characters.

Antiheroes need a lot of help. They're naturally complex characters who do things that make us want to hate them. So providing the reader with a peek into their past can go a long way toward fostering empathy or at least understanding.

Let's return to one of my all-time favorite characters we love to hate: Professor Snape from the Harry Potter series. Why do we hate him so much? For starters, he is the head of the Slytherin house. According to www.pottermore.com, Slytherin produces more than its share of dark wizards but also turns out leaders who are proud, ambitious, and cunning. The most famous Slytherin is Tom Riddle or, as he is famously known as, Voldemort. These are the wizards who play dirty and use magic in support of less-than-ideal causes. Professor Snape embodies the evil of Slytherin House as its fearless leader. But most of all, he speaks to Harry Potter with derision in his tone and treats the infamous "boy who lived" as if he is a lowly swine.

I despised Professor Snape. Until that scene in *The Order of the Phoenix* when Harry sneaks a peek at Professor Snape's worst memory in the Pensieve. Finally, I got a firsthand taste of how Harry's father, James, along with his schoolmates, tortured poor Severus Snape when they were students at Hogwarts. Severus was called "Snivelly" and made fun of for his greasy hair and runny nose. James cornered Severus in front of their classmates and used the "Scourgify" spell to wash Severus's mouth out with pink soap bubbles. Who knows how long the teasing would have continued if Harry's mother, Lily, hadn't stood up for Severus and demanded that James stop acting like an arrogant, bullying toerag?

That scene changed everything. Sure, I still loved to hate Professor Snape after that incident was revealed, but I certainly understood where his hatred for Harry Potter stemmed from.

We'll explore more on this concept in chapter five.

Hint: All characters in a story should be well rounded with good and not-so-good qualities. Readers love flawed characters. Still, part of what allows us to love these flawed characters is a glimpse into their past so we can understand how they came to be the way they are today.

CHAPTER FOUR

How to Effectively Write Backstory

While we will explore several effective methods for writing backstory into your novel, the key message to take away on this topic is that backstory—no matter how it is delivered—should blend in with your current storyline so that it feels natural to the reader. This is best accomplished if your backstory is inherently part of a scene, not a breakaway from your story.

Half the battle lies in figuring out a way to sneak in characters' pesky history. Let's look at an example from *Blackburn Castle* so I can walk you through step by step how to do this. Keep in mind that this is my process. You may find other ways equally as effective that work better for you.

Step #1: Sketch out your characters and major plot points.

For this exercise, I'm going to show you only what I wrote for the heroine's backstory and then we'll walk through how I incorporated one key element into the storyline. In order to level set where all of this going, here is the book blurb for *Blackburn Castle*.

> Victor Blackburn is living on borrowed time. **An ancient curse** violently claims the life of each Blackburn male on his twenty-seventh birthday. As his approaches, **his only hope of survival is a witch** who vanished long ago without a trace.
>
> Mercy Seymour eagerly counts down the days until the curse will claim Victor's life. She watched him murder her

mother, and only his death will free her of the hatred and anger she harbors.

When fate throws them together in Devil's Cove, desire simmers between the handsome pirate and the spirited bar-keeper's niece until they learn the truth about each other. Desperate for her cooperation, **Victor spirits her away to Blackburn Castle** in the Scottish Highlands, where forces of magic and mists from beyond the grave weaken her resolve, opening her eyes to the truth of the past.

As Victor and Mercy **unearth the fabled stones need-ed to break the curse**, they discover that the only weapon powerful enough to destroy hate is love. But will they have to sacrifice their relationship to save what means the most to them?

As you can surmise from the blurb, this storyline is rather com-plex. There is an ancient curse that can only be broken if my heroine, Mercy, who is a witch, unearths the fabled stones needed to break the curse. But she isn't willing to help the hero because he killed her mother. So the hero kidnaps the heroine and spirits her away to his ancestral home, Blackburn Castle, where the fabled stones are reputedly hidden. Let's dig into the backstory for the ancient curse, the fabled stones, and the heroine.

Everything in italics is backstory the characters in the current storyline are not aware of and unfolds slowly throughout the book.

- **Blackburn Curse Origins:** Elizabeth and Vivian Thorne are twin sisters and powerful witches who were born to Norse goddess Freya out of her unholy union with the Black Dwarves. The sisters both fell in love with Ambrose Blackburn. Ambrose was intended for Elizabeth (the older of the two siblings), *but he loved Vivian. Consumed by jealousy, Elizabeth seduced Ambrose one night using magic* and she became pregnant with his child *to entrap him into marriage.* Vivian was devastated and furious. *Ambrose was an honorable man and would have married Elizabeth except that* Vivian brewed a love potion and stole Ambrose *back*. Vivian's love potion was unbreakable because she harnessed the power of love imbued in the Amber Stones of Freya to brew the potion. Overwhelmed by his love for Vivian, Ambrose abandoned the pregnant Elizabeth and married Vivian instead. *Anger and hatred festered in Elizabeth over the years, while Vivian bore three sons to Ambrose. However, Elizabeth ultimately got her revenge. She arranged for the vampire Gregor to turn Vivian into a vampire. When Vivian woke after being changed, she attacked Ambrose and sucked his blood dry. Elizabeth then cursed Vivian's offspring to always look like Ambrose, and each first son of each generation would die at Vivian's hands in the same gruesome manner. Elizabeth put Vivian under a sleep spell in the family crypt only to wake long enough to murder her descendants, thus forcing Vivian to murder the love of her life over and over again for eternity.*

- **Amber Tears of Freya/Brisingamen Necklace:** Norse mythology says that Freya saw the Brisingamen necklace made by the Black Dwarves and fell in love with it. She begged to buy it, but the dwarves said it was priceless. However, they would give it to her if Freya laid with each of them as man and wife, four nights in a row. Freya conceded to their bargain and betrayed her husband, Odur, by wedding and bedding the four black dwarves. When Odur learned of her folly, he abandoned Freya. Freya was devastated and, crying, roamed the world endlessly in search of her husband. Her tears fell into the ocean and crystalized into amber stones. Freya gifted the amber tear to Vivian and the Brisingamen necklace to Elizabeth.

- **Mercy Seymour:** Mercy is a descendant of Elizabeth Thorne and grew up in Blackpool with her mother, Maude, and her father, Thomas. Her family has practiced witchcraft for years. Their patroness is the Norse goddess Freya. The strength of talent often skips generations. So Mercy is the most powerful witch in her family. For hundreds of years, Elizabeth's side of the family has hated Vivian's side of the family (i.e., the Blackburns) because of Vivian's unforgivable betrayal. There is a counter-curse written in Elizabeth's book of spells, *Tome of the Accursed*. However, in order for the spell to work, a descendant of Elizabeth must show mercy on the Blackburn family and forgive them of their past sins. This is why the heroine is named Mercy.

Maude is ready for the family rivalry and senseless deaths to come to an end. While everyone is aware of the curse, its origins are shrouded in mystery. When Mercy is seven years old, her mother sends her to stay with her aunt (Maude's sister) and uncle in Devil's Cove to keep her safe. Mercy is hurt and angry that her parents sent her away, because she is a powerful witch, even as a child, and can protect herself. It turns out that Mercy's father had an evil brother (the notorious pirate the Butcher) who got wind of the fact that Maude has two of the four stones from the original tear of Freya. He wanted all four stones and he needed Mercy to piece them back together with magic. The original tear of Freya is worth a fortune! Long story short, when Mercy's parents refused to divulge where their daughter is hiding, the Butcher killed Mercy's father and ordered the ten-year-old Victor to kill Mercy's mother, all of which Mercy witnesses through a scrying bowl. Mercy knows it was her mother's dearest wish that Mercy break the Blackburn curse, but she can't do it knowing Victor killed her mother. In order to ensure the Butcher never gets his dirty hands on the tears of Freya, Mercy casts a spell to conceal her location. Mercy is raised by her aunt and uncle in Devil's Cove where she works as a barmaid at her uncle's bar, The Black Serpent. She also earns extra spending money on the side concocting love potions and other serums for the town folk.

Step #2: Is this critical to the current storyline?

Recall from Step #1 that the storyline for *Blackburn Castle* is about a man who is cursed to die in a gruesome manner unless he can find the one witch capable of breaking the curse. The problem is, she isn't willing to help the hero because he killed her mother. So the hero kidnaps the heroine and spirits her away to his ancestral home, Blackburn Castle, where the fabled stones needed to break the curse are reputedly hidden.

Obviously, there is a lot more backstory on Mercy that I've left out. The current story doesn't begin until she is twenty-three years old. So a lot has happened in the intervening fifteen years since her parents died. Some authors interview their characters to flesh out all of the major events that shaped the character's line of thinking and behavior. I picked a specific birthdate for Mercy to determine her astrological sign, which informs her personality. Or you might decide each character's personality type based on the Myers-Briggs test. I outlined the main stores where Mercy liked to shop and which people in the town she was closest to and why. All of that is wonderful background information. But I didn't include that in the synopsis or make you read through it because it's not in the finished book.

Without a doubt, I needed a way to reveal that the heroine is a descendant of the Norse goddess Freya, who bestowed two gifts that are passed down the family line, because the tears of Freya and the Brisingamen necklace are integral to the current storyline.

Step #3: Choose the best method for a seamless delivery.

We will cover each of these methods of incorporating backstory later in this book, but for this exercise, here are the main approaches, as well as my logic for deciding which was most appropriate for *Blackburn Castle*:

- Flashbacks—Not applicable because Freya, Elizabeth, and Vivian aren't main characters in my current storyline.
- Memories—Not applicable for the same reason.
- Dreams—This could've worked if my heroine was psychic and visions came to her in dreams, but alas, she was not. Also, why would my heroine dream about Freya gifting these items to Elizabeth and Vivian during the story?

- Prologues—This, too, could've worked, but I had already planned to use the prologue to show the reader the scene where the hero kills the heroine's mother. When faced with the choice of one or the other, I decided that using the prologue to garner empathy for my hero was more important.

- Deep point of view—This was a possibility, but the backstory I wanted to reveal is complex and might be tedious for the reader if revealed through deep point of view.

- Dialogue—Winner! The history behind the tears of Freya and the Brisingamen necklace is interesting. With the right trigger, the facts could easily come out through a conversation between Mercy and another character.

After brainstorming possible scenarios, I decided the most natural way to present the backstory of the two gifts would be through dialogue between Mercy **and someone who didn't know the history**.

But the first ten chapters of the book take place in Mercy's hometown while she's living with her aunt and uncle. They know the family history. So the backstory had to come out after Mercy was abducted by the hero Victor and is on a pirate ship bound for Blackburn Castle, and helped sprinkle in the character's history throughout the book.

Step #4: Weave all the pieces together naturally.

Next I asked myself what would trigger a discussion between Mercy and another character about Freya's gifts. Be sure to consider all key elements of your story when brainstorming, including people, places, and things related to the backstory you want to reveal.

In this case, I knew that the *Tome of the Accursed* spell book played a significant role in the storyline because that's where the counter-curse was written. Since the Brisingamen necklace was lost years ago, I decided that the spell book would have a picture of the necklace embossed on the cover of the book. Further, two of the tears of

Freya (i.e. the fabled stones) were in Mercy's possession. In addition, everyone in the story was aware of the ancient curse and that the fabled stones were needed to break the curse. So, to narrow down my possibilities, I considered the following:

- Who was on the ship with Mercy that wasn't aware of the history?
    - o Dommick Sommerset, captain of the ship
    - o Eveline Sommerset, captain's wife
    - o Hatchet, the second mate
    - o All other crew members
- Which character was mostly likely to interact with Mercy and show interest in the backstory?
    - o The captain of the ship and the second mate are good friends of the hero, so they would be interested in knowing more about the tear of Freya in order to save his life. However, they are angry at Mercy for refusing to break the curse. All interactions between these two and Mercy turn hostile quickly or are filled with tension.
    - o The other crew members don't interact with Mercy because she is locked in Victor's cabin. So finding a way for Mercy to escape her room and then engage in a conversation with a random crew member would be difficult, not to mention awkward.
    - o Eveline is the perfect candidate for a discussion. The captain's wife was raised by a monk (Brother Anselm) and is deeply sympathetic to both the heroine and hero. She is a medium, so she shares a natural bond with the heroine, who is a witch. Winner!
- What would trigger the conversation?
    - o Eveline might be curious about the tear of Freya and why it is critical to breaking the curse.
    - o Eveline might notice Mercy's bracelet where two of the amber stones are displayed and inquire.

o   Eveline might notice the Brisingamen necklace embossed on the cover of the spell book and inquire.

o   Eveline might gently push the heroine to forgive the hero, which could lead into a discussion about the family history and ultimately the gifts.

Until this point in the story, a lot of focus had been on the tears of Freya because everyone knew they were needed to break the curse. However, nothing was yet revealed about the Brisingamen necklace, except for this brief allusion to it in chapter four: *Mercy closed the spell book and traced her fingers over the intricate design etched into the soft leather casing before setting it down.*

So I chose bullet point three above as the trigger for the conversation between Mercy and Eveline. What person on earth wouldn't show interest in an ancient spell book with a cool design embossed on the leather cover and ask questions about it?

There was just one problem. Mercy believed her spell book was left behind in her home town when Victor kidnapped her. Little did she know that Victor had grabbed the spell book while Mercy was unconscious and stuffed it in her luggage. Ugh. So first I needed the heroine to discover that the hero had brought her carpetbag, then the heroine had to find the spell book packed inside so she could have a conversation with Eveline about it. Whew!

Lights. Camera. Action.

Let's analyze the scene in chapter twelve when Eveline visits Mercy in her cabin and the backstory unfolds. Remember, Mercy was abducted, so she had rope burns on her wrists where the rope had been tied too tightly. One more point of note: Mercy had figured out Victor's true identity and planned to skip town to visit her uncle in London. So when the hero abducted the heroine, there was a packed bag in her bedroom.

"Oh, dear." Eveline moved closer and inspected the wounds. "Are you in a lot of pain? Perhaps I can fetch something from the galley to soothe your skin."

If Mercy were honest with herself, the burns were hardly noticeable. Still, she would welcome some relief. "Pity I don't have my belongings with me," she said. "I always carry aloe, an excellent ointment with varied uses."

"Well, I'm sure I saw a carpetbag beside the trunk earlier. Shall we investigate?"

Mercy nearly toppled her chair in her haste to stand. Were all of her draughts and potions within her reach? Just as Eveline said, the flower-patterned carpetbag lay nestled between the wall and the trunk. Mercy swallowed past the shout of joy screaming to be released and hauled her bag on top of the trunk.

Victor had brought her packed luggage! Her fingers worked the latches open with ease, and a few moments later, she lifted the *Tome of the Accursed* from the top. Had he known the significance of the spell book when he discovered it on her bedside table and packed it with her other belongings?

"What a beautiful book," Eveline said, peering over her shoulder. "I've never seen anything like it. Is that your family's book of spells? May I browse through it?"

Mercy hesitated, rubbing her hand over the soft leather casing. No one outside of her family had ever seen the spell book, much less touched it.

"Forgive me," Eveline said, stepping back. "I can see that it's precious. You needn't oblige."

But if Eveline was engrossed in the book, Mercy would have an opportunity to search through her inventory of potions. A sleep serum might work. She could put Eveline into a deep sleep and threaten Lord Sommerset to leave her under its influence until they returned to Devil's Cove. He was captain of the ship, after all.

Her stomach quaked as she handed Eveline the book, but she could not feel guilty. They'd all left her no other options.

Eveline traced her fingertips over the intricately designed necklace carved into the leather cover and then glanced up with a twinkle in her eyes. "Brother Anselm will be envious when I tell him I held an ancient spell book. Do you know how old it is?"

"**A little over four hundred years**," Mercy said as she rummaged through her belongings, searching for the small box of potions and ointments she had packed. Her heart galloped. "**It's been passed down through the generations, but it originated with Elizabeth Thorne, a formidable witch, if my family history is to be believed.**"

Closing the book, Eveline handed it back. "And the cover? Is there a story behind the necklace? It seems a rather odd object for a spell book."

Mercy nodded and tucked the precious treasure into the carpetbag while she relayed the brief history as she knew it. "**It's a replica of the Brisingamen necklace—the one the Norse goddess of love, Freya, received as a gift from the four Black Dwarves in exchange for a single night of pleasure.**"

Eveline's eyebrows arced high. "Quite a costly piece of jewelry."

An indelicate snort escaped Mercy as she glanced at her friend. "**Even more so than Freya imagined. Her husband was furious when he learned of her betrayal and abandoned her forever. As she searched the world for him, her teardrops fell into the ocean, crystalizing into blue amber and encapsulating her love for him. Elizabeth and her twin, Vivian, claimed to have been born to Freya out of her unholy union with the Black Dwarves. Presumably, the necklace and the tears were passed down through the generations, the necklace through Elizabeth's line, the tears through Vivian's line. It's a shame there is no evidence of the necklace's existence, because folklore proclaims it to have held mystical powers of youth and beauty.** I should have liked to inherit it along with the tome."

Time to dissect this scene and point out the key elements. I found a natural way for the heroine to discover that the book of spells was on board and tied it directly into the current storyline through Mercy's rope burns.

- Eveline notices the rope burns on Mercy's wrists (which arose from her abduction) and asks if she can get anything to soothe the pain.
- This gave me the opportunity to have Mercy mention that she always keeps aloe in her bag, if only she had it with her (i.e. because Mercy doesn't know her luggage in on the ship).
- Then Eveline says she thought she saw a carpetbag earlier.
- Mercy discovers the *Tome of the Accursed* inside the luggage, packed neatly on top.

In the first draft of this scene, Eveline noticed the book and asked to see it. Mercy immediately offered the book to Eveline and the conversation ensued about the backstory. But that wasn't good enough. I wanted to tie this scene into my current storyline even stronger.

Again, I brainstormed and realized that Mercy had been wishing in the previous chapter that she had her potions with her so she could try to use one to escape the ship. My heroine had been abducted. She wanted to get as far away from the hero as possible. So I tied that idea into this scene.

In the second draft, Mercy hesitates to give Eveline the spell book because no one outside her family has ever seen or touched the *Tome of the Accursed*. But she realizes that if Eveline is looking at the book, she won't be paying attention to Mercy. This will give Mercy time to slip a sleeping potion into her frock and spike Eveline's tea with it later. Her logic is that she can force the captain of the ship to turn around or else his wife will never wake up.

Oh, that is so much better! Instead of the backstory being the driver of this scene, the reader is focused on the current storyline of how Mercy is trying to escape her captor by drugging the captain's wife. Beautiful!

What I love about this final scene is that it takes the spotlight off the backstory a bit, so later when the significance of the Brisingamen necklace comes out, the reader has an "oh shit" moment. I can almost see them frantically paging back to this scene to reread the history. I've planted a doozy of a hint here, but it goes right over most of the readers' heads because they're more focused on whether Mercy will succeed in drugging Eveline.

> **Hint:** Figure out which aspects of your character's backstory are critical to reveal in the current storyline and then brainstorm and write scenarios that provide a natural setting to divulge the history.

Now that you've gotten a taste of how you can write backstory that feels natural into your current novel, let's explore these common methods of weaving in backstory:

- Flashbacks / memories
- Dreams
- Prologue
- Dialogue / Deep POV

CHAPTER FIVE

Flashbacks and Memories

Merriam Webster defines a flashback as "to focus one's mind on or vividly remember a past time or incident," whereas a memory is "an image or impression of one that is remembered." The use of flashbacks and memories to reveal backstory is common enough, but like all good things in life, there are pros and cons to doing so.

Con #1: Are you taking the reader out of the current story?

The benefits of taking the reader into the character's past must outweigh the disadvantage of pulling the reader out of the current action.

Remember, the reader bought your book based on the blurb. That's the story they want to read, not the history of how the characters came to be in their current position. Unless the past plays a critical role in the present, that is.

I disagree with the idea that using flashbacks and memories is for amateurs or indicates lazy writing. Further, I've read advice on this topic that says a writer should *never* use flashbacks in the first half of their story. Never say never. Flashbacks and memories are highly effective in showing the reader a pivotal moment that can garner empathy and understanding (i.e. "pros" of using this method).

> **Hint:** The key to effectively using flashbacks or memories to reveal backstory is to keep them as short as possible and tie them into the current storyline. Even better, integrate them with a powerful scene.

In Damon Suede's "Dark Heart RWA Workshop in a Box," he says, "Backstory shouldn't stop the story to drag readers into the *past*; backstory should drag the past into the *present* so characters decide on appropriate ACTION." I couldn't have said it better. This gets back to the concept that the past must have a solid link to the present so that the connection truly impacts the protagonist's GMC in your storyline.

Let's expand on that idea with an example.

I used flashbacks in *Devil's Cove* because I wanted the reader to experience firsthand two historical events that shaped the hero's life AND showed how the past was putting a monkey wrench in his current plans for revenge.

My hero, Devlin, is ornery and brash for the first half of the book. He was "lured to the haunted Devil's Cove Manor by an unquenchable thirst for revenge; a thirst matched only by his hunger for the blind, powerful medium he has coerced to aid him." That's from the book blurb. Somehow I needed to reveal what happened to Devlin that drove his need for revenge as well as the reason he hungered for the heroine he coerced to aid him.

Remember, Devlin hired Grace to rid his haunted mansion of ghosts (but the reader later discovers his true reason for hiring the medium). She did not want the job! But when faced with the choice of being carted off to an insane asylum by the town folk or taking asylum with Devlin in the haunted mansion to rid the place of evil spirits, she chose the latter. No one dared to challenge the pirate known as The Devil.

So in a scene where Devlin and Grace are searching the living room for signs of the supernatural, one of the side characters, Maribeth, an eleven-year-old girl under Devlin's charge, assuages her curiosity and boldly asks Grace how she became blind. In this scene, we are in Devlin's POV.

> When Grace described her attacker, how he'd smashed her face into the sand, when her voice faltered as she relayed the near drowning, all because she'd defended her mother's

honor, the floor fell from under Devlin and he was forced to sit back on the couch.

This cannot be.

The young girl Devlin had saved sixteen years before had been named Eveline. Eveline Mitchell. He would never forget that name; the events had set off a chain reaction that changed his life irrevocably. He'd pounced on Willie Jackson, and not a moment too soon. A fierce anger and disgust had welled inside him, and he had beaten Willie to within an inch of his life. The young girl had almost drowned over a bloody jest.

That day was both a blessing and a curse. He would do it all again to save Eveline, because he had never felt so proud of himself, a champion of the weak. Yet his mother had declared him a monster. His actions served as confirmation that he shared the same vicious streak as his father. He wasn't the same, dammit! His biological father was like that bloody bastard, Willie, drinking to excess and torturing helpless women.

Blood thrummed through his veins, and a dull ache throbbed where his finger ought to be on his left hand, a constant reminder of all he'd endured…

Sweat trickled from Devlin's forehead and caught in the blindfold tied securely around his head. He swallowed back the bile rising in his throat, hating himself for being a coward. Without making a sound, he tugged at the bindings on his wrists and ankles and cursed silently. Secure. If only he could see what was happening, he would be able to prepare himself for the worst. A gentle clank of metal on metal sounded to the left of him. The scalpels. He forced himself to take deep breaths to stay the trembling of his limbs. It would be worse for him if he showed any signs of fear. The Butcher was a sick bastard who fed off the tremors he evoked in his victims.

"Tell me why we're here," the Butcher said, whispering in Devlin's ear.

"Because you're a sick motherfucker." He regretted the outburst the second the words spilled from his mouth. Had he not learned a damned thing over the past year?

The Butcher's rumbling laughter rolled over him, and he bit down on his bottom lip, determined to keep his mouth shut.

"Yes, there is that," his tormentor said. *"The next time I give you an order, you'll obey without question. Do you understand?"*

Devlin ignored his question because there was no way he'd ever become the Butcher's whore and stroke his manhood to climax. He could endure the cutting, strangulation, and even listening to the monster masturbate after mutilating him, but he would not touch the cocksucker. Deep inside, he'd always known this day of reckoning would come. He'd only hoped it would've taken longer.

"Answer me!"

Devlin breathed through his nose and out his mouth.

The Butcher growled and clamped his hand over Devlin's, laying it flat against the wooden table at his side. *"No response? Let's see if this loosens your tongue."*

The blade cut into his flesh at the first knuckle of his pinky finger, and it was as if all the heat in his body gathered in that one spot. The black-hearted pirate chuckled and sawed deeper until he came to the bone.

"Cat still got your tongue?" the Butcher baited him.

Devlin ground his teeth together. The blade snapped through the bone and excruciating pain clawed at his extremities; despite his best efforts, he howled, *"Son of a bitch."*

"Not what I was looking for, but it's a start," the pirate said, squeezing the digit between his fingers. *"So much blood for such a small cut."* He inhaled deeply and suckled Devlin's pinky. The taste of blood always gave the man a hard-on.

Devlin wanted nothing more than to empty the contents of his lurching stomach all over the bastard. But he'd pay for that dearly.

"If you won't touch me, then you'll not touch anything." The Butcher prepared to make good on his threat, leveling the scalpel on the second knuckle.

> *Devlin braced himself and let his mind drift to the one place where he always found solace: Eveline. He imagined her angelic face framed by gold-burnished locks, frolicking in the ocean's waves and laughing as the water chased her to shore. His hand caught on fire when the blade severed his second knuckle, but he only grunted this time, lost in the serene beauty that was Eveline. Innocent. And worthy of everything he'd endured to save her.*
>
> *Eveline…*

This flashback scene occurs in chapter eight (about 25 percent of the way through the book). It is less than six hundred words and serves three purposes. Most importantly, I'm moving the current storyline forward by revealing this backstory. Past and present are intertwined.

First, the reader learns that the hero and the heroine have a shared past that significantly influenced the hero. He is inexplicably tied to the heroine in a way that touches his soul. Devlin had planned to use Grace to negotiate with the gatekeeper to Hell. When Grace was a blind chit he didn't know much about, he could sacrifice her easily on the road to his revenge.

Monkey wrench. Now my hero knows that the heroine is the girl he saved in his youth—the one person in the entire world who reminds him that there is a good person buried deep inside of him. Can he sacrifice her now after having saved her life once? This creates a major conflict for my hero in achieving his goal of revenge.

Second, the reader learns that the hero's mother thought he was a monster for beating Willie Jackson to within an inch of his life. This information becomes important in chapter nineteen, when Grace finally learns why Devlin wants Grace to negotiate a deal with the gatekeeper to Hell to kill his mother. Why does Devlin hate his mother so much? Because his mother sold Devlin to the notorious pirate, the Butcher, to use as his plaything. Devlin's mother was convinced that Devlin was as brutal as his father, who had beaten his mother. So the wallop Devlin delivered on Willie sealed his fate.

Notice that I did not reveal all of the backstory in chapter eight even though it would have fit naturally into that scene. The reader still doesn't know who Devlin wanted revenge against and why. So why not reveal this information in chapter eight? Because I wanted the reader to learn the truth at the same time as the heroine, Grace. We want to walk in Grace's shoes and feel her emotions real-time. If I had revealed the backstory about Devlin's mother selling him to the Butcher in this scene of chapter eight through his deep POV, the reader wouldn't have felt Grace's shock when she learns the truth in chapter nineteen. This is what is meant by "sprinkle in the backstory." You don't have to tell the reader everything upfront. Offer bits and pieces of the backstory throughout the current story to incite curiosity and keep the reader turning the pages.

Third, the reader experiences firsthand the type of torture Devlin was subjected to (i.e. reason he wants revenge against his mother) and how he drew on his heroic act in saving Eveline's life to get through torture without losing his bloody mind. Wanting revenge against one's mother is arguably unforgivable and certainly not heroic. But damn. After living through the torture in the hero's POV, we certainly understand his motives better. At the same time, we also understand, for the first time, *why* the heroine may have the power to steer him away from this unforgivable course of action.

Con #2: Caution: Confusion ahead!

A word of advice about writing flashbacks and memories in a way that doesn't leave your reader scratching their head and wondering what just happened. I differentiate a flashback with *italics*. Another option is to change the tense of the passage. So if your current story is told in present tense, the flashback could be written in past tense.

I've read blogs that suggest an author should clearly state the time and place of the flashback so the reader isn't confused, but I don't subscribe to that advice. If you weave the flashback seamlessly into your current story, there is no need to give the time and place. In fact, an author can stimulate the reader's curiosity by withholding that information.

> **Hint:** Memories can be introduced into the current story-line either through dialogue or the character's deep point of view.

In the following scene from chapter nine, the heroine, Grace, is drawing on her memories from childhood to piece together the fact that she is the bastard daughter of Lord Marcus Deveraux. This is a critical turning point in the current storyline because the reader knows that the villain Josephine wants revenge on Marcus through his last living relative. Notice that the part of the scene revealing backstory through a memory is only 322 words. We are in Grace's POV, and she is talking to her mentor, Brother Anselm, who raised Grace after her mother was sent to an insane asylum.

"Devlin seemed to believe I bear an uncanny resemblance to Lord Marcus Deveraux, both the color of my hair and eyes."

"The likeness is astonishing," Brother Anselm whispered.

Grace swallowed and a strange pressure gathered on her chest. She stood and cut a path to the hearth, following the crackle of the fire, and stretched out her fingers. *The soothing heat did little to prevent the shiver running down her spine when memories from her youth sprang to mind.*

"**When I was a little girl**," she began, twisting her hands together, "**I could hear my parents arguing in their bedroom late at night. They believed I was sound asleep, but I wasn't.**"

The wooden legs of Brother Anselm's chair scraped against the floor, but she continued her story, determined to lay it all out in her mind. She'd harbored the bothersome memories for too long and wished to be rid of them, as if voicing them aloud would relieve her conscience of their burden.

"**Father was the loudest. Even still I only caught a word or two. Strumpet. Bastard. Those were the words that struck me as odd, most likely because I**

didn't know what they meant at the time." Grace turned her back to the fire, facing Brother Anselm. "But I do now. Why would my father call my mother a strumpet?"

Silence greeted her. She lifted her chin, prepared to face the truth.

"Am I a bastard, Brother Anselm? Please tell me if Marcus Deveraux is my biological father."

Notice the italicized text above where I clearly indicate to the reader that a memory is about to be revealed. This isn't strictly needed since the next sentence starts with "When I was a little girl," so it's clear that Grace is talking about something from her past. However, I chose to include this foreshadowing because the shivers Grace felt when the memory struck her indicate something awful is about to be revealed. I want the reader on the edge of their seat.

Grace shares her memory through dialogue with Brother Anselm (i.e., the bolded text). This is natural in this scene because Brother Anselm is learning this information for the first time along with the reader. Grace came under his care after this event in her life. I loved weaving this memory into the scene because the reader feels Grace's tension and unease at finally piecing together why her father abandoned her. This adds depth to her character and presents her as a real human being grappling with her past. At the same time, this scene is important to the current storyline because it's tied to the villain's GMC. The reader learns that Grace is the biological daughter of Marcus and the key to Josephine getting her final revenge for whatever heinous crime Marcus committed.

Rather than using dialogue, memories can also be incorporated into the current storyline through the character's deep POV in a sentence or two. Here are several examples to demonstrate how simple it is:

This one is from *The Dragon Sorceress* (Destiny Is an Adventure Series). The heroine is sitting by a campfire with friends while celebrating the birth of "the chosen one" who will lead their people to freedom from the oppression of the dragon sorceress.

Though the fierce hunter in Kali longed as much as Drake to be the chosen one, another part of her rejoiced that it could never be so. The idea of facing down a fire-breathing dragon raised the hairs along her neck. She reached up to smooth them down, cringing as her fingers ran over the pockmarked skin, **remnants of the worst day ever—the one that stole her mother's life and left Kali forever scarred by the fire that had raged in her father's blacksmith shop**.

Kali was scarred for life in a raging fire that killed her mother—a memory the heroine revealed naturally through twenty-nine words in the current storyline. Kali's fear of fire is integral to her GMC. Shortly after this scene, the reader discovers that "the chosen one" wasn't born that day but rather "came of age." As it turns out, either Kali or her cousin Drake (both whom turned sixteen that day) is the chosen one and must hunt down the dragon sorceress and kill her. Kali's conflict throughout the story is her fear of fire.

In *The Vampire Queen* (Destiny Is an Adventure Series), Drake has just been told by a friend that the villagers are planning to capture him and his family and turn them over to the vampire queen. I call on his memories to lend credence to his shock.

What nonsense is this? Never in his lifetime would Drake have believed the villagers of his hometown would betray him this way. **Every single person in the village shared a memory of one sort or another with him; he knew all of their names, had helped build their homes or run errands for them when a family member was sick. Bert Maynard, the caretaker of The Spider's Webb Inn, was a distant cousin. And the cook, Mr. Allen, snuck Drake a hot bun whenever the old man stopped by The Elixir Shop for a bottle of tonic to ease the dry patches of skin that plagued his arms.**

The first draft I wrote stopped before the bolded text. But I later layered in specifics through his memories to give depth to his sense of betrayal. In this case, adding the backstory isn't strictly necessary. The current storyline could move forward without this information, but I hope you'll agree that the story is richer by including these eighty-six words. Readers want to connect with our characters and their humanity.

Here is another example from *Make Me Whole* in which the hero, Jacob, is reliving the moment in his life that caused his paralysis.

> His jaw clenched as he gripped the arms of his wheelchair, **and the moment flashed before his eyes.** Intense pain rippled up his spine once again from the memory of the impact of the boy crashing into him. He'd never seen it coming. But he'd never forget how it felt tumbling down the hill at breakneck speed, or the pain of a ski boot smashing into his lower back.
>
> That kid didn't belong on a black diamond course and knew it but bowed to peer pressure, changing Jacob's life irrevocably.
>
> **Dr. Lewis cleared his throat, bringing Jacob back to the present.** Jacob rubbed the lifeless flesh of his legs and gazed at the old man sitting ramrod straight in his broad-backed leather chair.

Do you see how easy it is to incorporate a memory into a scene in just a few sentences? I didn't name the specific time or place of his accident. The reader knew this was a memory by "the moment flashed before his eyes," and I easily brought the character back to the present with Dr. Lewis clearing his throat.

The best way to learn the techniques is to study more examples. One of my all-time favorite memory scenes is from the third book in the Tortured Souls series, *River Road.* My hero Hatchet is about to make love with the heroine, Hope. He hasn't been with a woman intimately for more than six months following the death of his last lover.

> Hatchet laughed and swatted Hope's hand away. "I'm supposed to be cherishing you. Turn around. You've entirely

too many layers on, and undressing you will try my patience."

"Don't rip my dress," she said, glancing over her shoulder. "This is one of my favorites."

"Don't rip my dress," Emma said, giggling as she slapped his hands away. "You've ruined one already, and I have so few."

Hatchet froze, closing his eyes. His hand stung from her slap, and his ears filled with her cute little snort, the one that always escaped before she gained control again. She gazed at him, her eyes sparkling with joy and love.

"Are you all right, Hatchet?"

Emma's image dispersed, like dandelion seeds caught on the wind. *Don't go!* He grasped for wisps of her fading image, desperate to hold on, but she was gone. At least for now, not forever … if he held on.

"I'm sorry, but I can't do this," he said, opening his eyes and meeting Hope's gaze. The widow was every man's dream for a pleasurable evening. She must think him daft, stopping on the cusp of undressing her. "All I have left are my memories, and I won't part with them for one salacious night in a brothel."

Her eyes widened, and she inched backward, her shoulders stiff. "A boardinghouse. Believe me, I understand your feelings, but you needn't insult me. This is my *home*."

He should leave before he made an even greater mess of the situation. At the doorway, he glanced back. "My sincerest apologies, Hope. I didn't mean to imply that you're … Dammit. I'm an ass, and you're a lady. I'll leave in the morning for Harmon Grove. If Isaac Moore hid your relic there, I'll find it."

With the asson back in her possession, she could banish the bloody curse. That is, if she ever spoke with him again after tonight.

This example illustrates how to "weave" backstory into the current storyline. Only a few paragraphs before this scene, the hero was fighting an internal battle about letting go of his past to pursue his future. He had convinced himself that Emma would want him to move on. And then this memory crashes into him. I could've written this scene such that the hero started to undress the heroine and froze from his guilty conscience. Boring.

Show, don't tell.

One more point I'd like to make is that writing this memory into this scene was a plot device to prevent my hero and heroine from falling into bed together in chapter seven of the book. My editor suggested their first love scene should come later in the book. Yet I wanted to show the reader that these two characters had chemistry, so I didn't want to delete the scene entirely. I needed a powerful reason for the hero or heroine to back out at the last minute. I loved the idea of the hero being the one to back out, and this heartbreaking memory was just the trick.

Finally, this scene significantly impacts the current storyline because Hatchet needs Hope to break the curse plaguing his family. He agreed to find Hope's ancient relic from Isaac Moore in exchange for her help in breaking the curse. So by insulting Hope during this scene, he has put his goal in jeopardy.

I hope I've convinced you that flashbacks and memories can be used effectively to reveal backstory. In fact, sometimes this is the best method!

CHAPTER SIX

Dreams

Dreams are a wonderful device for revealing backstory if executed properly. As with all other forms we've covered for weaving in snippets of the past, the dream must fit seamlessly into the current storyline. Talk about pulling a reader out of the story? Drop in a dream out of nowhere and your reader will be shaking their head.

So I rarely use dreams as a writing device because there are relatively few circumstances where something in the current storyline would trigger a dream in my character.

Advice #1: Find your triggering event.

Without a "triggering event," the dream feels out of place and jars the reader. However, there are circumstances when a dream is the perfect solution for the storyline. In *River Road,* the hero accompanied the heroine to the ritual where she became a voodoo high priestess. Part of the ritual included the heroine being submerged in a bathtub to the point of near drowning as a way of signifying her rebirth. This scene in chapter eighteen triggered a nightmare for the hero later that night. Check it out:

> *An eerie creak reverberated through the ballroom. Hatchet glanced up at the dark-green water weighing against the glass dome ceiling. Thousands of cracks rippled over the surface, more intricate than a spider's web.*
>
> *"Hatchet, help me!"*

He spun around, searching for the source of the desperate plea. Emma dangled by one hand from the escape ladder, screaming in pain as a man stepped on her fingers in his haste to exit.

Hatchet's stomach plummeted, and he shoved through the throng of guests clamoring to get out. Dammit! What had happened to the waiter manning the bottom of the escape ladder to ensure each guest ascended in a calm and orderly fashion? Emma should've been outside long ago.

"Hold on, Emma!" he shouted. "Don't you let go!"

Tears streamed down her cheeks, and she howled as another man trampled her hand. People shouted and slammed into his sides, but still he pushed forward, elbowing anyone who stepped in his path, glancing up frequently to gauge Emma's situation.

"I can't hold on." Her eyes were wide, frantic. "I can't hold on."

"You can," he ordered, scrambling up the first three steps of the ladder, his eyes trained on her. "I'm coming, Emma! Don't you let go."

Three more steps ... Sweat trickled over his forehead and into his eyes, but he blinked it away.

"Hatchet, I love you," she cried, her fingers slipping.

He growled and shouldered past another man. Another two steps. Her fingers released, and he braced himself with one arm hooked to the ladder, the other outstretched. Her body slammed into his arm, stalling her momentum, and she caught hold of his torso.

"I've got you," he said with a grunt, staring into her tear-filled, whiskey-colored eyes. A tremulous smile touched her lips. His heart thundered in his chest, and bile lurched up his throat. That was too damned close.

The glass dome belched, and Emma's eyes widened with terror as a torrent of frigid water crashed against Hatchet's back, knocking him off their perch on the ladder. His body slammed into Emma's against the nearby wall, and the pressure of her hold on his waist was gone in an instant.

The rushing water flipped him over. He spun in all directions, his hands seeking Emma, but he couldn't see a goddamned thing in the blackness surrounding him. His lungs began to burn, another body bumped against him, and he held on, but the arm was hairy, taut with muscles.

He couldn't tell up from down. Panic settled in his gut, and air seeped out of his mouth. The bubbles rippled over his chest. Follow the bubbles. He was upside down. Turning, he swam hard for the surface, but his soaked clothes weighed on him, sapping his energy. He couldn't breathe. His lungs were a blazing inferno.

Where was Emma? Oh, God, had he killed Emma?

Hatchet sat up, heaving in a gulp of air. His throat felt raw. His pulse raced. Everything was black around him. Goose pimples covered his flesh, despite the clammy air. All he could see was the raw terror in his beloved's eyes.

"Hatchet?"

"Emma?" he whispered.

A moment of silence.

"No, darling, it's Hope." She rubbed soothing circles on his back. "I'm here for you. Are you all right?"

A sheen of sweat gathered on his brow, and he lifted his knees, propping his forearms against them, willing his thunderous heart to calm. He hadn't dreamed of Emma's death in more than a month.

Do you have goose bumps after reading that dream? Keep in mind that *River Road* is book three of the Tortured Souls series and Emma died in book one. Hatchet was devastated by her death. He blamed himself, but the reader never knew exactly what happened. So I wanted to finally reveal to my faithful readers what transpired that fateful night when Emma drowned. But I needed to do it in a way that was natural in the context of the current storyline.

My first draft of this book did not include the scene of Hope's ritual to become a voodoo high priestess. I figured Hatchet had nightmares of Emma's death from time to time, so it was natural for him to have one after taking the heroine to the opera. That's a weak argument and doesn't draw a true connection between the current storyline and the backstory. The dream was simply a plot device to let the reader know what happened.

So I brainstormed with my critique partner and editor to come up with the idea of showing the heroine's anointment into the priesthood with the bathtub scene being the trigger for Hatchet's nightmare. At this point in the story, Hatchet has fallen in love with Hope, even if he won't admit the truth to himself. Watching her struggle in the bathtub while submerged under water is a terrifying experience for him given what happened to the last love of his life. That is a direct link between the current storyline and his backstory to form the perfect triggering event.

The beauty of this scene is that readers who read *River Road* as a stand-alone book aren't left scratching their heads from this dream, because Hatchet's nightmare reminds him that he's cursed. He had believed Hope's tarot card reading that he wasn't cursed. However, strange things had been happening in the storyline up to that point, and his nightmare shoved him over the edge. If he was truly cursed, he was putting Hope's life in danger by developing feelings for her. All the women he loves die. So he leaves after waking from the nightmare to visit voodoo queen Marie Laveau to finally discover the truth once and for all about whether he is cursed (i.e. the past emerged through his dream to push him into an action in the present that was relevant to the current storyline).

Advice #2: Haunted by the past.

Dreams work very well when the hero or heroine subconsciously suppresses an event from their past or if they're regularly haunted by that event. Of the sixteen books I've written, only four contain dreams. All four are gothic romances. Dreams lend themselves well to that genre. I used a dream as the opening to *River Road,* with the trigger being the hero's return to his hometown, which reminds him of his days as a soldier in the Civil War.

In *Blackburn Castle,* the hero dreams of a happy time in his youth when he was eating biscuits and orange marmalade. His dream was triggered by the heroine's scented soap because she had snuggled up to him in bed.

And in *The Secrets of Chateau Swansea*, heroine Maribeth finally remembers her true identity in a dream that is triggered by the hero insisting the heroine is not who she claims to be. Her conscious mind refused to accept the truth, but in her dreams, she remembers her past.

And in *Devil's Cove*, the heroine kept dreaming about being with a "lover" who made her feel cherished whether they were playing hide-and-go-seek in the dark forest or making love. The reader eventually learned that these dreams were actually memories of the villain's soul mate, Rosalie, whose soul resided in Grace's body. Isn't that deliciously creepy for a gothic romance novel? Here is an example from chapter ten. The italics denote the dream sequence and then comes Grace's reaction to the dream. Keep in mind that Grace is blind and she is a virgin.

An obscure and powerful ache built in Grace's nether region with a force that was both foreign and yet oddly familiar. The soft moss of the forest floor cushioned her back as her lover pinched the taut bud of her nipple. She couldn't hold back any longer and sought to extinguish the fire blazing through her body before it consumed her whole. With an instinct she didn't know she possessed, she opened her mouth to the gentle tugging on her lips and her tongue slipped into sweet oblivion. Her lover's tongue was bold and possessive as it explored every crevice of her mouth, inflaming her desire and filling her belly with the fluttering wings of a hummingbird drunk on the nectar of an exotic flower. Her lover's hand slipped between the wet folds of her womanhood and stroked with infinite care. She was on the edge of something raw and beautiful ... so close ... the sensations overwhelming in their intensity until she felt as if her entire body exploded in a thunderous wave of tingling from the very core of her being. Every single molecule of her body vibrated with the delicious aftershocks, and she collapsed, sated.

Grace bolted upright, **the vestiges of her dream alarmingly vivid in her mind**. She could scarce draw breath, and her body trembled from the ache between her damp thighs. The sensations subsided with each new draw of fresh air into her lungs. She had fallen from grace, into the fiery pit of insanity.

How did one dream of such raptures without an ounce of experience to draw from? Or little experience, at any rate. She ran the tips of her fingers across her lips. They felt bruised—so sensitive to the light touch. How could that be? She did not dare touch the sacred spot between her thighs for fear of what she might unleash. Never had she imagined such pleasures awaited her. Her dream had reawakened the wild and wondrous feelings Devlin's kisses had brought to life, only magnified a hundred fold.

He was an enigma.

Writing dreams into your novel can be a wickedly fun experience. What is so wonderful about this scene is that the heroine connects her dream to her feelings for the hero while at the same time recognizing that her dream makes no sense in the context of her life experiences.

Remember what I said about creating curiosity in the reader? Right now, I hope the reader is filled with as many questions as Grace. The reader doesn't find out that these dreams are actually memories of Rosalie until chapter twenty—ten chapters after this dream sequence.

This scene illustrates the fact that an author does not have to spell out for the reader the time and place for every flashback/memory/dream. Readers are smart and will infer a lot by what is written on the page. And, quite frankly, sometimes I don't want the reader to discover the truth until much later. That's half the fun in writing a novel.

When you read advice that says "never start your story with a dream" or "always tell your reader the time and place of the flashback so they aren't confused," what they really mean is that what you're attempting to do is difficult to pull off, so stick to a formula.

I call bullshit on that advice. Whenever someone says "you can't do X," I say, "watch me do it." Truly exceptional books often emerge when authors ignore traditional conventions. Write the story you want to tell.

A room of twelve authors told me I could not write a romance where the hero wanted to kill his mother. They said that isn't heroic and romance readers would never buy into that storyline. I disagreed and wrote *Devil's Cove* anyway. Arguably, these authors had a point because readers have a love/hate relationship with *Devil's Cove*. Either they love it or they hate it. I'm okay with that. Readers who truly love dark romance eat up the story. Imagine the satisfaction the reader has when the hero finally gives up his burning need for revenge through the love of a good woman.

I was also told that a hero could not kill the heroine's mother because readers would never forgive him. Really? In *Blackburn Castle*, the book opens with a backstory scene where the hero kills the heroine's mother under duress from the notorious pirate, the Butcher. My readers adored the hero, and some were frustrated with the heroine for waiting so long to forgive him for what he did. Writing their journey to forgiveness and love was a highly rewarding experience.

Do an internet search. You'll find all kinds of advice about not starting your story with the weather or with the hero/heroine driving into town, etc. The list is long for "don't do X." You can do anything you want so long as you knock that ball out of the frickin' park. That opening dream better pack a walloping punch.

CHAPTER SEVEN
Prologues

Some readers love prologues while other readers hate them so much they'll skip over the section entirely. That's a damned shame. If used properly, prologues are a fantastic tool for setting the stage for the current storyline.

Use #1: The suspense factor.

In chapter three, we covered a detailed example from *Devil's Cove* of how a prologue can be used to increase the suspense for the current story. The backstory was directly related to the villain's GMC and started the book with a bang.

Another wonderful example of this can be seen in *Sinister Ceremony* by Stacey Coverstone. You can read the full prologue in the "Look Inside" feature on Amazon. The author starts with a bone-chilling scene from 1898. Yet the current storyline is in the modern day. After reading that prologue, I was sitting on pins and needles, wondering how the events in the prologue would impact the heroine.

Do you remember that scene from *Nightmare on Elm Street* when the heroine walks outside to investigate a noise in the back alley after dark? I was yelling at the heroine not to go outside. Nothing good ever comes from that. My blood pressure was sky high. That's what I felt after I read the prologue of *Sinister Ceremony* and discovered in chapter one that the heroine was engaged to a descendant of the sinister lord of the manor from 1898. Oh man! I knew nothing good was going to come of that relationship. And the prologue leaves on a cliffhanger of sorts so the reader doesn't know the actual outcome of the scene or how it will play out in the current storyline. But I knew with certainty it was going to be one wild ride.

Use #2: The inciting historical event.

In *Blackburn Castle,* the prologue shows the scene where the ten-year-old hero kills the heroine's mother. In order to create immediate empathy for the hero Victor, I wanted the reader to experience this event in Victor's deep POV. I also used the prologue to inform the reader of the significance of the tear of Freya. Let's see if you agree that I accomplished that goal:

> With a chuckle, the Butcher placed the cold edge of his blade on Victor's neck. Sweat trickled down Victor's forehead as he lifted his gaze to Maude, but he couldn't see her expression through the watery haze in his eyes.
>
> "Do you think she'll spare your life and tell me where we'll find Mercy?" the pirate asked, his fetid breath filling Victor's nostrils. "You're worthless to me without the girl, and Maude knows it. **Your family is searching for two of the hidden stones in Blackburn Castle as we speak. But only Mercy can restore all four pieces into the original amber tear of Freya. It's worth a goddamned fortune!** Tell me where to find your daughter," he growled at Maude.
>
> Her eyes widened, and she shook her head.
>
> Victor's bottom lip quivered as another tear slid down his cheek. She wouldn't spare his life. **Why would she, when their families had been sworn enemies for hundreds of years?**
>
> The blade pierced Victor's neck, and his skin burned as it split open. A familiar pain, but this one would take his life. His heart threatened to burst from his chest, but he didn't dare move a single muscle in his entire body.
>
> **"If Maude refuses to tell me, you will fight her to the death,"** the Butcher said, wrapping one of Victor's hands around the hilt of the dagger. **"And then**

you can go home. Life is full of choices, boy, and only one of you will walk away. Do you choose life or death?"

The pirate jabbed their joined hands toward Maude with lightning speed, halting an inch from her heart.

Victor's bowels rumbled in his gut, but he held on tightly to the dagger, terrified of the Butcher's reaction should he let it fall to the floor. Lord give him courage to endure whatever fate awaited him, because he couldn't kill a woman.

"Stop this madness!" Maude said, holding out her hands in surrender. "They're innocent children, and the Blackburn curse must come to an end. No more death. I can't bear it anymore. Mercy is the key to Victor's salvation. Do you promise you won't kill them?"

Victor's mouth fell open. Why would she sacrifice her beloved daughter to save him, when not a single crewmember of *The Bloody Mary* had shown him mercy since his abduction?

"Everything will be all right, Victor," she said, her tone soft and reassuring, so much like the one his mother used whenever she wished to calm him.

He wanted to throw himself into her embrace, but the Butcher shoved him aside and grabbed her arms.

"Yes, of course. All I want is the amber stones of Freya."

A strangled cry escaped her lips. "Should you break your oath, I damn you to an eternity in the jaws of the hounds of Hell; may they rip you limb from limb."

The Butcher lifted his brow, seemingly unfazed by Maude's curse.

"Mercy is living with my sister in Devil's Cove."

"Was that so difficult?" the Butcher asked with a lopsided grin. He relinquished his hold on the woman and straightened the sleeves of his jacket. "There is no need for threats. I always keep my promises. Rest assured, *I* won't kill Mercy. Plenty of crewmembers on *The Bloody Mary* will relish the job when the time comes. I believe I also promised not to slit your throat."

He turned his steely gaze on Victor and bellowed, "Kill her now, or I'll hack off your leg and roast it for supper."

All of the blood drained from Victor's face; the moment of reckoning had arrived. The dagger trembled in his hands as he stared at Maude. She'd sacrificed her daughter for *him*. God give him strength, because he would rather lose a leg than betray her. His mother had raised him to protect the fairer sex, and he would make her proud.

The Butcher cuffed him on the side of the head, almost knocking him to the floor. "Are you deaf, boy?"

Heat pooled in Victor's ear, and he swiped away the snot trickling from his nose. Standing tall, he squared his shoulders and looked the bully in the eyes. "No, sir, I heard you plain enough. I'm no killer. You want her dead, you'll have to kill her yourself."

A meaty fist slammed into his nose, knocking him flat on his back as pain exploded in his head. Blood gushed over his lips and down his throat. He choked and spat, shaking his head to clear the stars forming in his eyes. His nose throbbed like the devil, no doubt broken.

"Cheeky blighter," the Butcher growled. "You're whatever I say you are. And today you're a goddamned killer. Ignore me again, and there's plenty worse in store for you. Kill her, *now*."

Victor wobbled to his feet and glared at the monster, funneling every bit of his anger into his next words. "Fuck you!"

With a howl of laughter, the Butcher grabbed him by the shoulders and ripped the shirt off his back. "Those are fighting words, you little son of a bitch. Don't have my whip, but you'll change your tune by the time I'm through with you."

"Leave him alone," Maude said, pulling Victor into her embrace, wrapping her arms around his head. "He's a child, for Christ's sake."

The bite of the pirate's blade sliced diagonally down Victor's back, transforming his skin into a blazing inferno. He heaved in a gulp of air. A second swipe of the blade brought him to his knees, ripping a scream from his lungs. *Goddamn the bastard.*

Maude sank to the floor beside him, holding up his head. Tears shimmered in her eyes. "You have to kill me, Victor, or you'll die. He will kill me next, and my husband's sacrifice will be for naught. You and all the Blackburn males must live. *Do you hear me?*"

"Please, don't make me," he rasped, turning his face away. The pain in his back was unbearable, but nothing compared to the anguish he'd feel if he murdered her. "My mother will never forgive me."

She held his face and captured his gaze once more. "You're wrong, my dear boy. If I forgive you, so will she."

That scene makes me cry every time I read it. Poor Victor wanted to make his mama proud by standing up to the Butcher and protecting Mercy's mother. He endured great pain by refusing to cave into the pirate's demands, and he would've sacrificed his life to save Maude. Instead, he honored her wishes and plunged a knife into her heart.

This backstory accomplished four things:

- By showing the scene where Victor kills Mercy's mother, the reader understands why he did it and immediately feels empathy for him. But I mess with the reader's head a little in the first chapter of the book when Mercy watches Victor dole out a nasty beating to another man in the alley behind her uncle's bar. Did the Butcher succeed in turning Victor into a heartless pirate?
- The first bolded text gives the history of the tear of Freya split between Victor's and Mercy's families. But do you see how I tied this in with the Butcher wanting all four pieces so he could restore the gem to single stone? I'm also revealing

backstory about how Victor came to work on the Butcher's pirate ship. In the Tortured Souls series, all three of the heroes met on *The Bloody Mary* and were tortured one way or another by the Butcher.

- The second bolded text brings out the fact that Mercy and Victor's families are sworn enemies without explaining why. This heightens reader curiosity.

- The third bolded text outlines an event that shaped the hero's future behavior. When the Butcher later dies and Victor is free to go home, he refuses to do so. The pirate's words ring in Victor's ears. Life is full of choices, but how could Victor choose to go home to his mother when Mercy could not because he killed Maude?

Now, I have a confession to make. Strictly speaking, *Blackburn Castle* starts with chapter one, not a prologue. My editor suggested this to avoid losing readers who skip the prologue. This first backstory scene was critical to setting the stage for the current storyline. So I dropped the typical convention of calling this scene a prologue and made it chapter one. To avoid reader confusion, I included the date and location at the top of chapter one and chapter two so the time jump was clear.

Use #3: The fairy tale.

In fairy tales and fantasy stories, use the prologue to show how the fable began. Think of the opening for *Sleeping Beauty,* which starts with "In a faraway land, long ago, King Stefan and his fair queen wished for a child. At last a daughter was born, and they named her Aurora." The king and queen threw a party to celebrate the birth of their daughter.

Among the guests were three good fairies, Flora, Fauna, and Merryweather, who bestowed gifts on the baby. But before the third fairy granted her gift, the evil fairy, Maleficent, made a dark, grand entrance. Furious at having been left off the guest list, Maleficent cursed the child to die at the age of sixteen. In an attempt to undo the curse, Merryweather bestows her gift through a counter curse spell. And so the current storyline begins.

Beauty and the Beast is another example of using the prologue to set the stage for the current storyline. The reader discovers that a curse was placed on the hero because he had no love in his heart. A witch turned the young man into a beast and he will remain so unless he can find a woman to love him despite his ghastly appearance before the last petal on a magical rose falls.

Some may argue that these types of prologues are trite and over-done. Personally, I love them. That's the beauty of books. Each reader will have a unique experience. We all have our likes and dislikes. If you want to start your book with a fable or curse or whatever, do it. Just know the risks of your choices. You might be casting a narrower net for reader interests. I write gothic romance because I love to read the genre. There are relatively few readers who love gothic romance. That's okay as long as I level set my expectations.

The hero in *Blackburn Castle* is cursed to die at the age of twenty-seven. I chose not to reveal the backstory of the curse in a prologue. Rather, the current storyline slowly reveals why he is cursed and how the curse can be lifted.

However, in *The Dragon Sorceress*, I chose to use the prologue to provide the reader with the backstory on the oppression of my fictional world, Aeon. This is a coming-of-age teen fantasy story. The current storyline is about two teenaged cousins fulfilling their destiny to defeat the dragon sorceress in order to free the world of Aeon from her dark oppression. When the story begins, the characters don't know whether Kali or Drake is destined to be the "chosen one," but Drake assumes he is the logical choice, given his physical strength.

The prologue sets the stage for how an ancestor of Arturo ends up being the chosen one to bring peace to Aeon. I started the backstory in the prologue by showing a critical historical event and then ended the event in chapter one through a recounting of the tale around a campfire. This method tied the backstory to the current storyline well and is unique.

The prologue is about two and a half pages long as compared to *Devil's Cove,* which was one and a half pages. Contrast that with most chapters, which are eight to twelve pages. The shorter the better.

Prologue – One Hundred Years Ago

Shutting his eyes against the pain, Arturo tried not to think about the blood seeping from the gash across his back. Her talons had ripped through his chain mail as though it were paper. The warm liquid pooled at his lower back, soaking his shirt and breeches. He prayed his instincts had been right and the dragon sorceress would morph into her human form. A second later he was rewarded with the telltale whoosh of air that always accompanied her transformation.

Searing pain flared in his back when she kicked him hard in the gut, causing his entire body to shudder. He groaned and held his arms over his torso protectively. Another blow like that might be the end of him in his weakened state, but he wasn't done with her. All he needed was a few more minutes.

"Good, you're not dead. *Yet.* Tell me, was it worth dying for?" the dragon sorceress asked, crooking her finger under his chin to lift his face. She stared intently into his eyes. "**I cannot be destroyed and will live on for thousands of years. You know that as well as any mortal.** I've lost count of how many times you've tried to kill me over the years. So tell me, dear friend. Was it worth it?"

"Aye," he said, his breathing shallow. He suddenly felt weak and tired. Rather than fighting to keep his eyes open, he rested them for a precious few seconds. Arturo knew what he must do, and prayed to the Heavens that he be granted the strength to look death in the eyes. All of his senses were alive—heightened by the awareness of his last breaths.

His eyes fluttered open and connected with hers. "**To live in constant fear is to not live at all. I will not have** died in vain. **The end of your time is coming. I promise you that, Marigot.**"

A glorious waterfall of black hair swayed on her back from her sudden laughter. "And how, may I ask, will my demise come about?"

"From the next great dragon slayer, of course."

"But we have already agreed that I cannot be slayed. **You have seen with your own eyes and have tried with your own hands to penetrate my dragon scales. And you, the best dragon slayer of all.** It is impossible!"

Arturo's mouth turned up in a slight curve as he beheld the black beauty before him. It was a pity that such angelic beauty was bestowed on an evil and heartless creature. "**Everyone and everything has a weakness.**"

Her shrewd eyes narrowed on his face. "And what, pray tell, is mine?"

"Vanity," he rasped and slowly clasped his gut with his hand. "I knew you could not resist the urge to change into human form and gloat over your death blow."

His eyes never left hers as he reached into his bag and whipped out his sword in one smooth movement, thrusting it into her heart. He fell flat on his face, having used the last ounce of his energy, and waited for darkness to overcome him. **Marigot's anguished cries fell silent when she splashed into the water nearby. His thoughts began to spin. Seconds later her hands grasped him roughly on the shoulders and shook him violently.**

"**You fool!**" **she screamed.** "**He who bathes in the pool of life shall be healed.**"

"**Healed,**" **he whispered, drawing his last breath,** "**but eternally scarred and vulnerable.**"

Marigot gasped in horror as she pulled back the torn cloth of her gown to reveal a wide scar marring her once beautiful skin.

"You'll pay for this dearly," she growled, continuing to shake him. But he was dead. She stood and raised her hands to the sky, shouting, "I will slaughter every last relative to join you in hell, Arturo. Burn your beloved village to the ground. Destroy your ships and crew. I will wipe Aeon clean of your existence. This I promise."

In a dramatic whirl of motion she spun and spun, transforming effortlessly into a dragon. **Though it was nearly dark, thin strips of sunlight permeated the canopy of forest leaves and shimmered against her icy blue dragon scales. Except, that is, for the long, dull patch of skin across her chest.** The dragon's eerie caw could be heard for miles as she tore through the sky on a path due North to the dragon sorceress's stronghold—Infinitas.

So let's talk about the main reasons why I chose to begin *The Dragon Sorceress* with backstory in the form of a prologue.

First, I am a fan of the "once upon a time in a land faraway" motif where the reader is introduced to the villain in a prologue or at the start of the story, like in *Sleeping Beauty*. This is especially true when the villain plays a relatively small role in the current storyline.

Second, the history of Marigot and Arturo plays a crucial role in the overall current storyline. The reader doesn't know this from the onset. Instead, I slowly reveal that the dragon sorceress wasn't always evil. In fact, Marigot was a princess who was betrothed to Arturo until he turned on her at the bidding of the prophetess Kaylee. Can you imagine being hunted by the man you dreamed of becoming your husband? Stories are so much better when the heroes are flawed and the villains have a grain of humanity. Nothing in life is ever black and white. But in the beginning, we want to root for the hero and curse the villains.

Third, the prologue shows the reader a lot about the fictional world. Magic is everywhere; from a sorceress who can morph into a dragon to the bag of carrying and the pool of life, the reader is immersed in magical concepts. And yet a dark villain rules with an iron fist, and the people are tired of living under her oppression and willing to die to improve their plight. However, even the best of the best humans cannot defeat the dragon sorceress. So the story begins with a clear picture of the insurmountable odds facing the main protagonists.

All of this could have been achieved by sprinkling in the background information throughout the story. How you choose to inform the reader of backstory is a stylistic choice. There is no right or wrong answer. This is your story. Tell it the way you feel is best. But whatever you choose, make it interesting.

Let me share a secret. I purposely misled the witness in this prologue. The reader may jump to the conclusion that the only way to kill the dragon sorceress is to catch her unaware in her human form or to shoot her in the heart where Arturo created a scar that left her vulnerable. I promise, that's not the way Marigot dies. Where would the fun be in that?

On a side note, know who your audience is before you publish a book, and find out their preferred method of buying books. I regret my decision to self-publish *The Dragon Sorceress* without first attempting to find an agent to represent me. After a dismal book launch, I learned that only 10 percent of sales for teen fantasy are ebooks. Contrast that with the romance genre, where 65 percent of sales are ebooks. This means to have a realistic chance at success, a teen fantasy needs to be on bookstore shelves. *The Dragon Sorceress* received a lot of four and five star reviews from librarians and booksellers on NetGalley, but it was offered for sale only through CreateSpace. Many booksellers refuse to purchase books through an Amazon affiliate. Lesson learned!

CHAPTER EIGHT
Dialogue and Deep POV

Our final topic for weaving backstory into your novel focuses on how to effectively use dialogue and/or deep POV to reveal nuggets from your character's past. What I love about this method is, it can be short and sweet. We covered a few examples in other chapters.

Caution #1: Does your conversation feel natural?

When two characters have a shared history, talking about that history at any length can feel awkward. It becomes quite obvious that the author is trying to impart background on the reader. This pulls the reader out of the story.

Let me give you an example of what I mean from *Blackburn Castle.* In this scene in chapter four, the heroine, Mercy, is brewing a love potion while talking to her aunt Cecelia. Here is the first draft of this scene:

> "Well, madness runs in our family," Mercy said. "I'm undecided on which of our ancestors was worse, Elizabeth or her sister, Vivian. Their story could fill the pages of *Grimm's Fairy Tales*; twin sisters fighting over the love of one man, potent love potion imbued with the tears of a goddess, and an eternal curse. Pure insanity!"
>
> Cecelia handed another vial to Mercy with a protracted sigh. "Poor Vivian must've been consumed by jealousy to double-cross Elizabeth and Ambrose in that horrid manner. They were engaged to be married. Sad business, that."

What's good about this scene is that the heroine is brewing a love potion in the current storyline, so this is a natural place for her to talk about her ancestors having brewed loved potions and fighting over the love of one man. Yay!

What's bad about this scene is that the heroine and her aunt are familiar with their ancestors' history, so this conversation feels awkward. However, with a few simple tweaks, the conversation and revelation of the backstory becomes a natural part of the current storyline. Here is the edited version:

> "Well, madness runs in our family," Mercy said. "I'm undecided on which of our ancestors was worse, Elizabeth or her sister, Vivian." **Their story could fill the pages of *Grimms' Fairy Tales*—twin sisters fighting over the love of one man, a potent love potion imbued with the tears of a goddess, and an eternal curse. Pure insanity**!
>
> Cecelia handed another vial to Mercy with a protracted sigh. **"Take care and never allow jealousy to cloud your judgment like poor Vivian."**

Notice how we changed a portion of the backstory to Mercy's internal POV rather than dialogue? Cecelia already knows the history of their ancestors. However, the bold /underlined internal POV works well because Mercy said she was undecided on which ancestor was worse, so she's mulling over their story in her head.

Also, we changed Cecelia's dialogue to a warning that is relevant to the heroine in the context of the current storyline rather than keeping it as a background info dump. This is more natural and drives home the same message. The reader realizes that Vivian got jealous of Elizabeth and let her jealousy cloud her judgment. *Holy moly*. Did Vivian brew a love potion and steal Elizabeth's man? Who cursed who? You want to incite curiosity rather than spoonfeeding the reader, sending her off to sleep.

Hint: Whenever possible, introduce backstory in a manner that will create curiosity in the reader. Don't tell all!

Caution #2: Too much detail about the past
ruins the reader experience.

Our readers are smart! You do not have to lay everything out on a silver platter. If executed properly, our readers will infer the important details from the scene. Don't believe me? Let's work through another example.

Instead of telling your reader that two characters were attracted to each other in the past (i.e. backstory), show your reader their attraction in a scene. Imply as much as possible rather than stating it outright. Let the reader infer from their interaction what happened in the past.

In *A Night to Remember,* the story begins at a charity ball where the heroine, Anna, is the hostess. She runs into a former college acquaintance, Brett, who was her dance partner in a ballroom dancing class. This is the first time they've seen each other since graduating from college seven years earlier.

On a side note, when I developed the storyline for this book, I knew it would kick off with a charity ball, so I purposely chose a backstory (i.e. they were ballroom dance partners in college) that would fit seamlessly with the current storyline. In doing so, I could naturally reveal their history in a scene at the charity ball:

> Brett hesitated before grabbing Anna's left hand and **placing a soft kiss on her bare fingers**. "Dare I hope this is a sign you're single?"
>
> "Why would it matter?" she asked with pursed lips. "I was never your type."
>
> His beautifully sculpted brow shot up in question. "You've always been my type—but stubbornly resisted my charms—despite all of my best moves." He shook his head softly. "It was cruel and unusual punishment."
>
> **She bit her lip, recollecting every one of his moves. Such sweet torture he had put her through!** Probably along with a host of other females.

"You tried your best moves on all the ladies," she said, **poking her finger into his chest** while a smile spread across her face. "I would've been another drop in the bucket."

He captured her chin between his fingers and thumb. "That's not fair. As I recall it was the other way around. The ladies were making the moves on me." He shrugged. "Can't hold that against me. Being the star quarterback came with some drawbacks."

A grin tugged at her lips. "Oh, really? Most guys are dying to have women crawling at their feet."

"Guess I'm not most guys." **He caged her between his arms, bracing his hands against the wall.** "All I ever wanted was you."

She dragged in a rough breath. **Could his words be true? Had she made him out to be a rogue because of her own insecurities and fears that she might not be enough for him?**

"How about a dance for old time's sake?" he asked, stepping back and holding out his hand. "Let me hold you in my arms again."

In this scene, I show the reader the attraction between Anna and Brett. They can't stop touching each other. He kisses her fingers. She pokes him in the chest. He cages her between his arms. Also notice the way Anna's thoughts reveal more of the backstory and how she felt about Brett in college. This scene is a natural part of the current storyline, and yet the entire dialogue reveals the characters' backstory while showing their attraction.

Caution #3: The obvious choice is probably the boring choice.

In *Ticket to Love*, the heroine is a police officer who wants to become a detective. One of her conflicts (i.e. GMC) is that her family wants her to drop her career in law enforcement to take up her rightful place running the family's bed and breakfast. In order to drive home the idea that this was a real conflict, I needed to show that the heroine, Kristy, truly loves certain aspects of running her family's B&B.

Check out this scene from chapter two in which Kristy is called to a scene outside a restaurant in the pedestrian zone of her small town. The hero parked his car and trailer illegally in order to unload his sister's furniture easily, because his sister is moving into the apartment above the bakery located next to the restaurant.

> "Hey, Shorty," I say, grinning at the chef. "What's up? Got a message from dispatch. You called in a complaint? By the way, the onion rings you added to the menu last week"—I kiss my bunched fingertips and they explode in the air—"delicious...no, out of this world."
>
> I'm no dummy. **The fastest way to improve the chef's mood is to compliment his cooking skills. This tactic has served me well in the past.**
>
> "Good evening, Officer Stone." Chef Marcus's shoulders straighten, and he preens like a peacock. "Thank you. I'm glad you enjoyed them. **Coming from another accomplished chef, I'm flattered. My sister still raves about the eggs Benedict you whipped up at your family's B&B.**"
>
> **Mmm... That was one of my favorite meals to cook for our guests.**
>
> Alex snorts in disbelief. "Why can she call you Shorty?"
>
> "Because he's my tribe." I offer the chef my fist. He bumps me with his own. "We share short-people problems." I point my finger at Shorty. "Top shelf at the grocery store."
>
> The chef nods. "Step stool in the kitchen."
>
> "Good one." I chuckle and shrug. "He calls me 'Shorty,' too, when I'm off duty. Tribe member privileges. Sorry, but you guys exceed the maximum height criteria. Guess you'll have to make do with our names."

Short and simple. The key is to look for natural ways to integrate the backstory. I could've written this scene with the hero's sister moving into the second floor of the clothing store where she worked, next door to the jeweler. Instead, I chose to have the sister move above a bakery, next to a restaurant. This choice allowed me to introduce a piece of backstory into the current storyline seamlessly. The reader might not even realize I'm feeding them a nugget about the heroine's history because it isn't obvious. But I've planted the seed here that my heroine loved cooking for the guests at the family's B&B.

Caution #4: Longer is not better.

Reserve long stretches of dialogue or deep POV to reveal backstory that is most critical to the hero or heroine's GMC. For the most part, shorter is better when it comes to weaving in backstory. I generally try to keep backstory short and sweet, like my last example. You'll see this holds true in chapter nine of this book when I take you through an entire book from start to finish.

However, there are no hard and fast rules, and there are times when longer passages are warranted.

This holds true when you disclose backstory that directly impacts the main goal, motivation, or conflict in the current story. Let me show you an example from my small-town contemporary romance novel, *Ticket to Love*. Before we dive into the scene, let's read the book blurb:

> The first ticket I wrote him was for a parking violation, the second was in a pedestrian zone, the third ... I never wrote that one. That was our ticket to love.
>
> Until it wasn't...
>
> Turns out my one-night stand is actually my best friend's wedding planner. He's hanging out in our small town for the next three months, meeting with my friends, negotiating deals, and **oh—he's also the main suspect in my first police investigation**. The case I must solve to become a detective. And the crux of it all? I'm falling head over heels for the guy.

I've dreamed my whole life of this promotion. I thought I'd never find love. Now I'm afraid I might lose both.

The main storyline revolves around Kristy conducting an investigation in which the hero, Don, is a prime suspect. The dialogue in my next example is far more involved than the earlier example for a valid reason. I needed to reveal his shady past to cast doubt on the hero's trustworthiness through a credible source. So here is a conversation between the heroine and an old police academy classmate about the hero. I trimmed out the fat for purposes of this exercise:

"Hey, Kristy!"

I glance up. A man dodges cars while crossing the street, waving me down. **Stan Evans. We met over a year ago at the police academy, but this is our first run-in since then.** He took a job here in Grand Rapids if I recall.

"What brings you into town?" He gazes into the shop. "You're not getting married, are you?"

"Definitely not. I'm the maid of honor." I point inside. "You met the bride-to-be at our graduation. Do you remember my best friend, Sophia?"

His eyes narrow on her, and he nods. **"Is that her fiancé? Shit, I hope not."**

The fine hairs on my neck bristle. Stan knows everyone and everything.

"You know Don?" I ask with the lift of an eyebrow.

He snorts, then meets my gaze. **"We went to high school together.** His uncle is bad news. Got hauled into the station last week for another suspected B&E. One of the best con artists around."

That can't be right. "You sure we're talking about the same guy?"

Stan folds his arms. **"Yeah, that's him. He has a younger sister, Tonya. Strange bunch of misfits. None**

of the kids at school wanted anything to do with that family. They're all bad news."

But Don said Tonya was the only family he had left. Was that only a figure of speech because he cut ties with his uncle?

"What are you implying?" I want specifics, tangible evidence of wrongdoing. "Does Don have a record that you know of?"

He shakes his head. "Nothing he ever got caught for. What's he doing in there anyway?"

"Sophia hired him as her wedding planner. The testimonials on his website are impressive."

"Did he make them up?" Stan sniggers. "Don must be desperate for a date, looking for inroads with the bridesmaids. **Still a loser, I see."**

"Don is good at what he does. Give the guy a break. Maybe he's changed since high school. Kids don't pick their relatives."

"Sure," he says, walking away backward. **"Still, keep an eye on the gift table! You never know if his uncle taught him a few tricks. Wouldn't that be the scam of the century?"**

This conversation raises red flags about the hero while introducing information about his past. Is he or is he not a criminal? This gets to the essence of the conflict between the hero and heroine. She is a cop. He is a suspect in her investigation. Can she trust him when he says he is innocent?

Don had told Kristy that he didn't have any living relatives during their one-night stand. This happened before Don became a suspect in Kristy's investigation. Why did Don lie? His uncle is a criminal and Stan plants the seed that perhaps Don is too. Kristy tries to brush this off by saying that Don isn't guilty by association. But later in the story, when money is stolen at one of the bridal events, this conversation resurfaces in her mind. Who should she believe?

The man she's falling in love with or another cop who knew the hero growing up?

Caution #5: When POV and backstory don't mix.

Similar to what we discussed in the chapter on dreams, there should be a "trigger" or logical thought progression from the current storyline into the character's deep POV about backstory. Let's look at an example of backstory written in deep POV from my contemporary romance, *Fair Game*. The heroine, Leah, does not date doctors. So, of course, her love interest, Jared, is in medical school. Even worse, Jared is Leah's best friend's older brother, who usually acts like a complete jackass around her.

Chapter one of the book starts with Leah attending Jordan's twenty-fifth birthday party and "tricking" Jared into dancing with her all evening. She does this as a favor to her best friend, Jordan, so that Jared is occupied all night while Jordan makes the moves on his best friend.

Well, Leah and Jared end up having a fabulous time at Jordan's birthday party together. The guy is H.O.T., and Leah can't get him off her mind the next day. But…Leah's rule for not dating men in the medical profession is grounded in a deep, personal experience. This backstory forms the foundation for the romance conflict. Check out how I worked it into the current storyline at the beginning of chapter two:

> I set my car keys on the kitchen island and **put my earphones in while searching for my *new* favorite song, *The Other Side* by Jason Derulo**. Jordan and Grannie would be back from the bakery within thirty minutes and had already grabbed a bite to eat. So I went about collecting the ingredients I needed for a killer turkey on wheat sandwich. Having been Jordan's best friend ever since we met in middle school, I knew my way around the Billettes' kitchen like it was my own.

I sashayed across the kitchen floor, grabbed a small plate from the cupboard and began slicing tomato, onion and lettuce while moving my hips to the sexy beat of the music.

Closing my eyes for a few seconds, I relived the moment when Jared first pulled me into his arms on the dance floor, grinding his rock-hard body against mine. A small shudder passed through me as I recalled his sexy smile—square jaw with five o'clock shadow—and those penetrating dark eyes. Like I was the only person alive.

Was the charming and hunky guy who'd danced my feet off at Tequila Blue truly my best friend's brother? **Jared was always a self-centered jerk around me. Well, maybe not always, or certainly not in the beginning of my friendship with Jordan. His salty attitude started around the time I entered college. Perhaps the knowledge that he was going to be heading to medical school had puffed Jared up and brought out the true jackass in him.**

No surprise there! His personality fell in line with my other experiences. **I had only to look to my biological father, Richard, to know what kind of men gravitated toward the medical field: self-centered, egotistical and arrogant. It took a certain amount of narcissism for a man to believe himself capable of healing human frailties, and to place that God given talent before all other things in his life...even his own "little princess."**

I snorted and reached for **the diamond pendant necklace my father had given me for graduating college. Cold and impersonal—just like our relationship. Why couldn't he understand that I had no interest in being showered with expensive gifts? I would have traded every single damn gift he ever gave me to have him show up at one of my dance recitals. Experience had taught me a bitter lesson and for that reason, I promised myself never to date a man in the medical field. Ever. I'd already had my heart broken by my father** time and time again and I had absolutely no intention of repeating that heartbreak with a boyfriend.

Like I told Jordan, there are plenty of fish in the sea so I would gladly bypass the sharks. With that thought reverberating in my head, the song on my phone switched over to the next on the play list, as if confirming my decision to move on.

I reached for the mayonnaise and nearly jumped out of my skin when a pair of hands grabbed me by the hips. I swung around wielding the butter knife, prepared to defend my life.

"Whoa, girl," Jared called out, stepping back a pace and lifting his hands. "What the hell do you think you're doing?"

My eyes popped wide open as I stared at Jared in abject horror. Not because I had almost stabbed him, but rather because he stood half naked before me with sweat still glistening off his ridiculously sculpted torso. The sweat had gathered at the top of his gray spandex shorts, just below his belly button, where a trail of dark hair disappeared into the fabric.

I closed my eyes and took a deep, calming breath to prevent my gaze from wandering even further down along his body. Jared was a cocky bastard and didn't need any more encouragement or ammunition for puffing himself up.

"Don't sneak up on someone like that," I scolded and turned back to my sandwich, so my traitorous eyes wouldn't lust after his body. **I reminded myself Jared was off limits. No way. Not happening.** "I could've stabbed you. Shit! That scared me."

Notice the logical thought progression of the heroine in this scene.

- The playlist music triggers Leah's thoughts about Jared and their awesome time dancing the night before.

- She can't believe how wonderful he was, because normally he's a jerk.
- His salty behavior started once he began medical school.
- That leads Leah to think about her father, who is a surgeon.

And there you have it – she touches on the backstory in her deep POV. Now the reader knows why Leah has a heartfelt reason for never dating men in the medical profession. And more importantly, the past is dragged into the present so the heroine is called to action in the storyline. She was "wavering" on her resolve not to get involved with Jared. The past nudges her back on track [reference last bolded text in the above example].

Fair Game was the third book I wrote. In hindsight, Leah's deep POV on her father could've been shortened to only the part about her father being a self-centered jerk. The section in bold only, where Leah reaches for the pendant necklace, could've (and quite frankly should've) been deleted. There is a scene later in the book where Jared challenges Leah on her opinion of her father and she points to the fact that Richard only gives gift but never spends time with her.

On a side note, the romance conflict in *Fair Game* is one of those "no-no" concepts that most editors puke all over. "I don't date cops" (or surgeons or fill in whatever you want) doesn't usually make for a strong enough conflict. Remember when I said I call bullshit when people tell me I can't do something? Never say never.

The reason I chose this conflict is because I wanted to write a romance story that was grounded in the concepts from Gary Chapman's *The Five Love Languages*. I adore this book, and the concept he teaches makes a helluva lot of sense.

Leah assumes that all people in the medical field will be like her father and put their career and money before family. She doesn't want that kind of life with her future husband. That's reasonable. What she doesn't realize is that her father expresses love through "gift giving" because he grew up poor and never had the finer things in life. From his viewpoint, he has been showering his daughter in love. But Leah feels loved by spending quality time with people. So the fact that her father always worked and never spent time with her hurt deeply.

Can you guess Jared's love language? He is also a "quality time" person. So even though he is going into medicine, he always makes time for the ones he loves. I showed this throughout the story, with the first example being in chapter one when Jared shows up at his sister's birthday party and stays all night.

I also amped up the conflict by having Jared hold Richard in high esteem. Even better, the two men worked together on a special project at the university, so Jared interacted with Leah's father directly. This is an example of where I plotted my story and then worked backward to decide which backstory details pushed my characters; buttons and forced them into action the current storyline.

Ah, I love *Fair Game*.

> **Hint:** Finding unique and interesting ways to incorporate backstory into your novel is fun for the author and interesting for the reader.

In *Date Night*, the heroine, Jordan, and her grannie work on a scrapbook together to memorialize all of the major milestones in Jordan's life. They do this to honor her dead father so he can "share" in her experiences. After they scrapbook, each of them writes a letter to Jordan's father. This was a fun and unique way to offer the reader some of the key background information.

I challenge you to think of fun and interesting ways to incorporate backstory through dialogue or deep POV. Don't use an entire scene when a single sentence will do. But if the past event is critical to the current storyline, give it the weight it deserves. Employ humor. Or keep it serious. There are infinite ways of imparting backstory through the use of dialogue and deep POV, so explore and have a blast while you're at it.

CHAPTER NINE
In Closing...

Wow! That was a lot of information to digest. Your head may be reeling right now. Thank you for staying with me on the journey to discover how to write backstory into your novel. We've covered examples from different genres so you could see firsthand how to put these techniques into practice.

I've armed you with tips and tricks and shown you how to incorporate your characters' pasts into their current storyline in a way that feels natural. While all of the messages covered in this book are important, a few key points are imperative to remember and apply consistently in every story:

- Anything related to the past that is introduced into the current storyline **must** be solidly linked to a character's present GMC, whether it's the hero, heroine, or villain.

- No matter which method you choose to incorporate backstory, find a way to drag the past into the present that feels natural to the reader (i.e. logical progression of thought or triggering events that arise out of the current storyline).

- Always ensure that your characters behave in a manner consistent with his/her upbringing and the major events that shaped his/her life.

- When used properly, backstory will add a level of depth to your characters that shines through to your readers and keeps them enthralled.

- While there are no hard or fast rules, here is the list of methods to incorporate backstory and when they really pack a punch:
  - o Prologues—great for increasing the suspense in the current storyline, showing how a fairy tale or fable came into existence or showing the inciting event that shaped the protagonist (i.e. GMC).
  - o Dreams—work well when the protagonist is suppressing memories or is haunted by a tragic event.
  - o Flashbacks/memories—let the reader walk in the shoes of the protagonist and build empathy or understanding for the character's actions or intentions.
  - o Deep POV—always a good way to introduce backstory but look for creative ways to trigger thoughts of the past in the character's mind or you risk putting your reader to sleep.
  - o Dialogue—arguably the easiest to use when all else fails but make the conversation as natural as possible.
  - o Other—limited only by your imagination and can include news articles, letters, scrapbooks, diaries, or spells, to name a few.

All of the concepts we discussed are crucial to master if you want your story to resonate with readers, but how do you pull everything together? I think the best way to illustrate how to weave backstory into your novel is to show you through a practical example. If you are interested in seeing how I incorporated the background of my characters into the current storyline of *The Secrets of Chateau Swansea*, please continue to chapter ten. Otherwise, I wish you luck with your next release.

If you enjoyed reading *How to Write Backstory Into Your Novel* and found this book helpful, please take a moment to write a review on any of the major retailers. I love hearing from readers, so please feel free to contact me through my website www.rcmatthews.com. I'm also active on Twitter and Facebook, so you can drop me a line there too.

Other resources I've read / used and recommend:
Understanding Show, Don't Tell (And Really Getting It) by Janice Hardy. Her book contains many excellent examples and works through the concept at the sentence, paragraph, and scene levels. The author also provides wonderful guidance on how to identify when you're telling so you can decide whether you ought to show instead. That's half the battle!

Another excellent tool to help you identify when you're "telling" is the online editor AutoCrit. I used that program for six of my books. Eventually, avoiding the words that are indicators of "telling" becomes second nature.

2,000 to 10,000 Writing Faster, Writing Better, and Writing More of What You Love by Rachel Aaron is a wonderful resource to help you organize your thoughts and put structure to your writing process. Her method can be applied by both plotters and pantsers.

R.C. Matthews is the author of contemporary and historical romances featuring bold, sassy heroines and magnetic alpha heroes. Warning! The chemistry between her characters is off-the-charts hot, so read at your own risk. She resides in the Midwest and is surrounded by men: her husband and three sons. During her free time, you'll find her watching *The Walking Dead*, reading a fabulous book, or hanging out with her family.

Discover books by R.C. Matthews

Gothic Romance
Devil's Cove
Blackburn Castle
River Road
The Secrets of Chateau Swansea
Forsaken (coming October 2019)

Contemporary Romance
Date Night
Fair Game
Begin Again
The Mastermind
A Night to Remember
Little White Lies

Erotic Romance
Make Me Whole
Breaking His Rules
Who Needs Love When You Have a Cyborg Lover?

Teen Fantasy
The Dragon Sorceress
The Vampire Queen

CHAPTER TEN

A Practical Example from Start to Finish

In the following pages, you will find my entire story *The Secrets of Chateau Swansea,* which is about 280 pages. I've highlighted every instance of backstory in bold text and provide commentary in the footnotes on why I chose to include that specific bit of backstory. This story is both a gothic romance and a cozy mystery, so for all of the backstory related to the cozy mystery, I have underlined the text that relates to past events critical to solving the mystery.

Hopefully, after reading the entire story, you can finally understand what your editor or critique group means when they say to sprinkle in the backstory. As always, let's start with the book blurb since this is the story that inspired the reader to part with their money and invest their precious time reading. Ready. Set. Go!

> An heiress. A working-class man. A star-crossed love on a haunted estate.
>
> Psychic Maribeth Sommerset investigates a grisly murder in a haunted chateau at the bidding of the estate's steward, Arthur Dunn. He plays a dangerous game of deception, landing himself at the top of Maribeth's suspect list. But even as she falls for him, she can't help but wonder if he's the man of her dreams or a deadly fraudster.
>
> Amid scandalous secrets and destructive lies, the killer claims a second life, and Maribeth scrambles to unravel the secrets of Chateau Swansea before she becomes the next victim.
>
> Light your candle, shore up your courage, and enter a haunted estate for a thrilling Victorian gothic romance!

Let me say a word about the goal, motivation, and conflict of this story since all of the backstory included within the book should be integral to the GMC of the hero or heroine. Below is my outline using Debra Dixon's wonderful charting method. I highly recommend her book, *GMC: Goal, Motivation and Conflict.*

	Heroine External	**Hero** External	**Heroine** Internal	**Hero** Internal
Goal Wants…	Maribeth is a psychic who wants to solve haunted mysteries; because	Arthur wants to shield his employer's good name; because	Maribeth wants to find someone who loves her despite her sordid past; because	Arthur wants a life free of deception and to be respected by others; because
Motivation Because…	She empathizes with victims and her unique gifts shouldn't go wasted; but	Stanley changed Arthur's life irrevocably for the good when he hired him; but	She doesn't quite belong to the social class of her guardian; but	His parents are traveling fortune-tellers who earn a living off lies; but
Conflict But…	As an heiress in the 19th century, finding work proves difficult.	In order for Arthur to shield his employer, he must incriminate himself.	She fears rejection by all men due to the scars she bears from childhood.	Deep down, Arthur worries he isn't worthy of respect, given his past.

Within the first chapter of the story, the reader learns that Maribeth is the ward of a marquess and heiress to a sizable dowry. In contrast, the hero is a working-class man. Marriage between the gentry and the working-class in 1889 simply wasn't done! This creates an immediate and natural inner conflict for why the hero and heroine cannot be together (i.e. the romance conflict). If the hero gives into his desire to claim Maribeth as his wife, he will damn her to a life of ridicule by society.

What isn't revealed in the blurb is the hero's abhorrence of the heroine's choice of profession. However, this becomes evident by the end of chapter one and adds to the romance conflict (i.e. what keeps the hero and heroine apart).

Also notice that Maribeth worries she may become the next victim. But why? Read on to find out more.

Below is background information on each of my characters. **Spoiler alert!** If you would rather read the story and revisit their background later, please skip to chapter one of the book. Otherwise, continue. But be forewarned, the backstory is complex.

Anything that is "discovered history' (i.e. unknown to the two main characters at the time the current storyline starts) is in *italics*. Everything underlined is revealed in the book. In addition, I've indicated the chapter where the backstory appears and the method I used to reveal it. Here is my legend:

Dialogue = DIA
Deep POV = POV
Dream = DRM
Letter = LTR
Suppressed memory = SM
News article = NEWS

So, after each relevant section of backstory, you will see [C# – Method]. Notice that I spread the history over the entire story save for the very last chapter. That's what I call "sprinkling in" backstory. Little by little, the past merges with the present. Also take note of all the background that is not underlined and, therefore, not revealed in the current storyline.

Welcome to the cast of *The Secrets of Chateau Swansea*.

Maribeth Sommerset (heroine): *Bella Turner was born in Swansea, England on April 28, 1869, to Arabella Brown and Stanley Turner [C10 – DIA]. Her mother died in childbirth [C6 – DIA] and Bella was raised at Chateau Swansea by her loving father [C10 – DIA]. He often read to her from* The Owl *and the Pussycat [C5 – SM] and rocked her in a rocking chair [C10 – SM]. They shared a special bond. She was his "merry Bella." [C17 – DIA] He commissioned a beautiful playhouse to be built in* *the forest on the Chateau Swansea estate. A swing hung just outside the playhouse, and Bella fell once, cutting her palm [C11 – SM / C23 – DIA].*

Father and daughter were happy until Stanley married Caroline Wilson, the evil step-mother. Caroline and Bella had several altercations. *One time, Bella dropped a vase in the foyer and Caroline slapped the child's hand viciously [C5 – SM]. Caroline also forced Bella to carry out a séance in front of a group of strangers [C7 – DIA / SM]. Caroline also encouraged the governess to lock Bella in a dark closet without a lantern as punishment [C15 – DIA / SM]. Bella disappeared (i.e. presumably was abducted) at the age of four while her father was away on a business trip [C7 – DIA / C22 – DRM]. She was placed under the care of the sister of Chateau Swansea's housekeeper [C22 – DIA]. The trauma of Bella's abduction caused her to forget everything about her life prior to the abduction [C22 – POV]. Bella called the housekeeper's poor sister "mama" [C4 – POV], and her "mama" called the child Maribeth (derived from "my merry Bella" [C22 – DRM], see more under* Stanley Turner*).*

NOTE: To be clear, Maribeth has suppressed memories of her life as Bella, which manifest themselves in the current storyline in a way very similar to what a clairvoyant would experience. So while Maribeth had shown signs of only being a medium (i.e. psychic) up to this point in her life, she wonders if she is also clairvoyant like one of her guardians, Eveline Sommerset. Writing these suppressed memories was so much fun! I took my own challenge to look for interesting ways to incorporate backstory.

Shortly after her abduction, Maribeth started to work as a trapper girl [hints of this in C1 revealed in C7 – POV] in the coal mine known as Wheal Turner [C24 – DIA]. About a year later, the foreman of the coal mine sold Maribeth to a slaver, and she never saw her "mama" again [C19 – DIA].

While sailing from England to South Africa on the slave ship, Maribeth stole food from the kitchen and received ten lashes of the whip for her thievery [C19 – DIA]. Another pirate ship captained by Dominick Sommerset (known then as Devlin Limmerick, "The Devil") [C4 – DIA] invaded the slave ship carrying Maribeth.

Dominick took pity on the girl and rescued her [C19 – DIA] because he too had been sold into slavery as a child. Maribeth lived on Dominick's pirate ship [C1 – POV] for five years and developed a close relationship with the captain as well as the first and second mates (Victor Blackburn and Charles "Hatchet" Moore). After Dominick gave up pirating to reclaim his title as the Marquess of Covington and settled down in Devil's Cove, he became Maribeth's legal guardian and she took his surname [C4 – DIA].

When Dominick hired a gifted medium (Eveline) to rid the haunted Devil's Cove Manor of evil spirits, Maribeth soon discovered her own abilities to speak with the dead. While they lived at Devil's Cove Manor, there was a disaster and many people were reputedly killed by Josephine, also known as the gatekeeper to Hell [C4 – DIA]. Living in a truly haunted manor provided many opportunities for Maribeth to hone her skills. Especially when Dominick, Eveline, Victor, and Hatchet fled unexpectedly for Blackburn Castle without her, leaving her under the care of Brother Anselm.

Shortly after returning from Blackburn Castle, Dominick and Eveline departed for their honeymoon. Meanwhile, Victor and Hatchet headed to New Orleans so Hatchet could finally put an end to the curse hanging over his head. Maribeth was again left under the care of Brother Anselm. Or so they thought. She wasn't going to be left behind a second time and instead stole away on Victor's ship [C1 – POV]! Good thing she did, too, because her skills as a medium eventually saved Hatchet's life [C4 – DIA].

Soon thereafter, Maribeth settled into a blessed life with her guardians Dominick and Eveline at Devil's Cove Manor. Maribeth wanted for nothing. She later attended Château Mont-Choisi finishing school in Lausanne, Switzerland, where she became fast friends with Edith [C1 – POV and DIA]. She was suddenly surrounded by ladies who came from privilege and wealth. One did not speak of having worked in a coal mine or being whipped for stealing. She was a "lady" and expected to conduct herself accordingly. But Maribeth never quite fit into that crowd. She longed for the adventures of her youth when she sailed on a ship or hunted ghosts [C1 – POV].

Her guardian generously bestowed a dowry on her. However, he made a deal with Maribeth. If she could prove that she could support herself by working as a psychic investigator, he would give Maribeth her dowry outright. Otherwise, Maribeth had to attend a ball given in her honor to search for a husband [C3 – DIA].

And so begins the story of *The Secrets of Chateau Swansea*.

Arthur Dunn (hero): Arthur Dunn was born in 1860 in Mayhill, England. His parents were fortune-tellers who performed in the traveling circus. They were frauds and swindled people out of their hard-earned money [C2 – DIA]. Arthur despised their way of life because he could never put down roots or develop true friendships [C7 – DIA]. His mother was exceptionally talented at reading body language in order to give accurate readings [C10 – DIA]. In turn, Arthur learned tricks of the trade from his parents and was adept at lying/deceiving others [C4 – POV], which also made him capable of detecting other fraudsters. All he wants is to "belong" to a community and live an honest life.

When the circus came to Swansea, England, Stanley Turner visited the fortune-tellers because he was desperate for any information on his daughter's whereabouts. She had been missing for six years. After listening to the man's plight, Arthur refused to collect the fee his parent normally charged. Arthur told Stanley not to listen to a word his parents had said. Stanley appreciated his honesty and took sympathy on the nineteen-year-old Arthur. Stanley offered Arthur a position in his household as the understudy to the steward **if** Arthur would help him locate Bella [C10 – DIA]. Arthur jumped at the opportunity for "decent" work. Stanley wanted Arthur to interview young ladies claiming to be Bella and apply his "bullshit" barometer [C10 – DIA]. Over the years, Arthur interviewed more than fifty candidates, so he was skeptical of anyone claiming to be Bella Turner.

His parents didn't keep in touch much after that point, except to occasionally ask for money [C10 – DIA]. This was fine since Arthur finally had what he always wanted. He fit in well as a servant to the master of Chateau Swansea, and <u>he had no illusions about his station in life. There was a socially acceptable hierarchy in the world that he gladly adhered</u> [C4 – POV / C26 – DIA] to in order to maintain the life of a respectable man.

<u>Arthur grew close to Stanley during the ten years working at Chateau Swansea [C2 / C6 – POV] and the men developed a genuine affection for one another. So much so that Stanley gave Arthur power of attorney over his vast empire if Stanley should ever become incapacitated and his one legitimate heir died (i.e. his cousin, Mr. Young). Further, if Bella was not found by her twenty-fifth birthday, the Turner wealth would belong to Arthur [C13 – DIA].</u>

Out of affection for Arthur, <u>Stanley gifted a house on the estate to Arthur</u> [C10 – POV] so he would enjoy some privacy and finally have a home of his own. Arthur was beyond grateful to Stanley for all that he'd done for him. <u>So when Caroline Turner demanded that Arthur engage in an affair with her, he adamantly refused [C10 – DIA and POV].</u>

Caroline ensured Arthur knew his place in society. He never crossed the line by presuming himself to be "better" than he really was. Not that Caroline Turner would have allowed that in her household either. <u>So while Arthur enjoyed Stanley's friendship in the privacy of their own company behind closed doors, he respected his employer enough to always address him in public as Mr. Turner [C23 / C26 – DIA]. Needless to say, Arthur was one thousand percent devoted to his employer [C2 / C6 / C10 – POV].</u>

And so begins the story of *The Secrets of Chateau Swansea.*

Arabella Brown (heroine's mother): Arabella Brown was born in England. Her father was an English merchant well known and respected in Swansea, and her mother was a French artist. Her parents built a beautiful manor house and called it Chateau Swansea in honor of her mother's heritage. <u>Arabella became a famous clairvoyant [C1 – DIA].</u> After her parents died in a tragic accident and Arabella fell on hard times, <u>she turned one of the rooms at Chateau Swansea into a séance chamber where she held frequent</u>

rituals for a fee [C1 – DIA]. Guests were invited to stay overnight, and she entertained them with readings and other amusements.

One day, Stanley Turner came to the chateau with friends. Arabella and Stanley were an unlikely pair, but they fell in love. [C10 – DIA] *Although Stanley begged Arabella to marry him, she refused for two years because she didn't wish to harm his reputation as a businessman [C26 – DIA].* He owned numerous coal mines, and, as a wealthy man, he enjoyed a high social ranking in the town of Swansea. Only days before Arabella gave birth to their daughter, Stanley convinced her to marry him. But Arabella died of complications shortly after childbirth [C10 – DIA]. Her ghost lingered on the estate [C2 – DIA], for she could not leave her daughter motherless. And so Chateau Swansea became known as a haunted estate.

Stanley Turner (heroine's father): Stanley Turner inherited his wealth from his family who were in the business of mining coal in the Rhondda Valley. He was rich and happy but a bit more on the serious side. When his friends suggested a weekend at Chateau Swansea to experience a séance, he was skeptical but willing. He soon fell in love with the famous clairvoyant, Arabella Brown, and would've given up everything to be with her. Yet she refused him time and time again, even after becoming pregnant with his child. He finally convinced her to marry him so that her child would be legitimate. But marital bliss lasted only a few days because Arabella died shortly after childbirth. *On her deathbed, Stanley promised to give a ruby ring to their daughter once she was older in remembrance of Arabella [C25 – DIA].*

Stanley loved his daughter fiercely and raised her at Chateau Swansea where she could be close to her mother "in spirit" and grow up where her mother grew up. He eventually remarried in order to give Bella a mother figure in her life. He chose Caroline Wilson because she came from a good family but was not too proud. She was also young and would have plenty of energy to raise a toddler girl. However, everything changed when they were married. Caroline loved Stanley's wealth and the social status they enjoyed [C2 – DIA].

Stanley was devastated when his four-year-old daughter Bella was abducted while he was on a business trip. He searched everywhere for her and hired the best investigators, but nothing was ever discovered. *A year after his daughter disappeared, there was a disaster at one of his mines called Wheal Turner. Almost all the workers died [C16 – NEWS]. Stanley sold his coal mines and invested in steel instead and made a fortune during the industrial revolution [C24 – DIA].* He used the money to continue his search for Bella.

However, six years later, he was still no closer to finding her. That's when he visited Arthur's parents at the traveling circus and made Arthur an offer of employment to continue his search for Bella. His marriage to Caroline deteriorated quickly after Bella's disappearance. *She was cold and didn't understand his need to turn every stone looking for his daughter [C8 – LTR].* He became more distant. *She turned to other men for sexual gratification. Stanley didn't care anymore [C6 – DIA].*

That was, until Caroline got pregnant by one of her illicit lovers [C3 – NEWS] and demanded that Stanley accept the child as his rightful heir. The timing was impossible because Stanley was on business in America. He refused to acknowledge her child as his and instead threatened to divorce Caroline upon his return from America [C8 – LTR]. She confessed to having arranged for Bella's abduction and promised to divulge the truth if Stanley would acknowledge her child as the rightful heir [C16 – LTR]. He agreed to her terms in a letter but secretly made arrangements for a divorce [C22 – DIA].

Their relationship was over. He would take back control of his house and life. *So he sent his favorite photograph of Arabella to an artist to be turned into a painting that would hang over the fireplace in his bedchamber [C16 – POV]. Once completed, he commissioned a frame from the best shop in Swansea [C8 – DIA].*

When he returned from America, he called his solicitor to the house to exchange the divorce papers. *Caroline was furious when he entered her bedchamber and handed her the papers on the balcony. She ripped the papers up, threw them in the fireplace, and told him Bella had died in the explosion at Wheal Turner [C22 – DIA].* Caroline had made Bella work in one of Stanley's dirty coal mines. *He earned his wealth off his daughter's back [C24 – POV].* Stanley simply indicated that he would draw up another set of divorce papers. *She charged at him, and he stepped aside [C22 – DIA].* Caroline fell over the edge of the balcony and landed in the pond below. Her neck snapped on impact. Stanley *is crushed by the news of Bella* and falls into a catatonic state [C2 – DIA].

And so begins the story of *The Secrets of Chateau Swansea.*

Caroline Turner (heroine's evil step-mother): Born to a lawyer and homemaker, Caroline Turner wished for more in life. She was ecstatic when she met Stanley and he proposed marriage. So what if he had a toddler? Bella had a governess to raise her. Everything was wonderful in the beginning. Stanley was an attentive and generous husband. But after one year, he started working again and traveling. Caroline became bored while he was gone. And the ghost of Arabella Brown began haunting her [C2 / C8 – DIA] whenever Caroline mistreated Bella. Especially when Caroline tried to use the child to offer séances in Arabella's old séance chamber [C7 – DIA]. The ghost's reaction scared the bloody hell out of Caroline. Finally, Caroline could not take it anymore and devised a plan to get rid of the little brat once and for all. Perhaps then Arabella would go to Hell where she belonged.

Caroline threatened to fire the housekeeper if she didn't help her kidnap the child. So the housekeeper said her son would abduct Bella and her sister would take the child [C22 – DIA] for a small monthly stipend. The only issue that remained was how to get the child off the premises without raising an alarm. Caroline waited until Stanley was on a business trip. Then Caroline's sister, Helen, visited in her carriage. While Bella played in her playhouse in the forest, the housekeeper's son snuck up behind her, stuffed a rag in her mouth and put a bag over her head [C22 – DRM]. He deposited her in Mrs. Marsh's carriage, and Mrs. Marsh had the child delivered to the housekeeper's sister in the Rhondda Valley on May 5, 1873 [C25 – DIA and LTR].

But that wasn't enough. Caroline wanted to torture the girl the way she had been tortured by Arabella's ghost. So the child was sent to work in one of Stanley's coal mines. One year later, an explosion at Wheal Turner killed all the workers. The disaster was so bad that many of the bodies were never recovered. The housekeeper's sister reported back through Mrs. Marsh that the child never surfaced after the explosion [C25 – DIA and LTR].

So when Caroline told Stanley that Bella was dead, she believed that was the truth.

Below is the list of potential suspects for the murder besides Arthur, the ghost of Madame Brown, and Stanley Turner. Every good mystery has multiple suspects.

Mrs. Marsh (Caroline Turner's sister): Helen Marsh and Caroline Turner were very close as sisters—obviously, since Helen carried out a criminal act on behalf of her sister. But Bella was a little brat, and she was given to a loving replacement family. Helen married the chief investigator on the police force. One week before Caroline's death, Helen and Caroline held a séance in Arabella's séance chamber; the ghost of Arabella was furious [C2 – DIA]. Helen knew Caroline was pregnant and that the child wasn't Stanley's. She was always aware that he had threatened her sister [C2 – DIA].

Emily Hawkins (Chateau Swansea housekeeper): Ah, and so we come to Mrs. Hawkins, the housekeeper. She had been a faithful servant first to Arabella Brown and then to Stanley and Caroline Turner [C2 – POV]. Emily's son and daughter were teenagers. Her husband was sickly. The housekeeper had mouths to feed. The housekeeper position paid very well. She couldn't afford to lose the income. So when the lady of the house threatened to fire her without a reference if she did not help, she went along with the abduction and arranged for her sister to take Bella. Her sister was a wonderful woman and would treat the child with love [C22 – DIA].

Mr. Gabriel Young (Stanley Turner's cousin): Stanley's cousin would inherit the Turner fortune if Bella Turner could not be found. In fact, he counted on inheriting so he could pay of his mounting debts from gambling [C6 – DIA]. The day before Caroline Turner died, Gabriel and Caroline had a verbal spat. Gabriel visited to beg for an advance on his inheritance. Caroline badmouthed him for his poor manners, and Gabriel goaded her by saying he would turn her out penniless once Stanley died. Caroline smugly informed him that she was pregnant with the next rightful heir [C9 – DIA].

Edgar Webber (Chateau Swansea butler) / Mr. Keppler (gardener): The snooty butler and the gardener were both reputed to have had an affair with Caroline Turner, so either man may have been the one to kill her in a jealous fit of rage.

Mrs. Pickering (Chateau Swansea cook): Caroline threatened to toss her out because the mistress of the house was growing fat from the deliciously rich fare served by the cook.

Enjoy the book!

Chapter One

Swansea, England
1889

A crack of thunder rumbled through the pane of glass separating Maribeth Sommerset from the torrential downpour. Inside the café of the Inn at Oxwich, she was protected against the elements. Outside, nobody strolled on the sidewalk or dashed across the street to hail a hack. The otherwise bustling street was empty, save for a single coach parked outside Chapman Brothers across the way.

A gentleman exited the frame shop, his shoulders square and his jaw tight. The wind whipped the edges of his black coat around his legs and his hat flew off, tumbling away on the sidewalk in a wicked dance. Within seconds, his black hair was plastered against his forehead.

He barked orders to the coachman, who jumped off his perch, rounding the box to open the coach door with haste. Shaking his head in apparent disgust, the gentleman flipped open an umbrella as two more men walked out of the shop with measured steps, carrying a sizeable package wrapped in brown paper. Their arms were stretched to the limits, their hands braced on each end of their bounty.

Droplets of rain pelted against the sleek outer surface of their raincoats, but they didn't allow the fierce weather to distract them from their duty. What sort of portrait warranted a visit to the framer on such a bleak day?

"Have you heard a single word I've said in the past five minutes, Maribeth?"

She glanced away from the curious scene across the street and met her best friend's perturbed stare. "I'm sorry, Edith, but I confess that I have not. What were you saying?"

A wry smile greeted her. "Mama believes Lord Bolton will attend your coming out ball next month in London. He rarely ventures into society. You will be the talk of the *ton*. What if he makes an offer for your hand?"

Maribeth rolled her eyes. "Let's hope not. I'm far too young for marriage."

"You're twenty, which is far too old for coming out," her friend countered. "It's time you took a husband. As a married woman myself, I cannot accompany you on these adventures much longer. God willing, I will be with child soon."

"My prayers are with you," Maribeth said with a smile. "However, I cannot promise that I'll marry someday. My future doesn't include a townhouse in Piccadilly or pushing a pram through Hyde Park. I'm afraid Château Mont-Choisi was a frightful waste of my guardian's money. Finishing school did little to improve my prospects of marriage."

She peered outside once more, tilting her head to see beyond the back end of the coach to where the men still wrestled with the large package. The commanding gentleman with dripping dark hair motioned for the lackeys to turn the oblong painting horizontal.

"Madame Bisset would shudder to hear you confess as much," Edith said. "She vowed to make a lady of you, and contrary to your arguments, I daresay she has."

Me, a lady? Even so, she wouldn't make a suitable wife. **Maribeth rubbed the pad of her thumb against the tips of her fingers, seeking the gritty remnants of her youth, but they were washed away long ago. The secrets of her past lay beneath the surface, hidden from everyone. If exposed, her**

scars would scandalize the ladies and gentlemen of her acquaintance.[1]

Across the street, the driver had taken his seat at the helm. The gentleman with the umbrella followed the progress of the departing coach for a moment before venturing into the street, headed straight for the entrance of the Inn at Oxwich. His stride was brisk and without fanfare.

"Should I pen a note to Lord Covington," Edith asked, "requesting that he invite this gentleman to your soiree? You simply cannot take your eyes off of him. He is handsome, I grant you."

Why must Edith turn the focus of every discussion to suitors? Maribeth took up a forkful of her cherry tart. She bit into the confection, savoring the richness of the gooey center.

"You have an overactive imagination, Edith. My mind is presently fixated on the sinister dealings of a madman. Who fetches artwork in the midst of a storm? Did you notice the crest on the coach? That package is being delivered to Chateau Swansea, former residence of the most famous clairvoyant ever to grace this earth."

Edith stared over the rim of her teacup, her eyes widening. "Well, there's the pot calling the kettle black. Your imagination knows no bounds. Dark, mysterious transactions do not occur within the four walls of the Chapman Brothers' establishment. Even Queen Victoria is known to have commissioned one of their frames. Their craftsmanship is unparalleled."

Only her best friend would spout that trifling bit of news and ignore the titillating piece of gossip regarding a renowned clairvoyant.

"How very unkind of you to point that out," Maribeth said. "My musings were far more entertaining. Perhaps we'll see this mysterious painting during our visit to Chateau Swansea today." Tossing her linen napkin onto her plate, she stood. "Shall we go?

---

[1] This passage provides the first hint that the heroine and hero might be compatible despite their social class differences (i.e. the romance conflict). The heroine's memory arises out of something her friend said in the context of the current story. In addition, this nugget only hints that something from Maribeth's past is scandalous (i.e. the heroine's inner conflict). This incites curiosity in the reader.

Our hired carriage will arrive soon, and I forgot my notebook upstairs. Come, let us be off."

Edith groaned. "But the weather is dreadful. I do not relish the thought of traveling in this rain."

"Oh, hush." She snaked her arm through Edith's, dragging her friend to the adjoining entrance of the hotel lobby.

A pox on the weather! These were the moments she lived for. **They were as close as she ever came to the adventures of her youth when she lived on a pirate ship.**[2] Once they were inside the infamous, reputedly haunted chateau, her friend would be silenced by the sheer beauty of the place. The photographs Maribeth had uncovered while planning for this trip were quite promising.

"I'll never understand your wanderlust and morbid fascination with ghosts," Edith whined. "I will fall into a dead faint should we encounter one during our tour of the séance chamber."

"Then I will stay close by your side and catch you."

Few beyond Maribeth's guardians ever understood her. Exploring the supernatural was as vital to her well-being as breathing air. Nothing would please her more than touring the Continent in search of specters and solving impossible mysteries with her God-given talent.

This wasn't the eighteenth century! A young lady of means could travel to distant, exotic places or pursue a career. Edith was far better suited for embroidery and pincushions. But finding clients willing to pay for Maribeth's services as a medium was proving difficult. Still, she would not abandon her dream.

Edith paused at the base of the grand staircase and squeezed Maribeth's hands. "Be serious, for once. My greatest wish is for our children to grow up together. Promise me you'll dance with all the willing gentleman at your ball and fall in love."

---

[2] Maribeth was raised unconventionally. She loved living on a pirate ship and viewed that time as adventurous. This means she has interacted regularly with men below her social class in the past. The reader can surmise from this that Maribeth might be capable of falling in love with the steward (i.e. the romance conflict). This backstory is naturally revealed here because the heroine is about to embark on an adventure while visiting a haunted chateau.

Love was for gently bred ladies, full of hope **and untouched by fate's brutal backhand**. There were too many tortured souls in the world who could benefit from Maribeth's gift. **Besides, after stealing away on a ship bound for America and communicating with ghosts, why settle for marriage and a house in London?**[3] Her purpose in life was self-evident, and she would fulfill it, if given the opportunity, even at the risk of disappointing her best friend.

"Of course I will dance every set." **She owed as much to her guardians, Dominick and Eveline, Lord and Lady Covington.**[4] "But don't hold your breath waiting for one of my suitors to make an offer of marriage."

"Whyever not?" Edith asked, cupping Maribeth's cheeks. "You're lovely."

"No, I'm not. I speak whatever words come to mind, my tongue is as pointed as an arrow's tip[5], and I cannot recall the proper placement of silverware when setting the table." With the arch of an eyebrow, she dared her best friend to refute the truth. Edith's silence served as all the confirmation required, and she continued, "Besides, a husband would only deter me from the one true love of my life."

Edith sighed. "Haunted houses."

"Just so," she said with a smirk. "Don't forget the abbeys, castles, and dilapidated schools."

Tugging on her gloves, Edith waved her away. "You are impossible. Go fetch your notebook while I inquire after our hired coach."

---

[3] Maribeth was "touched by fate's brutal backhan" (external motivation and internal conflict), which is vague but intriguing. This should stimulate the reader's appetite to know more about what happened to her. Also, Maribeth had stolen away on a ship bound for America at one point in her life, so she is a bit reckless or impetuous. All of those intriguing aspects of her personality point to a woman who might shirk the dictates of society and marry a steward (i.e. the romance conflict).

[4] Maribeth's social status becomes evident here. She is the ward of a lord and lady (i.e. the romance conflict). However, this comes out quite naturally as part of the current storyline's conversation over her coming out ball.

[5] This is an example of Maribeth's personality being consistent with her background. She was raised on a pirate ship with a bunch of sailors, so she has a colorful vocabulary, as you'll see later in the book.

Lifting her skirt, Maribeth dashed up the stairs.

"Miss Sommerset, wait!" the bellman called out.

She glanced over her shoulder and stopped as he approached with an envelope outstretched in his hand. "This arrived for you earlier."

Turning to accept the missive, she read the direction on the letter as he strode away. Lady Eveline Covington, 687 Gatekeeper Lane, Devil's Cove, England. Probably a note to remind her to meet her guardians in London soon.

She glanced up and her gaze connected with the darkest brown eyes she'd ever known. The gentleman from the frame shop stood near the doors to the hotel, holding his wet cloak over his arm. He was neither tall nor short. His trousers and jacket were serviceable, neither refined nor tattered. Nothing about him drew attention, except the utter stillness of his stance and the intensity of his stare. An odd look flittered over his face for an instant, with a slight parting of his lips. The exact nature of his expression eluded her.

Perhaps awe, mayhap disgust.

Either way, his perusal of her person was blatant and thorough. Her heart thudded a maddening rhythm in her chest. She refused to look away. Nay, she could not turn away. Why did she fascinate him? Perhaps he despised the curls in her hair, left to hang freely down her back. Or her almost child-like stature. Admittedly, she was small, even for a woman. But she wasn't a circus act to be gawked at.

"Excuse me, Mr. Dunn, a coach has arrived," the bellman said, gesturing outside.

The spell the gentleman had woven around her senses broke. She fled the rest of the way up the stairs, her pace brisk until she closed the door of her bedchamber behind her. Sagging against the door, she closed her eyes and inhaled. She was a grown woman, not a freak of nature. Dozens of gentleman were attending her ball to claim her hand in a dance.

Because of the dowry Dominick bestowed upon me.

She would not think about her coming out ball or the rude gentleman in the lobby any longer. This may very well be the last holiday she took with Edith. She would enjoy the afternoon touring

Chateau Swansea. After packing her notebook into her reticule, Maribeth hastened to rejoin her friend.

Edith sat primly on one of the benches, observing the patrons moving freely between the hotel and café.

"You needn't have hurried," she said with a bite of irritation lacing her words. "Our hired coach was hijacked by *your* gentleman, a Mr. Dunn, I believe."

Maribeth leveled an icy glare on the bellman. "Quite ungallant of you to allow him to steal our ride in this foul weather."

"My apologies." The bellman nodded briskly.

Forty-five minutes later, they were finally on their way to the chateau. The storm raged on, wind and rain assaulting the carriage. Maribeth could scarce see the outline of her best friend sitting across from her in the cabin. Soon, the air turned cold and damp.

A mounting pressure weighed on her chest as the foggy memories of her youth crept into her mind. Hours of solitude in a dank, cold enclosure. No lamp to light her way, no food to warm her belly. Hungry, so very, very hungry.[6] She shook her head and clutched her reticule, focusing on the lantern hanging just outside the window instead of the confined walls of the hack. *Breathe. You're not alone.*

"Tell me again of the gown you're wearing to my ball," Maribeth said to Edith. With such an agreeable topic, her friend would fill the cabin with cheerful chatter for the rest of their journey.

As soon as they left the city streets behind, Maribeth sought a glimpse of the red bricks and sloping roof of Chateau Swansea through the window. The massive structure sat on the rise of a woodsy cliff in the distance. At least the rain had abated, but the storm left a horrid chill and the heavy scent of worms in its wake.

"Whoa now," the coach driver called out ten minutes later, bringing their vehicle to a halt at the end of the driveway, behind several other coaches. Apparently, many other tourists wished to

---

[6] The cold, dark conditions in the carriage ride trigger memories from her past. This relates to her sordid past. Maribeth worked as a trapper girl in the coal mines. Notice the reader doesn't learn that detail yet. Keep them curious to know more.

view Swansea's greatest attraction for a small fee. Maribeth held the admission tickets safe in her reticule.

"Turn about," a man shouted outside. "Turn about, I say! Nothing to see here. The chateau is closed to visitors tonight."

Drat. What wretched luck. Maribeth poked her head outside the carriage window for a closer look. She hadn't traveled all this way only to be asked to leave. Men crawled over the landscape, congregating near a pond that encircled the right side of the mansion. What had caused them to close their doors to guests for the night?

"Pardon me," she said, waving the man in her direction. "We're here on holiday and will be departing soon. When will the chateau open to the public again for the next tour?"

The older gentleman yanked on the lapels of his black suit jacket and scowled. "I can hardly say. Off with you!"

A moment later, the hack crawled forward in the line of other carriages making the turn in the driveway to leave. She surveyed the grounds. Several constables in black uniforms huddled around a white sheet strewn on the grass at the edge of the pond. The closer they drove to the head of the circle drive, the more apparent it became that something was amiss.

"Is that a dead body?" Edith suddenly whispered. "God in Heaven..."

Maribeth pounded her fist on the roof of the hired hack. "Stop the coach!" She grasped the handle to the door.

"What are you doing?" her friend shrieked, tugging on Maribeth's sleeve. "We must leave at once. You heard the gentleman. The chateau is closed to visitors."

But not investigators. This might be the luckiest evening of her existence. She had less than a month to prove to her guardian that she could support herself in her chosen path in life. A bit of rain and a bad-tempered servant wouldn't hold her back.

"Wait here," Maribeth said, jumping from the moving coach. "I'll only be a moment."

She lifted her skirt and trudged through the knee-length grass toward the men gathered near the pond. Goodness, but her dress was a nuisance. Before she managed five steps, someone caught her arm from behind and yanked her to a halt.

"Where do you think you're headed?" The surly man from the road glared at her, his steely blue eyes boring into hers. He was so close she could make out the silver whiskers interspersed in his black sideburns.

"I beg your pardon," she said, yanking free of his hold. "I'm here to offer my services. Where might I find the master of the house?"

"That's enough, Webber," another man said from behind. "I'll handle this matter."

Maribeth whirled around, coming face to face with none other than Mr. Dunn. What business did he have here? Not that she cared one whit about him, except that he owed her a favor. Webber's footsteps receded behind her, and the odious man resumed barking orders for the coaches to evacuate the premises.

"I apologize if Webber alarmed you," Mr. Dunn said, folding his arms at the base of his lower back. "The butler is distraught at present. What can I do for you, Miss...?"

"Maribeth Sommerset," she said with a lift of her chin. "And you are Mr. Dunn. You *stole* my hired hack earlier at the Inn at Oxwich. Don't even try to deny it. The bellman confirmed the truth. That wasn't well done of you!"

His eyebrows lifted, and a spark of amusement ignited in his lovely brown eyes. "I beg to differ, madam. Hired hacks are, by definition, 'for hire.' The driver accepted my generous offer to pay a premium fare."

Cheeky fellow. Men shouldn't steal coaches from ladies. His mama would be appalled by his behavior.

"Even so," she said, tugging on her gloves, "I'm sure the bellman informed you that the hack was ordered by me and my dear friend. You should be ashamed of yourself."

He coughed into his hand and glanced away, but not before she saw the undeniable curve of his lips. Running off with a lady's carriage wasn't amusing. After months of planning this trip, she'd almost missed her opportunity to tour Chateau Swansea on his account.

"Excuse me," he said, meeting her gaze once again. "I do apologize for any inconvenience. I'm the steward of Chateau Swansea and had urgent business to attend here."

Steward. Well, that changed everything. He was the right-hand man of the master of the estate. *Bloody hell.* Had she offended him with her quick temper? She dug inside her handbag and plucked out one of her trade cards.

"Apology accepted," she said with a smile. There was no reason to quibble over a silly coach. She thrust the card into his hand. "As I said, I'm Miss Maribeth Sommerset. Private psychic investigator, at your service." She gestured to the group of men near the pond. "I communicate with the dead. I'm staying at the Inn at Oxwich through Saturday should you need my assistance. My rates are reasonable and negotiable."

Did she sound professional and assured? This being her first legitimate opportunity to offer her services, she couldn't truly say.

He stared at the rectangular card, his brow pinched. She knew every printed word by heart, though she had yet to hand one out. Until now. Her palms began to sweat, and she glanced beyond him to the activity by the pond. From this distance and angle, the white sheet was no longer visible.

One of the constables sketched furiously on his notepad, while another scanned the perimeter of the pond. Yet a third spoke with a harried woman who worked her hands nervously in the folds of her apron. The scene suffused Maribeth's veins with a tingling warmth. A real investigation!

"Leave. At. Once!" Mr. Dunn said, enunciating each word.

Her gaze snapped to his, taking in his stony expression. Had she misheard him?

He pointed to the hired hack she'd arrived in. "Get out! The last thing I care to deal with in this moment is another lunatic come to swindle the Turner fortune. Disgraceful! You should be ashamed of yourself, taking advantage of a grieving man. The master of the house isn't accepting visitors today or any time in the near future."

Lunatic. Disgraceful.

His accusations reverberated through her, sprouting roots in the depths of her soul. She had anticipated skepticism from her first client. But not anger or derision.

"I'm—" She choked on the next word. *Sorry?* No, she wouldn't apologize for pursuing her dream. Heat flooded her cheeks, but she held his gaze. "I didn't mean to intrude. I was only trying to be helpful. Please, excuse me."

She ran back to the hack, her eyes brimming with unshed tears.

"Move on, driver!" she shouted, plopping into the seat beside Edith.

"Maribeth, what—?"

"I don't wish to speak of it!" She laid her head on her friend's shoulder.

The ride to the inn passed in utter silence. Maribeth emptied her mind of all thoughts. She would not cry or rail against the injustice of the situation. **One could dream, but it did not follow that those dreams would come true. Life had already taught her that important lesson.**[7]

"Would you care to join me for a cup of tea in the café so we can forget this nasty business?" Edith asked when they entered the lobby.

"Of course." Tea and conversation would keep her mind occupied. As she strode by the wastepaper basket, she paused and clutched her handbag. Should she toss the remainder of her trade cards away? After all, dreams rarely came true.

No, the opinion of a single working-class man would not set her off course! In a day or two, after the chief investigator got his bearings, she would pay him a visit.

---

[7] Maribeth has had her dreams crushed in the past (i.e. related to the heroine's external motivation / inner conflict), but the details aren't revealed yet. Only six bits of backstory were revealed throughout chapter one, and each reference was no more than a sentence or two.

Chapter Two

She wasn't supposed to cry.

Caressing her trade card in his trouser pocket, Arthur Dunn sighed. He'd admired Miss Sommerset in the hotel lobby yet never imagined she was a fraudster. Not this fragile, hauntingly beautiful woman with a quick wit. Perhaps he'd been a mite too forceful, for which he was hardly to blame. **Most charlatans of his acquaintance, of which there were more than he cared to admit, would rage at his accusation if called out.**[8] He'd had half a mind to throw the trade card back in her face, and yet... *What kind of fool am I?* A part of him wanted a keepsake.

He rubbed the back of his neck, working on the tension knots gathered there. Nothing about this day was going as planned. First, that damnable portrait required every last inch of space in the coach, forcing him to find another ride back to the chateau. Second, upon his arrival, he witnessed an inflamed argument between the master and mistress of the house, which resulted in her death. Third, he had caused a lady to cry. At least trouble always came in sets of three. One could hope the worst of his day was over.

The hired hack carrying the psychic rambled away, and in its place rolled a far more troublesome prospect. *So much for hoping.* Arthur gritted his teeth and strode to the carriage, heading off the butler, who'd also noticed the chief inspector's arrival.

"Hold your tongue," Arthur said under his breath, his gaze boring into Webber. The entire scene was about to dissolve into a drama of the worst sort without the additional theatrics Webber would contribute if allowed to do so.

---

[8] The hero has experience with fraudsters. He views the heroine as a fraudster, which adds depth to the romance conflict.

The butler turned up his nose. "I will wait my turn for questioning, but I assure you, I shall have my say."

Of course he would; nothing ever stopped the butler from speaking his mind. A coachman folded down the steps to the carriage and opened the door.

"Take me to my sister this instant!" the chief inspector's wife said, alighting from the box with an enormous parasol and a peacock feather protruding from a dainty hat. Combined with the voluminous navy skirt of her gown, Mrs. Marsh painted the picture of a bird run amok by tigers at the zoo in Regent's Park.

Once on the ground, her gaze locked on the constables surrounding the body near the pond. "Goodness, is that the poor soul who perished?" She shook out her fan and pumped the apparatus vigorously.

"Helen, please," the chief inspector said, jumping out of the carriage after her. "This is a formal investigation. You may wait inside the parlor, and I will send Caroline to you once I've had the opportunity to question her myself. Someone lost their life today. We must make every effort to get to the bottom of this. Webber, please escort my wife to the parlor."

"I'm afraid that won't be possible, sir," Webber said.

Chief Inspector Marsh lifted his brow. "Pardon me?"

"Webber!" Arthur hissed. "Please do as you're told."

Mrs. Marsh's keen gaze skipped between them. "What do you mean, Webber? You have never denied me entry into my sister's home."

Clenching his fists, Arthur steadied himself. He'd wring the butler's neck when the day was over, but there was no stopping the man from having his say.

"All I meant is that your husband cannot send your sister to you," Webber said, ignoring Arthur's heated stare, "because she has joined her Maker."

Mrs. Marsh held her tongue for a full ten seconds before his message sank in and she screamed, "Caroline isn't dead, you bloody fool! I don't believe it. Let me pass."

The full-bodied woman shoved the butler aside and lifted her skirt, storming into the high grass on a direct path to the men guarding the body, while Chief Inspector Marsh looked to Arthur for confirmation.

"Yes, it's true," he said on a sigh.

The chief inspector's lips pressed into a thin line, and he inhaled sharply before trudging after his wife.

Arthur poked his forefinger into Webber's chest. "Get the rest of these carriages out of here! Then gather the staff in the kitchen. No one leaves until the police have spoken with every last one of them."

Without waiting for a response, Arthur dug in his heel and turned to follow the chief inspector and his wife. The wet earth sucked at his boots with each step, and his pants clung to his legs, damp from the high grass soaked with rain. His feet were cold, but at least the rain stopped entirely by the time he arrived at the scene.

Mrs. Marsh wept in her husband's embrace, her wails piercing the air. The chief gestured for the body to be covered once more. Bits of algae stained the edges of the sheet green and filled Arthur's nostrils with a faint, musty odor. The housekeeper, Mrs. Hawkins, stared from the sideline, shaking her head.

"Come, allow Mrs. Hawkins to bring you to the house," the chief inspector said, patting his wife's back. "You needn't stay any longer."

Mrs. Marsh looked up with tear-stained cheeks and pounded her fist against her husband's chest. "You will make him pay for this! Do you hear me?"

Her husband nodded. "We will apprehend the culprit, I promise."

"I already know who did this," she shouted. She pulled herself out of his embrace and rounded on Arthur. "Stanley Turner is a murdering scoundrel, and he will rot in the gallows! Where is your employer?"

Arthur suppressed every urge to react. He held his expression bland and his breathing normal. His employer's future depended upon Arthur's discretion. **After all the man had suffered in his lifetime, and after the second chance he'd given Arthur to**

improve his own life, Mr. Turner deserved a thorough investigation, not a lynching.[9]

"He is in his bedchamber and stands ready for questioning after his solicitor arrives," Arthur said in an even tone.

She glanced at her husband. "Why call for his lawyer unless he's guilty? Caroline told me he was angry with her, and she feared for her life. He has gone too far."

"Are you sure about this, Helen?" The chief inspector took her by the shoulders.

She nodded. "I learned the news last week at tea. Caroline said he threatened to kill her.[10] I'm telling you, my brother-in-law is guilty."

Chief Inspector Marsh eyed the other detectives and constables, who nodded their consent. Their afternoon had suddenly freed up in a matter of minutes. *Disgusting pigs.* Stanley Turner might hang for the crime simply because the police were too lazy to complete an investigation. Despite what Arthur had witnessed, he would not allow his employer to be trussed up and shipped to Newgate without due process. Even the lowliest scum on Earth deserved a fighting chance, and Mr. Turner was the best of men. He would get a fair trial!

Arthur cleared his throat. "Do you have evidence of these threats? A note from her, perhaps?"

Mrs. Marsh narrowed her gaze on him, her face pinched. "Of course not! A lady does not write such things down."

"Circumstantial evidence," Arthur said, turning his attention to the chief inspector. "Mrs. Turner's death was a horrible accident. But I suppose the coroner can conduct an autopsy and confirm or deny foul play?"

---

[9] There is a level of respect and gratitude Arthur holds for his employer, because his employer gave him a second chance (i.e. the hero's motivation). At the same time, this begs the question what kind of jaded past Arthur lived that might put a romance with the heroine in jeopardy (i.e. the romance conflict).

[10] Oh, the first piece of history related to the mystery comes out. Remember, all backstory that relates to the murder mystery is underlined in the book. I won't comment individually on each of these.

With a brisk nod, the chief inspector said, "Indeed. Quite right. Henderson, please inform the coroner his services are needed at once."

Mrs. Marsh's mouth gaped like a fish in open air before she found her voice again. "You would desecrate my sister's body? I am a highly respectable witness."

"Hearsay," Arthur added. "What proof is there that Mr. Turner was angry with his wife? Her pin money has been consistent ever since my employment. Every scheme she pursued, he supported: dinner parties, visits to Bath, an exorbitant wardrobe. Ask any one of the staff."

Stomping her foot, Mrs. Marsh growled. "Stanley Turner is guilty of murdering my sister. You are defending him to secure your own livelihood as steward to his estates!"

"Helen, that's quite enough." Chief Inspector Marsh motioned for Mrs. Hawkins. "Please, take her inside the house."

"You believe me, don't you?" the chief's wife asked the house-keeper.

Her desperate expression did little to stir Arthur's compassion, and he doubted Mrs. Marsh would find a champion in Mrs. Hawkins. She'd been a loyal staff of the master of the house for years, preferring his level head to that of their testy mistress.[11]

"I've already given my testimony," the housekeeper confessed with her hands folded securely over her waist. "The ghost of Chateau Swansea chased Mrs. Turner over the edge of the balcony. Only minutes before the incident, I heard ghastly moans and felt a chill sweep through me." She shuddered and took a deep breath. "I warned the mistress not to hold a séance in Arabella Brown's room. The former mistress of the house does not take kindly to those who mock her memory."

What nonsense is this? The reputed ghost of Chateau Swansea was nothing more than a myth. Other servants within the house laid claim to encountering the ghost, **but Arthur had yet to find any**

---

[11] I'm being a little sneaky here and planting information that "leads the witness" with respect to Mrs. Hawkins. From the first encounter until the very end, I present the housekeeper as a deeply loyal staff member of Mr. Turner.

credible evidence of her existence in his ten years working on the estate.[12] Still, if the housekeeper's testimony diverted the attention away from Mr. Turner or encouraged a full investigation, Arthur would hold his tongue.

Tears trickled from Mrs. Marsh's eyes, and she swiped them away. "You heard the ghost's wails? <u>Caroline spoke of cold rooms and her personal items gone missing. Especially gifts from Stanley. Arabella is a jealous mistress, even in the afterlife.</u> We didn't mean any disrespect when we held the séance. Quite the opposite, in fact." The chief's wife lifted her hand to her forehead. "I'm feeling faint. God in Heaven, did I provoke my sister's murderess?"

Chief Inspector Marsh rubbed his eyes, and a wary frown settled on his lips. His gaze shifted to the second-floor balcony of Mrs. Turner's bedchamber. The fall had likely broken the victim's neck. But proving whether or not a ghost was involved would be impossible.

Arthur did not envy the position the chief found himself in. But he was thankful to Mrs. Hawkins nonetheless. Her testimony bought at least another week or two for Arthur to track down the truth, especially if he added an element of uncertainty through his own testimony.

"Calm yourself, wife," the chief inspector finally said. "There is no evidence of a ghost haunting Chateau Swansea."

One of the constables standing off to the side raised his hand. "Permission to speak, sir?"

Chief Inspector Marsh waved him on.

"<u>There are fifty-two accounts of ghost sightings on file at the station in the past twenty years</u>," the constable said matter-of-factly. He tilted his head in thought. "<u>Well, more if you include the entire</u>

---

[12] This further supports the idea that the hero turns his nose up at anyone who believes in the paranormal (i.e. the romance conflict). In addition, he has been a faithful servant for ten years (i.e. hero's motivation).

county. However, Chateau Swansea comprises over eighty percent of the documented sightings."[13]

Arthur's lips twitched, but he held himself in check. The young puppy babbling about ghosts was doing a splendid job of muddying the waters.

"Why do you know these facts, Henderson?" The chief inspector folded his arms and glowered at his man.

Henderson swallowed and looked to his peers, as if seeking advice on how to respond. "I was on duty when Mrs. Turner filed her latest sighting. Excuse me, but I was intrigued and read through the other files."

"Very well." The chief rubbed his forehead. "Interviewing the staff will take several hours. Mrs. Hawkins, can you escort my wife inside and arrange for tea?"

"I will not step another foot in that house," Mrs. Marsh declared, her face contorted. "My life is in danger. The séance was Caroline's idea, but I participated in the evening's event. No, no. Jennings will drive me home and return with the coach later. While your men conduct the interviews, I will contact a reputable medium. Truly, I will not find a moment's peace until we learn the truth."

A reputable medium? Arthur glanced away, masking his grin with his hand. Such a person did not exist. Actors and actresses, every last one of them.

"As you wish." The chief wrapped his wife's arm around his and escorted her back to the coach, saying, "I'm sure whoever you hire will ease your mind."

Arthur stared at their receding forms. The situation was getting out of hand. If Mrs. Marsh hired a medium to investigate whether the ghost of Chateau Swansea had killed her sister, she would surely pay for the answer she sought.

Perhaps not with malicious intent. Mrs. Marsh wanted peace of mind; she wanted Stanley Turner to hang for her sister's murder. Only then could she live without fear of retribution from the ghost

---

[13] Don't forget that the town of Swansea and the chateau where the story is centered also have a history. Bring out the fun details whenever relevant to the current storyline.

of Madame Brown. The distraught woman would voice her worst fears to the medium and pray that the ghost had not killed her sister.

Every medium worth his or her salt knew a hefty bonus awaited them at the end of their services when they delivered the *desired* result. What a disaster!

"Excuse me," Arthur called out while jogging after the pair. He caught up in a matter of ten strides. "You're grieving, Mrs. Marsh, and shouldn't be charged with such an exhausting task. Please, allow me to arrange for a reputable medium."

She eyed him warily. "Do you know the first thing about these matters?"

He bowed. **"My parents were traveling fortune-tellers. I'm quite adept at identifying authenticity in this particular field. I believe I may already have the perfect candidate."**[14]

He handed her Miss Sommerset's trade card.

"Private psychic investigator," she read aloud. "Where did you get this?"

"She came by this afternoon to offer her assistance. In fact, she departed only moments before you arrived. Perhaps she had sensed what had occurred. I'm stymied myself."

All the blood drained from Mrs. Marsh's face, leaving her deathly pale. She shoved the card back at Arthur. "Hire her at once. I'll pay whatever she asks."

He nodded but said, "The estate will pay for her services on behalf of Caroline Turner. I wouldn't have it any other way."

"Quite right of you." The woman leaned heavily on her husband. "I expect a full report within a week."

Not a problem. Arthur could have a report within two days if he wished. All he needed to do was negotiate the right price. He glanced at the trade card once again. *Miss Maribeth Sommerset, what is your price?* After the way he'd treated her earlier, the cost would be steep, indeed.

---

[14] Arthur's parents were traveling fortune-tellers. Through the story thus far, the reader can surmise the hero's disdain toward anyone who earns a living off of the concept of spirits, the dead, or reading futures (i.e. the romance conflict).

Chapter Three

Maribeth awoke Friday morning to the dull thud of rain on the windowpane. Another foul day in Swansea, a perfect match for her mood. What did she expect when traveling in March? She rose from bed, dressed, and completed her ablutions swiftly. Edith was an early riser and would call on her at precisely—

Knock. Knock. Knock.

Eight o'clock in the morning. Maribeth spat a mouthful of tooth polish into the basin and rinsed with water. With a final glance in the mirror to ensure her unruly hair hadn't fallen out of its pins, she headed for the door.

"Good morning, Edith," she said with a modicum of joviality, lest her friend pry more into the prior evening's events. "You look lovely on this fine day."

"That's a bit much," Edith said, drily. She wrapped her arm through Maribeth's and they headed down the stairs to the breakfast room. "What do you have planned for our last day in town?"

Maribeth waggled her notebook. "Swansea Castle. I will read you my notes on the history of the castle over breakfast."

"How very thoughtful of you," her friend said with a smirk. "I'm quite beside myself without this week's *Titbits*. Do you think there is a copy to be had?"

The emphasis on sensational human interest stories appealed to many readers. Even Maribeth conceded that the short articles and stories were often entertaining.

"Find a table for us in the breakfast room, and I'll inquire," Maribeth said, beelining toward the concierge desk. The odds were not in their favor, but it couldn't hurt to ask. If nothing else, she could pick up a copy of the daily newspaper. A deep, morbid curiosity burned in her soul to know what had occurred at Chateau Swansea.

Unfortunately, the bellman only produced a copy of the local newspaper. However, the front page news title Maribeth read aloud at the breakfast table did not disappoint.

Swansea Evening Post
Swansea, England
8 March 1889

GHOST OF CHATEAU SWANSEA STRIKES

Special to Swansea Evening Post

Swansea, March 7.
At 4:30 o'clock this afternoon, the dead body of Mrs. Caroline Turner was recovered from the pond on the estate of Chateau Swansea. An examination of the remains shows that her neck had been snapped, but there were no other signs of trauma. Whether the neck injury was caused by the deceased's fall from her second-floor bedchamber balcony or other fiendish means is uncertain. The only eyewitness to her demise, a Mr. Arthur Dunn, steward of the estate, reported that Mrs. Turner fell off the balcony. Others within the estate reported hearing eerie wails and creaking floors immediately preceding the incident. Even the chill of the dead was present. From this, it is evident that the murder was committed by the ghost of the infamous clairvoyant Arabella Brown, former owner of the estate.

Although the nefarious spirit of Madame Brown has been said to spook visitors in the past, this is the first murder at Chateau Swansea attributed to her. Police and medical men familiar with the details of the case are stymied by the facts. However, one disturbing piece of evidence has been uncovered from a confidential source that points to foul play. Mrs. Turner was said to be early with child, despite the fact that her husband

<u>only returned last week from a seven-month business trip
abroad.</u>

Wraith or wrath?

Maribeth set the news article on the table and whistled. "Well,
there is a story to rival any in the *Titbit*."

Snatching the newspaper off the table, Edith perused the article
again. "Eerie wails and creaking floors. The ghost of a clairvoyant
haunting the chateau. Is any of the story true, do you think?"

Good Lord, she hoped so! In her two years pursuing work as a
psychic investigator, Maribeth had visited less than a handful of truly
haunted mansions, perhaps four during the whole of her life. **Devil's
Cove Manor stood at the top of her list as the worst. Her
childhood home housed hundreds of lost souls at one point.
These days, only two ghosts could be found on the vast
property.**[15]

"Without access to the chateau, eyewitness testimonies, a post-
mortem report, and other evidence, I can only speculate." Maribeth
sipped her Earl Grey tea. "Under the circumstances, there is a high
probability that Mrs. Turner's spirit lingers on the estate. Murder is a
nasty business. She would sing like a blue tit if I were given the
opportunity to communicate with her."

Edith's gaze suddenly moved beyond Maribeth's shoulder, and
her eyes widened. What had gotten into her friend? She looked as
though she'd seen a ghost.

"And what if I offered you that opportunity?" a gentleman said,
sliding onto the bench seat beside Maribeth.

She glanced at him and stiffened. Of all the men on this planet,
Mr. Dunn was the last she expected to find posing such a question.
He'd made his thoughts on her chosen profession quite plain the day
before, brutally so.

---

[15] This lends credence to the heroine's goal to become a psychic
investigator and solve mysteries. Being around spirits is nothing new
to her. She was raised in a house full of them.

He lifted one infuriatingly handsome eyebrow. "Would you seize the chance or tell me to go to Hades?"

"The latter, sir. I do not care to deal with lunatics either."

His grin was sudden and breathtaking. She might have stared at him all day but for the gasp from across the table that garnered her immediate attention. *Yes, focus on Edith and her poor manners.* She tried as best she could, though the heat permeating off Mr. Dunn's leg warmed her thigh and the rich leather scent of his cologne muddled her thoughts. Why must he sit so close and crowd her? She felt his stare to her very core.

"What are you doing?" Edith mouthed, shielding her lips from the gentlemen with her hand, as if that kept him from following the gist of their conversation.

Maribeth leveled a glare on their uninvited guest. "Would you be so kind and give us a private moment?"

"Of course." He stood and retreated to the bar, leaning against it while watching her intently.

"Take the offer," Edith hissed a moment later.

"Why should I?" Maribeth took a fortifying gulp of tea and glanced once more at Mr. Dunn, ensuring he was a safe distance away. "He called me a lunatic and disgraceful, *and* he accused me of taking advantage of the situation. I wouldn't help him for one thousand pounds."

Her friend's lips twitched. "You would forego ten years' worth of wages because he hurt your feelings?" She grabbed Maribeth's hand from across the table and squeezed. "I knew it! You dream of a marriage proposal after your ball, but you're afraid to believe in happily ever after. In that case, refuse the wretched man."

Of all the ridiculous notions! Edith knew very well that—Oh, her friend was sly. *Of course, I'm acting like a silly chit.* When it came to business, she must set aside her feelings.

"You are a terrible friend," Maribeth groused.

"I am the best of friends." Standing, Edith flicked her head in Mr. Dunn's direction. "At least inquire after his change of heart. Who cares what the man thinks of you? **Lord Covington will not renege on his offer to sign over your dowry if you provide**

evidence of your work history. But first, you must find work.[16] Her lips parted in a wicked grin. "Charge an unreasonable fee! That blaggard should pay for his disrespect."

Maribeth blew out an uneasy breath as her friend sauntered away. Her stomach fluttered with an intense yet foreign sensation. Was her dream within her grasp?

"May I?" Mr. Dunn asked, gesturing to the empty bench across from her.

She nodded, motivated by the possibility that she stood on the precipice of a new career. "You were quite rude yesterday. Why the sudden change of heart? Out of respect for the deceased, I will give you five minutes of my time to explain."

"My employer will hang for a crime he didn't commit if you do not help him," he said with his penetrating gaze. "His estate will pay for your services on behalf of his deceased wife. Her sister, a Mrs. Helen Marsh, fully supports your involvement in this criminal investigation."

"Why?"

He folded his hands, laying them on the table. "Mrs. Marsh fears retribution from the ghost of Madame Brown."

A slight tick in his jaw caught Maribeth's attention, and she detected the merest hint of derision in his tone. So he didn't believe in ghosts?

He glanced at the newspaper folded on the table. "Only those closest to the investigation are aware that the sisters carried out a ritual in the former owner's séance room. We wish for you to discover if the ghost of Madame Brown murdered the lady of the house for her blatant disrespect, and if she plans to strike again."

"Do you believe the ghost will kill Mrs. Marsh?"

---

[16] Ah, Maribeth gets to keep her dowry if she can prove that she can support herself through her work as a psychic investigator (i.e. heroine's goal). This could have been revealed earlier when Maribeth said she had less than a month to prove to her guardian that she could support herself. This is what "sprinkling in" backstory means. Adding this earlier would've slowed down the pacing of the story. I planted the seed earlier and let it grow here.

Mr. Dunn tapped his forefinger on the table, shaking his head. "What I believe is irrelevant. That is the question you're tasked with answering. The chief inspector is supportive of your involvement as well. There will be no barriers."

She'd never heard of an opportunity such as this.

"He wishes for his wife to find peace of mind," Mr. Dunn added.

"I see," Maribeth said, her shoulders relaxing. "Malevolent spirits can be temperamental and unpredictable. A healthy dose of fear is wise under the circumstances."

However, despite the legendary stories of the former mistress haunting the mansion, the likelihood of ghostly intervention was remote. Maribeth didn't possess the training required to carry out a full criminal investigation, but she could certainly help uncover the truth of the ghost's involvement in the events, if any.

"Do you believe Mr. Turner killed his wife?" Maribeth asked.

"I wouldn't know."

"According to the paper, you were the only eyewitness."

"My vantage point was from the driveway, looking up. I'm not sure what I saw. Husband, ghost, secret lover? Who can say for sure?"

That wasn't enough. An alliance would only work if he was honest with her. She needed to know everything. Could she trust him? Her instincts demanded she walk away. He knew more than he was telling her. The seconds ticked by, and the dull murmur of other patrons filled the silence.

"Listen here," he added, leaning closer. "As the news article intimated, Mrs. Turner dallied with her staff and found herself in a precarious position. She was thirty-six years old, her husband fifty-five. Perhaps she was lonely. I am neither judge nor jury. But what I do know is that Mr. Turner sits in his bedchamber in a catatonic state and is entirely defenseless. He is a good man. He deserves a thorough investigation and a fair trial. The police department cannot be impartial. Surely, you must see that. We have one week to conduct our own investigation alongside the police."

Maribeth regarded him closely. "We?"

"You must use your 'sight' to prove a malevolent ghost resides at the chateau. Give me one week. You may stay in one of the guestrooms at Chateau Swansea, and I'll introduce you to the staff. You'll have free reign over the estate. The victim's sister places great faith in those gifted with the power to communicate with those beyond the grave. If you have the right credentials, she'll believe whatever you say. Simply name your price."

A bark of laughter escaped her. He thought she could be bribed? No wonder he held so little respect for those in her trade.

"You will pay me whatever I want, so long as I say the ghost of Chateau Swansea killed Caroline Turner while the true killer remains at large?"

Unbelievable. She stood to leave, but he grabbed her wrist from across the table. Her skin tingled under his touch and she sucked in a breath. "This discussion is over. Kindly let go of me."

"Please, stay." He relinquished his hold immediately, settling back on the bench. "You misunderstood my meaning. I expect you to conduct a thorough investigation and report your findings, whatever those may be. Justice must be served, no matter who is found to be at fault."

Mrs. Turner's family deserved the truth behind her demise, and a cold-blooded killer might still roam the halls of Chateau Swansea. Whether Mr. Dunn believed in her skills or not, she needed this job to launch her career as a private psychic investigator.

"Fifty pounds and a glowing letter of recommendation. That's my price."

"Done." He stood and gestured for her to proceed him. "Gather your belongings and inform your friend that you'll be accompanying me to Chateau Swansea. My carriage awaits us outside."

Chapter Four

Arthur handed Miss Sommerset into the coach, noting the slightest hint of lemons as she passed by. The white silk of her gloves contrasted starkly with his brown leather ones. She wore a fine wool coat in deep burgundy with twin capes. Her trunks carried many more equally costly garments, no doubt. He would do well to remember she hailed from a household of wealth and privilege.

"Tell me of your past experiences as a medium," he said the moment they settled opposite one another and the coach lurched forward. "Mrs. Marsh will want a full account from me. The uncanny timing of your arrival on the estate yesterday convinced her to offer you the job. Still, she'll request your résumé. Did you sense Mrs. Turner's death, perchance?"

Miss Sommerset's eyebrows arched. "I'm a medium, not a clairvoyant. My visit was purely coincidental. I had purchased admittance for the Thursday evening tour of the chateau."

She was merely a tourist seeking a thrill while on holiday. That would not impress the chief's wife. He drowned out the clattering of the horse's hooves and turned his mind to spinning this fact in the medium's favor. But he came up with nothing. He would keep this bit of news to himself.

"More's the pity," he said before he reined in his sarcasm. "What else might I offer as evidence of your credentials? Provide me with a story or two, if you please. When did you first learn of your talent?"

"At the age of eleven." She rested her hands on her lap and regarded him in a serious manner. **"Shortly after moving to Devil's Cove Manor with my guardian, I became highly attuned to the presence of the dead. Perhaps I always sensed my abilities, but Eveline"**—she cleared her throat—**"Lady**

Covington encouraged my interest. She, too, has the sight."[17]

But of course! This was a juicy morsel he could sink his teeth into. **Devil's Cove Manor enjoyed a reputation as a haunted estate that rivaled that of the chateau.**[18] Mrs. Marsh might swoon with delight upon hearing this.

"Are the rumors true?" he asked.

"I'm afraid you must be more candid," she said. "Many rumors surround the estate."

And its notorious owner. He studied her for a moment. This was her opportunity to enthrall him, yet she held her stories close to the vest. His mother would've given a performance worthy of any stage. Perhaps Miss Sommerset was still sour with him for his earlier rudeness.

"While interesting," he said, "the rumors regarding whether or not Lord Covington masqueraded as the pirate, 'the Devil,' has little to do with your qualifications."[19]

Her eyes widened a fraction.

Leaning his elbows on his knees, he propped his fists under his chin. **"Tell me of the gatekeeper to Hell. Did you communicate with Josephine before she massacred all those people?"**

Rumors of the paranormal activity had spread like wildfire nine years ago after twelve guests perished during a ball held on the haunted estate. It was all his parents spoke of for a month straight. How far would the lovely Miss Sommerset go to impress her new employer?

---

[17] This supports the heroine's goal of becoming a psychic investigator. It's only natural that the reader would want to better understand where the heroine's interest comes from. By having Mrs. Marsh demand more on Maribeth's qualifications, the current storyline allows a natural means for divulging all of this backstory.

[18] In order save his employer from the gallows (i.e. hero's goal), Arthur must convince Mrs. Marsh that Maribeth is a reputable medium so she'll listen to her final conclusions, which Arthur plans to influence in his favor. The fact that the heroine's childhood home was known to be haunted is favorable.

[19] Ah, now it comes out that the heroine's guardian used to be a pirate. This is key backstory with respect to the romance conflict. Maribeth's childhood was truly unconventional. Will she fall for the steward?

Her smile was angelic, disarming. "You surprise me, Mr. Dunn. I didn't take you for a fool who subscribes to fantastical rumors."

Touché. An involuntary grin escaped him. **Evidence of a mystical creature had not been discovered in the ensuing investigation, despite numerous eyewitness accounts.**[20] Besides, the little imp would never confirm rumors that might tarnish the reputation of her guardian, Lord Covington. Even a marquess could not withstand such scrutiny.

"You wound my pride. Your tongue truly is as direct as an arrow," he said. Though, truth be told, he appreciated a woman who spoke her mind.

"Excuse me? Why would you—" Her eyes widened. "Were you listening in on my conversation with Edith in the hotel lobby yesterday?"

"Every single word; a riveting conversation. Your friend is quite right." His gaze lowered to her lips, pink and rosy. They parted and her breathing quickened.

"Which part?" She swallowed. "That I'm lovely or impossible?"

"Both."

The medium met his gaze head on. Yesterday's unshed tears had vanished, and in their place was a steadfast resolve. She was a beautiful woman with those captivating eyes and golden curls at her temples, but rather young to be traveling unaccompanied. What was Lord Covington about, allowing her to stray so far from home without a proper companion?

"Why do you stare at me in that manner, Mr. Dunn?"

"My apologies." He did not often give into his curious nature. But she confounded him. "Your eyes are the most unusual shade of green. Did you inherit them from your mother? Or father?"

She averted her gaze, suddenly taking interest in the lappets on her jacket. **"My father, I believe. My mother's eyes were a**

---

[20] This long passage highlights the heroine's past. News of the paranormal happenings in her childhood home was widespread. The hero has the first inkling that maybe—just maybe—the heroine is legitimately a medium and not a fraudster (i.e. the romance conflict). The fact that Maribeth refuses to shed a questionable light on her guardian, even at the risk of her reputation, is admirable.

lovely shade of coffee brown from what I remember. I was only five when..."[21] Her gaze went to the window, and she cleared her throat. "But that is neither here nor there."

He marveled that Miss Sommerset had any memories of her mother, given the age at which she came under the care of her guardian. His own memories before turning six were foggy at best. But she was right. They had wandered far from the topic at hand.

"So what encounters with spirits can you speak of?" he asked. "Enthrall me, please."

She wet her lips. "My first communication with the dead involved friendly spirits. Through prayer and quiet reflection, I connect with ghosts on this plane of existence, unless they ignore me. But they're lonely creatures, so most engage in conversation. I can also conjure their physical forms in my presence. While others cannot see them, I do."

His jaw slackened, but he held his mouth shut by sheer strength of will. "A rare talent, indeed." In fact, few mediums had the audacity to lay claim to the ability lest they be proven false. Yes, he could work with this to impress Mrs. Marsh.

"Have you solved any cases, Miss Sommerset?"

She pursed her lips. *Ah, the first sign of impending deceit.* What lies would she conjure to secure her position? He waited patiently.

"No," she finally said, straightening her shoulders.

His brow lifted of its own volition. "None?"

She lifted one forefinger. "But my communications with a ghost in New Orleans saved an entire family from a deadly curse. A slave girl's soul was trapped in a mirror on the plantation. I set her free."

---

[21] Maribeth had a mother with brown eyes, but the reader can surmise she doesn't remember her father. Further, something happened when she was five, but what? This hints of the heroine's sordid past (i.e. her internal motivation). Although not expressly said, Arthur is starting to show curiosity about Maribeth. He has been searching for Bella Turner for a decade and along comes a woman who meets her description and is about her age. Her eyes are green, like Arabella Brown's. An interesting fact the reader can piece together later in the story if the reader is astute and paying attention.

Interesting, to say the least. Miss Sommerset was proving to have a wonderful imagination, after all. With a little coaxing, he would surely discover more to please Mrs. Marsh's need for sensationalism.

"And what of séances and talking boards?" he asked, drumming his fingers on the bench. "What experience do you have with either?"

Her nose scrunched up. "None whatsoever."

He rubbed his temples, warding off a headache. How could this be? "Every respectable medium offers séances and a turn with the talking board. I'll tell Mrs. Marsh you're well-versed in the art, but there is no need in this investigation. She'll never accept you otherwise."

"You'll tell her no such thing!" Miss Sommerset scowled. "Is this your idea of a jest? Séances and talking boards are forms of entertainment. Gifted mediums do not employ these tricks of the trade. You offend me, sir."

What was her game? He took in her flushed cheeks, rigid posture, and the spark glinting in her eyes. She meant every word that spilled from her lips. *Fascinating.* Smoke and mirrors truly offended her.

"I will not be mocked," she said, pinning him with a nasty glare. "Do you expect me to lie and offer false witness? I assure you, I will not. Please, turn the coach around. Find another medium for your circus act."

Confidence and authority radiated off her in waves. She was steadfast in the belief of her craft. Beautifully sincere, and exactly what he needed. Even if she proved to be a fraud in the end, of which he had no doubts. **He was raised by the best of them, was a fraud himself.**[22] Still, she would serve his purpose well. What good would come of admitting he did not believe in ghosts or mediums? A little lie never hurt anyone in the pursuit of justice.

---

[22] Arthur reverts to believing the heroine is a fraudster (i.e. the romance conflict), but we also discover he considers himself to be a fraud. Why? Stay tuned. This is tied to the hero's conflict. He must lie on purpose and act like a fraud himself in order to take the pressure off of his employer as the main suspect.

"Accept my sincerest apology," he said, lowering his voice an octave, probing into the depths of her eyes. He laid his hand over his heart. "I did not mean to cause offense. Truly. While skeptical, I keep an open mind. The chateau may be haunted. There are enough documented accounts to fill a desk drawer. Please reconsider, for Mr. Turner's sake."

She cocked her head to the side, but said nothing. Did his pledge ring true?

"Are you a steward or an actor, Mr. Dunn? You say all the right words as though scripted."

Her jest sliced through the tension building between them. A medium with a sense of humor. How charming.

"Steward, of course. You'll stay and investigate? By week's end, you may leave with a letter of recommendation and fifty pounds richer for your trouble."

The carriage rolled to a stop, and he glanced out the window. They had arrived at Chateau Swansea. He needed her to uncover the potential motives of the other residents on the estate. Caroline Turner stirred up trouble in every aspect of her life. With enough viable suspects, the police may never discover the truth behind her death, and his employer could avoid Newgate.

"I'll stay for one week," she declared as a footman opened the carriage door.

Miss Sommerset exited before Arthur could offer his assistance. Was she avoiding his touch after the shock of attraction they'd shared in the breakfast room? She may find his company irksome, but the way she stole glances while she thought he wasn't looking clearly indicated that she found him attractive. He hurried after her, his gaze landing on the swell of her bottom as he alighted from the carriage. An unbidden ache churned in his loins, and he looked away.

There was no time for a dalliance when his employer's future lay in limbo. Not to mention that she was accustomed to mingling with the gentry, while he was paid to serve them. No, come the end of the week, Miss Sommerset would collect her fifty pounds and board the first train out of Swansea.

One week would suffice to confound the police. **His skills of deception were rusty, but telling lies and evading the truth were ingrained in his blood.**[23] All he must do was bend Miss Sommerset to his way of thinking. Simple, really. Even after insulting the spitfire, she had agreed to stay, hadn't she?

---

[23] Again, Arthur isn't all that he seems. His past shaped him to be skillful at deception. And while he doesn't like it, he's willing to tap into those skills when needed (i.e. the hero's goal).

Chapter Five

Chateau Swansea sat in serene tranquility against a backdrop of fluffy clouds. Breathtaking green pastures beckoned to the west, leading to a dense forest. Today the pond stretched around the east side of the chateau with a glass-like surface. Only ripples trailing a pair of swans marred the water. Every aspect of the façade invited Maribeth's eyes for a closer look, from the rich burgundy bricks to the bell tower and cherrywood double doors adorned with wrought iron knockers.

A haunted chateau on the cliffs of Swansea. *Delightful.* She breathed in deep, filling her lungs to capacity. The scent of damp earth with a hint of edelweiss filled her nose. All frivolous thoughts and worries were vanquished from her mind. In this space, she connected with life beyond this earth.

A cool breeze kissed her cheeks, but nothing else stirred her senses. She walked to the front entrance of the chateau, leaving Mr. Dunn to instruct the footmen about her trunks. Her senses were on alert, her mind open to everything around her.

The decorative etchings on the doors spoke of an older age. Intricately carved vines fell in a tangled web from the upper corners all the way down the sides. In a few sections, carved sprigs of edelweiss sprouted in glorious defiance: a symbol of courage. *Enter with courage in your heart, but be forewarned of the traps awaiting within.* So very clever of Madame Brown. Clairvoyance was both a blessing and a curse. The secrets of one's past or future sometimes ought to remain unknown.

Taking the simple knocker in hand, Maribeth rapped on the door twice in quick succession. A vibrant energy permeated her gloves. She stepped away, holding her breath as the dull thud echoed in the shallow enclave of the entrance. Every nerve ending in her body vibrated with anticipation of what lie within.

"You needn't knock," Mr. Dunn murmured from behind.

The warmth of his breath tickled her ear and sent wicked little shivers racing down her spine. She exhaled in a whoosh, glaring over her shoulder. Goodness! *You are not a ninny to be scared out of your wits by a few simple words.* Yet his proximity and masculine scent was frightfully disturbing to her senses.

His eyes shone with a hint of amusement as he walked around her, gesturing to the door. "May I?"

The double doors creaked and the butler peered through the center crack at Maribeth, his visage stern.

"Ah, our psychic has arrived," Webber said with a sneer, stepping aside. He folded his hands at the base of his back and stared straight ahead as they entered. "The séance room is down the corridor, third door on the right. Shall I escort you there posthaste? With a bit of good fortune, you'll solve the mystery of the murder before tea is served."

Maribeth froze, her sharp wit silenced by his ice-cold greeting. So Webber was also a skeptic and wary of her talents? God willing, she would make a convert of the butler and steward by week's end.

"Ignore him." Mr. Dunn set his hat on the side table and pulled off his gloves. His unwavering gaze met Maribeth's. "You'll find Webber has a droll wit and unruly sharp tongue. And he often forgets his place, I'm afraid."

The butler harrumphed and stalked out of the foyer. Though similar in height and build to Mr. Dunn, Webber exuded the formal indifference of a butler with perfection. His age and station afforded him a modicum of respect, but even Maribeth had her limits.

"Excuse me while I deposit my belongings in my office," Mr. Dunn said with a crisp bow. He disappeared down the corridor to her left and she took stock of her surroundings.

A winding oak staircase commanded the center of the foyer. Halfway up, a balcony overlooked the entrance, behind which a gilded mirror hung. Down the center of the wood stairs ran a carpet in rich hues of gold and sapphire. Maribeth's gaze traveled up the walls, which were covered in alternating strips of textured wallpaper and panels of wood. Decadent, to say the least.

Nothing in particular about the space spoke to her spirit. She pulled off her gloves and stuffed them into the pockets of her coat. Perhaps if she trailed her fingers over the table or if she wrapped her hand over the balustrade, she might find a connection.

The air held a dash of lemon polish, filling her nostrils with the soothing scent. She surveyed the side table with interest. The style was simple yet pleasing, with two drawers and a dark finish to complement the tiled floors. Bending, she inspected a chip in the detailed pattern of one of the tiles. The design mimicked a snow-flake, except these were black on white. The chip was so large, her forefinger fit easily into the hole.

A resounding crash echoed in her ears, the shattered pieces of a vase blurred her vision, and a jolt of pain seared across her hand. Unbridled fear slammed into her gut, stealing her breath. She shot to her feet and stumbled backward, her heartbeat racing, pounding against the walls of her chest.

"Is anything amiss?"

Whirling around, she found Mr. Dunn staring at her in the most peculiar manner. His gaze shifted to the rapid rise and fall of her chest. She was behaving like a fox in the hunt: spooked.

Is anything amiss? She hardly knew the appropriate response. Her deep breaths and irregular heartbeat subsided with his presence. Whatever had just happened … the experience was foreign and all together unwelcome.

Hello, is anyone here?

She focused on the chip in the tile, half expecting a spirit to rise from the depths of the floor. Sensing the footprint of past lives on objects was nothing out of the ordinary, but hearing the crash of a vase and feeling the sting of a slap? Those were odd, indeed. She'd heard of similar experiences from her mentor, but Eveline's mother had been a clairvoyant as well as a medium. Was this a latent skill lurking in Maribeth's psyche?

"Miss Sommerset, are you all right?"

Her head snapped up, and she held Mr. Dunn's concerned gaze.

"Of course," she said with a feeble smile. "Thank you for asking." Only five minutes into her stay at the chateau, and she'd given the impression of being a complete nut case. Little wonder he was a skeptic. "It's just ... I'm sensing the presence of a frightened child." She pointed to the troublesome spot on the floor. "Do you know the history of that chip?"

He ran the tip of his shoe over the crack, shaking his head. "This old thing? I haven't a clue. This pockmark predates me. Maybe you'll have better luck inquiring with the housekeeper, Mrs. Hawkins. She has been employed here for more than two decades."

"Thank you, I will, Mr. Dunn."

His head cocked to one side as he cleared his throat. "You may address me as Arthur if you wish. We will work closely together over the course of the coming week. Formalities can be tedious in such circumstances."

"Very well, Arthur," she said without hesitation. Social conventions were never her strong suit. "And I give you leave to use my given name as well."

"So it is settled." Arthur gestured to the staircase. "Shall I show you to your quarters for the next week?"

She nodded and followed him to the second floor. A grandfather clock chimed the one o'clock hour. The house was otherwise quiet, eerily so. Had the chateau always been this deserted? From what Maribeth recalled during her research of the haunted house, Mr. and Mrs. Turner were childless.

Arthur stopped before the last door on the west wing. "I've given you the Orange Blossom room. My apologies in advance. Mr. Turner's cousin, Gabriel Young, and his wife arrived earlier this week. They're expecting houseguests to visit any day. You're staying with us only a week, so I thought this bedroom would suffice."

"I'm sure this will be fine," she said, entering.

Daylight filtered through the window, illuminating the single bed and dresser painted white. A washbasin and mirror stood in the corner. The entire room was simplistic, except for a lovely mural on one wall. She recognized the scene immediately: a cat gazing longingly at an owl in flight, all by the light of the moon.

Arthur had assigned her to a child's bedroom? Strolling farther inside, she picked up a book from the bedside table. Flipping to the first page, she read a few lines aloud. "The Owl and the Pussycat went to sea in a beautiful pea-green boat. They took some honey, and plenty of money, wrapped up in a five-pound note."

Peals of laughter rang in her ears and warmth spread throughout her body. She closed her eyes, savoring the sense of happiness reverberating through her. The young girl who owned this book had cherished every word.

Hello, little girl, are you here? Come speak with me. We can be friends, if you like.

"A silly story, if ever there was one," Arthur said, disturbing the quiet moment.

Maribeth grinned as she stroked her hand over the colorful illustration. **"This was one of my favorites as a child, especially when a brooding pirate read it to me. Before meeting Eveline, my guardian—"**[24]

The steward's brow shot up and she snapped her mouth shut, tossing the book onto the bed. She shouldn't share such stories with a stranger. Better she get on with her purpose for being here. She turned her attention to unbuttoning her coat.

"Go on," he said. "You had a fascinating childhood. I would love to hear more."

Arthur leaned his shoulder against the wall, folding his arms over his chest while scrutinizing her. Why did he study her so intently with that enigmatic turn of his lips? Men never watched her every move with interest or engaged her in more than small talk. Her fingers trembled, and she looked away. Speaking about her childhood was out of the question.

"I'm told the daughter of Madame Brown favored that book as well," he finally said.

"The child who slept here?" she asked.

---

[24] The heroine divulges some of her past. She too loved this book (more on this later), and admits out loud that her guardian used to be a pirate (i.e. the romance conflict). The revelation of backstory is triggered by finding the book on the bedside table in the course of the current storyline.

The gleam in his eyes was inscrutable. <u>"No one else has stayed</u> <u>overnight in this room since the child disappeared many years ago."</u>

Her chest tightened, and she swallowed past the bile rising in her throat. Something terrible had happened to the girl, every fiber of Maribeth's being confirmed the truth of the matter.

"I thought perhaps..." The steward pressed his lips together as if thinking better of voicing his ideas aloud, but the cat was out of the bag.

"You thought my sleeping in this room might nettle the ghost of her mother into seeking me out?"

He rubbed his jaw with a small measure of contrition reflected in his eyes. "Rather coldhearted of me, I suppose. Would you prefer accommodations in the servants' quarters?"

"Certainly not." As her gaze swept through the bedroom, a tingling foreboding grew in her belly. "Your intuition was spot on."

"Does anything scare you, Maribeth?"

He sauntered behind her and peeled the coat off her shoulders. His left hand brushed hers as he tugged on one of the fitted sleeves. She held her breath, attuned in every way to his presence; his heady scent, the sound of his soft breathing, his body heat radiating on her back. She wanted...

She truly could not say what she wanted. Her experiences with men outside her family circle were limited. But she had witnessed Edith with her husband in unguarded moments when they thought no one was looking. Did she wish Arthur would press his lips on her nape or steal a kiss?

Maybe.

"I have nothing to fear from the ghost of Madame Brown," she said, turning to gaze up at him. But his nearness and the way he purred her name in that seductive baritone was more than a little unsettling. Ghosts rarely gave cause to be feared. But a handsome man who consumed her with every look...

He folded her coat and placed it on the end of the bed.

"I'll settle in here later," she said, clearing her throat. "What was the little girl's name?"

"Ah, ah, ah." He shook his head. "I'm afraid you must discover that on your own."

Her eyes narrowed. "A test of my skills? I could simply inquire with Mrs. Hawkins."

"But you won't. I sense your pride doesn't permit you to travel the easy route." He smirked.

Bastard. Of course his observation was dead on. She dearly loved a challenge. "Can you show me the scene of the crime?"

A hint of admiration glinted in his eyes. "Of course, right this way."

She hurried after him with one furtive glance over her shoulder at her new quarters. What did she have to fear? Nothing, except failure to communicate with any spirits.

Chapter Six

At several inches less than six feet, Arthur was not a tall man. However, walking beside Maribeth down the corridor, he was a veritable giant. The top of her head barely came parallel with his shoulders, yet she often met his direct stare with one equally as bold.

But whatever had transpired in the foyer during his absence had rattled her. Or she was a talented actress. He couldn't recall any of the other mediums who visited in the past having a similar experience, and in the foyer of all places. *I'm sensing the presence of a frightened child.* Why would Maribeth say that? She was hired to discover whether or not the ghost of Madame Brown lingered on the estate. Little of what the minx said or did made sense.

A flicker of doubt ignited in his chest. Would he prevail in controlling her final report to Mrs. Marsh come the end of the week? The medium was headstrong, but then so was he. Everything he set into motion was going splendidly. She was sleeping in the bedroom he'd assigned, and he was granted the favor of using her given name. In his experience, nothing built a false sense of friendship and camaraderie quicker.

"You'll discover the layout of the chateau is rather simple," he said, pausing when they reached the stairwell again. "Guests are quartered in the west wing, while family quarters can be found in the east wing. The third level is reserved for the servants' quarters."

Maribeth glanced in the direction of her bedchamber with a furrowed brow. A telltale sign she was deep in thought, and an endearing one at that. What keen observation would she share this time?

"Why was the girl's bedroom in the west wing?" she asked.

Quite astute of her to notice the incongruity. He could reveal the whole of the story and assuage her curiosity, but he would not. Perhaps later in the week, after he'd had an opportunity to observe her further.

"The former mistress of the house favored the west wing for the family's living quarters," he offered.

"I see." She nibbled on her bottom lip for a moment in the most distracting way. A sign of nerves, perhaps?

"Which bedchamber belonged to Madame Brown, if I might inquire?"

"The room adjacent to yours," he murmured.

Did the news set her heart fluttering? *Unlikely.* She hadn't even flinched when he spoke of Madame Brown's ghost. Mrs. Marsh would not easily concede her beliefs regarding her sister's murderer, so she must be strong.

"However," he added, "the connecting door was sealed years ago. You needn't worry about unwanted visitors in the night."

She met his gaze. "A lock will not deter a ghost, but I appreciate the concern. Before we enter Mrs. Turner's bedchamber, tell me what you know of the events preceding her death. The more I know of what transpired, the better my chances of connecting with her spirit."

"You truly believe Mrs. Turner's spirit lingers here?" he asked, unable to stop himself. There was a purity about her that made him want to believe in her abilities.

"I do," she said, strolling into the east wing. "Her death was tragic, and her spirit may roam the estate until the matter is resolved. Tell me all you know."

Arthur inventoried the sequence of events in his mind. What might he reveal, what ought he conceal? His account of the events could guide her ultimate conclusions and lend her an air of authenticity. Best he not leave Stanley's fate to the medium's imagination.

He paused before Mrs. Turner's bedroom door and peered down at Maribeth, demanding her full attention. "When I arrived at the chateau that afternoon and alighted from the coach, I heard shouting from above. Frantic, shrill cries from the mistress of the house."

"You're certain the shouts were hers?"

"Without a single doubt. Her voice was distinctive, and she was known for bouts of hysterics."

This much was true. His heartbeat skipped, and he avoided Maribeth's unnerving stare. The way she studied him ... God, he desired her. Could she read his thoughts as readily as she claimed to see the dead? If she read his mind now, what would she think or say? That he aspired to something far beyond his grasp. The mistress of an estate might dally with her servants, but a young lady such as Maribeth ... no, she would never consider anything beyond a working relationship with him. Or would she?

He mentally shook himself of the ridiculous thoughts and continued, "Upon hearing the commotion, I looked up. Mrs. Turner stormed across her balcony and suddenly pitched forward over the ledge, arms flailing. Almost as if she had been shoved from behind, though I saw no one else from my vantage point."

The muscles in his throat spasmed after telling the lie, but his voice held steady. He was sorely out of practice. Still, his prior experience did not fail him. The trick of delivering falsehoods in a believable manner lay with staying as close to the truth as possible.

"And the cause of death?" Maribeth asked, folding her hands primly at her waist. "The fall was a mere ten, perhaps twelve feet. I've jumped twice that distance off the side of a ship in my youth. Did she drown before your eyes?"

He drew in a harsh breath. Had he let Mrs. Turner perish? The insinuation was there, lingering between them. *Damned impertinent of her.* Gritting his teeth, he managed a tenuous hold on his temper. Snarling at Maribeth would not further his cause or endear him to her. He was many things, but a cold-blooded killer was not one of them.

"Her neck snapped upon impact with the pond. Ask the coroner yourself, if you do not believe me. Besides, Mrs. Turner was a strong swimmer, so I knew she was fatally injured when I dragged her limp body out of the water."

"My apologies, Arthur," she said, patting his forearm. "I believe you. Please understand, I must assess everyone's character and reactions on my own. I'm sorry if I offended you."

He nodded briskly and opened the door to the suite, gesturing for Maribeth to enter. She walked inside and her shoulders shuddered. Wrapping her hands over her upper arms, she rubbed briskly. The room was rather chilly without a fire in the hearth, but with her long sleeves and high-necked dress, she ought to be comfortable.

"The newspaper article mentioned other witnesses," she said as she strolled through the chamber. "Who spoke of eerie wails and creaking floors?"

"Mrs. Hawkins, the housekeeper, as well as Mrs. Pickering, the cook."

He folded his arms as she ran her lithe fingers across every available surface, occasionally closing her eyes and breathing deep. A sense of calm serenity surrounded her. Her steps were cautious, her focus absolute. He may as well have not existed for all the attention she afforded him.

"Would you care to inspect the balcony?" he asked, unlocking the double glass-paned doors.

She nodded and followed him outside. A lounging chair covered in a bold, floral pattern filled one corner. The short ledge around the perimeter, which barely reached Arthur's shins, held several potted plants.

Maribeth sat on the ledge, exactly in the spot where Mrs. Turner fell, and she peered over the edge to the pond below. After bracing her palms on the ledge, she met his gaze. "This is where she tumbled, is it not?"

"Yes, indeed." He dipped his head in acknowledgment. A lucky guess for a cunning lady. *Let the show commence.* "Is Mrs. Turner here with us?"

Turning her face skyward, she breathed in and out with long, measured breaths, closing her eyes, no doubt for dramatic effect. At least the woman was not predisposed to talking to the dead out loud. He found such one-sided conversations laughable.

"I'm afraid not," she finally said on a sigh.

Why didn't she leap at the opportunity to demonstrate her skills? This was the murder scene. If any connection was to be found, surely it was here. *Confounding.* He had no other word for the woman. Except *inexperienced.* She was green and had yet to hone her skills of deception.

"What did Mr. Turner say when questioned?" she asked, pulling him from his musings.

"Nothing." Arthur lowered himself on the foot of the chaise longue and stretched out his legs. "By the time his solicitor arrived to attend the interrogation, Mr. Turner's mind had slipped into oblivion."

She lifted an eyebrow. "Do you think he knows what occurred?"

Arthur shrugged. "He resides across the hallway, and the incident occurred shortly before the scheduled Thursday tour. As such, Mr. Turner would've taken to his quarters to avoid the throng of visitors." He focused his gaze on the doorway into Caroline's chamber, away from Maribeth's prying eyes. "I venture he must've heard something, at the very least."

"Perhaps creaking floors or the wails of a malevolent ghost?" A hint of humor tinged her words. "Why do you suppose the rumors of the ghost of Madame Brown persist?"

The corners of Arthur's lips curled up. "Well, for one, where is the sense in touring the séance chamber if it isn't haunted by the infamous clairvoyant who resided here?"

"I see." Maribeth folded her legs at the ankle, tapping her booted heels against the stone ledge. "So your employer is an opportunist?"

A gruff laugh escaped him. "By no means. The tours were his wife's idea. She held a macabre fascination with the dead." Among other things. "Even more so, I believe she enjoyed torturing Mr. Turner. He visited Chateau Swansea for a séance a few years before he met and married Caroline. When the former mistress died in childbirth, Mr. Turner acquired the estate and accepted guardianship of Madame Brown's daughter. I believe Mr. Turner held an enduring love for the clairvoyant. Some say Arabella was jealous of Caroline living in her home and raising her daughter."

The *tap, tap, tap* of Maribeth's boots against the ledge stopped, and she shook her head. "The Turners were married ages ago. Why would the ghost attack now?"

"Because Mrs. Turner held a ceremony with her sister in the séance chamber only a week before the incident. This is why Mrs. Marsh worries the ghost may have murdered her sister."

Her mouth formed a little O and her brow lifted with interest. "That's right. You mentioned this at the inn. A first attempt?"

"Second," he corrected. "<u>There was one other séance a few years after the Turners were married. However, something occurred back then that scared the wits out of Mrs. Turner.</u> She only found the courage recently to try another séance."

"Poppycock!"

Arthur shot his gaze across the balcony to where Gabriel Young leaned in the doorway with his arms folded. How long had Stanley's cousin been listening in on the conversation? The squirrelly bastard.

"Do not fill Miss Sommerset's head with these ridiculous notions." Mr. Young straightened and bowed. "Gabriel Young, at your service. While I applaud every effort to unearth the truth of what happened to our dear Caroline, I cannot condone speculation of ghosts." His face scrunched. "<u>Most likely, my cousin killed his wife in a fit of rage, else he wouldn't sit motionless all day and night, like a statue, in his bed. Murder has a way of messing with one's mind, I imagine. Not that I blame him. Caroline drove everyone insane.</u>"

Had Mr. Young offended Maribeth with his denouncement of ghosts? With a little luck, this would spur her on and provide even more reason to prove their existence. After all, her livelihood was at stake should the rumors be false.

"That's a rather bold claim," she said, standing. "One might deduce Mr. Turner's condition stems from grief over his wife's death. Yet you presume the worst."

"Nonsense. Theirs was never a love match." Mr. Young waved away the possibility of a grieving husband. "<u>My cousin has been estranged from his wife for many years. He tolerated Caroline's lovers, so long as she was discrete. But she crossed a line this time. Surely, you're aware she was pregnant with another man's child.</u>" He shook his head, with a downturn of his lips. "<u>Disgraceful behavior</u> <u>after everything my cousin gave her.</u> The *lady* of the house was <u>rumored to be having an affair with one of the servants on the estate.</u> <u>Imagine my cousin's state of mind if he'd found out. One of his</u> <u>servant's whelps to inherit his vast fortune?</u>"

Mr. Young pierced Arthur with a penetrating stare, leaving no doubt as to who he believed that servant to be. Maribeth's eyes flickered with interest. Devil take him, but he wouldn't allow Stanley's cousin to muck up this investigation.

"Perpetuating rumors is ill-advised," Arthur said, coming to stand beside Maribeth. "Especially when you attempt to wrap me in the fold. <u>Everyone knows of my disdain for the mistress of Chateau</u> <u>Swansea, most especially her roving eyes.</u>"

"Yes, legendary," his nemesis said with a bored expression. "<u>What better way to conceal the forbidden relationship?</u>"

Oh, what utter drivel! Arthur had never desired the harlot a single day in his entire employ at the estate. But why argue the point further? The man was insufferable.

"<u>Interesting that he blames his cousin,</u>" Arthur said, <u>turning his</u> <u>attention to the medium, "though hardly surprising. As the Turner</u> <u>heir, Mr. Young would profit handsomely should the master of the</u> <u>house be found guilty of murdering his wife. He also had the most to</u> <u>gain when Mrs. Turner died, along with the *whelp*.</u>"

"You offend me, sir," Mr. Young said, lifting his chin. "Pray that the police find the murderer and Stanley rouses from his grief, else you will find yourself performing in a circus act again for your insolence. <u>Do not forget, I hold the power of authority over my</u> <u>cousin's affairs should the doctor find him incapable of running the</u> <u>estate.</u>"

A rush of blood surged through Arthur. "Oh, yes, the vultures circle above when their prey is weak. <u>Have your creditors become</u> <u>relentless as of late?</u>"

Mr. Young sucked in a breath, his fists clenching and unclenching. A moment passed in awkward silence, then he tipped his head. "I wish you luck in your investigation, Miss Sommerset, and hope you discover the truth soon so that I might move on with my life.

Who wants to inherit a decrepit old mansion reputedly haunted by ghosts?"

Turning, Mr. Young stormed out of the bedchamber.

Decrepit? Hardly. The chateau stood on rich land and represented only a fraction of the family holdings. Whoever inherited the Turner fortune would be set for a lifetime, and their heirs after them.

"<u>Were you tupping Mrs. Turner?</u>" Maribeth asked, rounding on him.[25]

The air rushed out of his lungs, as though bludgeoned with a ramrod. She hadn't exaggerated in the hotel lobby when she claimed to speak her mind.

"I do not 'tup' anyone! If I desire a woman, I take her to my bed and worship her body for hours." His gaze raked over her bosom and back up to her puckered lips, leaving no doubt about his desire to carry *her* off to his bedroom.

Her eyes suddenly widened, and she clapped one hand over her mouth. A deep scarlet stained her cheeks, but she rallied her spirits soon enough. "Pardon the vulgarity of my question, but I must know!"

He closed his eyes, grappling for composure. *Lord, help me.* His brazen behavior hadn't affected her in any discernable way. He was a fool, imagining he might capture her interest for a dalliance. She was within her right to question him as an investigator assigned to the case. He'd do well to remember that.

"<u>No, I was not.</u>"

A muscle in his jaw ticked under her scrutiny, and damn her if she didn't stare directly at the spot. She was far too observant for his peace of mind.

"Was her death truly an accident?" she probed. "Tell me what you saw."

"I already told you my account of the incident."

---

[25] Here is another example of Maribeth's behavior being consistent with her backstory. She speaks her mind and says things inappropriate for a lady of her wealth and class because of the unconventional upbringing she had. Without revealing her past earlier in the book, the reader would be confused by her mannerism and occasional outbursts.

She folded her arms. "But you're withholding something. I don't know what or why. Is Mr. Turner truly unwell, or are you shielding him from the authorities?"

Regardless of what he said, she wouldn't believe him. He was fast learning that Maribeth did not easily fall prey to the influence of others, not even him. Taking her hand in his, he pulled her through the bedroom and out the door. He didn't stop until they entered Mr. Turner's bedchamber across the hallway.

"There," he said, pointing to a man propped against pillows in his bed, his gaze fixed in front of him. "Speak with him if you wish. He is but a shell of his former self. Lord, but I'd rather see him stand trial than live this pitiful existence."

His breathing came in harsh pants. This was no way to live. **He wished for so much more for the man who had given Arthur a new life, one far away from the ugliness of traveling city to city and earning a wage with treacherous lies.**[26]

A nurse bounded to her feet from her chair at the bedside. "Mr. Dunn, can I be of service?"

Maribeth squeezed his hand before letting go. He closed his fist, capturing the heat of her touch as he approached the bed. His employer did not react to his presence whatsoever, which stung deep in his heart. They had developed a close bond in the ten years Arthur had worked on the estate. Why did Stanley stare blankly past him? Surely, their friendship counted for something.

"Good afternoon, Stanley," he said, swallowing. "I've brought you a visitor. Come, say hello. I told you about Miss Sommerset last evening. Remember? She's a psychic, like Arabella was."

If anything could stir Stanley's interest, it was that bit of news. Yet the older gentleman didn't bat an eyelash.

"Any change, Mrs. Bartley?" he asked.

---

[26] Sprinkling in more details about Arthur's upbringing and how his employer saved him from a life of lies and constant travel (i.e. the hero's motivation). This is essential so the reader can later understand why Arthur is willing to lie in order to protect his employer. Further evidence, also, of his disdain for the heroine's chosen profession (i.e. the romance conflict).

She shook her head with a pitying glance in her patient's direction. "He hasn't uttered a word since he came under my care. Barely eats or drinks. We must find a way to get through to him."

Maribeth took a position beside the bed, in the seat the nurse had vacated. Arthur leaned his shoulder against the bedpost and cocked his head, studying her. She sat so close to his master, her shoulders back, so self-assured.

"Hello, Mr. Turner, my name is Maribeth. I'm so sorry for your loss. I've been hired by your steward to investigate the incident with your wife. I promise to do everything within my power to bring justice. Is there anything you wish to share with me?"

She was full of surprises. Why introduce herself by her given name? It was an unconventional move for a lady. Perhaps that was her intent. Though a brilliant tactic, a minute ticked by and still her question went unanswered.

She laid her hand over Stanley's. "Can I relay a message to Mrs. Turner for you? I speak with the dead."

Arthur's breath hitched in his throat. His gaze flashed to Stanley. But his master didn't blink, didn't flinch. Arthur jammed his hands deep in his pockets lest he grab the old man and rattle his teeth in his head. He could at least force Stanley to moan, to move, to react.

"May the Lord's peace be with you," she whispered before standing and nodding her head in the direction of the exit.

Arthur closed the bedroom door behind them, and the lock clicked into place, echoing down the empty corridor.

"So you're not protecting him from the police," she declared. "The poor man. We must help him by discovering the truth."

That much was obvious, but he didn't know where to begin. "And how do you propose we do that?"

"I must speak with Caroline Turner." Her eyebrows scrunched, meeting at the bridge of her nose. "But I didn't sense her presence in her bedroom. Let's visit the second-most likely place where she would linger."

"Which is?"

"The séance chamber, of course. Take me to the place where the inciting event occurred."

A vibrancy encompassed her whenever she spoke of her craft. He suppressed a smile. *Of course.* Maribeth's powers of deduction were sound and lent her a certain credibility. His fingers itched to rub her cheek and feel her exuberance firsthand.

"An excellent suggestion," he said, clenching his fists at his sides. "There is a framed picture hanging on the wall that you'll wish to see. Hard evidence of the ghost of Madame Brown."

"A ghost captured on film?" She covered a burgeoning grin behind her fingers. "This I must see."

He offered her another titbit for strengthening whatever tale she chose to spin of ghosts, and she laughed at the prospect. His chest tightened in the most peculiar way as he trailed after her. If he was not careful, he might find himself entirely under *her* spell. But with Mr. Young's threats ringing in his ears and Stanley still unresponsive, Arthur must beguile Maribeth into forming the right conclusions, or he would be the one telling fortunes to earn his keep.

Chapter Seven

"Ye who believe shall find what ye seek. Ye who doubt must turn about."

Maribeth read the inscription embossed in gold script across the center of the door to the séance chamber. Madame Brown certainly had a flair for the dramatic. Though, for some inexplicable reason, she sensed the clairvoyant had truly honored their craft while extracting a living from her talent.

Am I any different?

"Do you believe?" Arthur asked, his voice somber.

With every fiber of her being. This was her calling, and she would find what she sought within. The raw energy of the chamber zinged through the door handle and into her palm. This was one of those defining moments in her life. Would she rise to the task or stumble and fall?

"I do," she whispered.

Arthur covered her hand with his, halting her from opening the door. His intense gaze bore into hers. "Mr. Turner's life is in your hands, Maribeth. Please have a care with it."

Licking her lips, she pushed the handle down. The latch clicked and her heart pounded, sending a rush of adrenaline through her veins. Touring Madame Brown's séance chamber was a dream, but entering with Arthur as her sole guide was sheer bliss.

He pushed the door wide open. "Go on, enter."

A hazy swirl of energy greeted her, crowding her space and mind, cloying to her skin like the early morning dew on grass. *Filthy little beggar!* Loathing crept up her spine, inch by inch until it wrapped around her throat. She could scarce breathe. Small white dots swam in her periphery, and she swayed. God, she must flee;

leave this menacing place immediately before she lost all of her faculties. Her body shook violently and the world spun on its axis. What was this—?

"Maribeth!"

Her body wracked once more, and her surroundings came into focus. Arthur held her shoulders, shaking her again and again. His grip was firm yet gentle. Worry lines creased the corners of his eyes. And his lips, those beautiful, sensual lips, were inches from hers, moving rapidly. What was he saying? She concentrated on his mouth, forcing all else from her mind until his words permeated the haze engulfing her.

"What in the devil is the matter with you?" Arthur groused, gripping her shoulders tighter, his fingers probing through the fabric of her gown.

The warmth of his hands and desperate gleam in his eyes soothed away the bite of his words. Perhaps she had been foolish by taking on an investigation of this magnitude without someone by her side to ground her. **Her mentor, Eveline, rarely communicated with spirits without Brother Anselm by her side. But the monk was growing too old to travel with Maribeth, even if she wished for his company.**[27] Arthur would have to fill that role.

"The spiritual energy here overwhelmed me for a moment." She extricated herself from his hold and peered around the cavernous room. "Thank you for the little shake. Your touch grounded me."

Air hissed through his teeth, and he stormed away only to turn around and face her again. His face was ashen. "Must you be so dramatic? You needn't go out of your way to impress me with your skills."

Why was he rattled by her episode? He didn't care what happened to her. Or did he? She studied him through her lashes. With each passing second, color returned to his cheeks. If given a choice, would he abandon her or stay by her side?

---

[27] The heroine is so focused on her goal of becoming a psychic investigator that she ignored an important lesson about the toll the job takes on her mind and body. As you will see in the next few paragraphs, the hero is stunned by Maribeth's reaction. He is beginning to wonder if the heroine isn't a fraud.

"Ye who doubt must turn about," she said, folding her arms over her chest. "Madame Brown and I agree on that score. Your negativity might hinder my progress. Perhaps it's best you leave. I can ask Mr. Young or one of the other servants to assist me."

"No." His jaw tightened, and he rubbed his hand over the tense muscles. He was a man caged, fighting some inner battle. "My apologies. I've never seen ... your reaction took me by surprise. Will that happen again?"

A flutter rippled in her chest. If he held her body close to his again, stared at her with a mixture of concern and desire? She couldn't predict her reaction, except to say he made her feel foreign sensations. Lovely, yet terrifying.

She shrugged. "Maybe, maybe not. I cannot predict the future."

"Then I'll stay with you." He gestured to the head of the séance table where a framed photograph hung on the wall behind a commanding throne. "Time for you to meet the ghost of Madame Brown."

Suppressing an urge to snort, Maribeth closed the distance and studied the picture of the séance room. A young girl sat on the throne, a skittish gleam in her eyes. Guests filled the seats around the table, where firelight glowed from six candles, flickering off their joined hands. Behind the girl, a beautiful woman stood, her smile triumphant.

"Do you see the shadow of the ghost standing behind Mrs. Turner?" Arthur asked over her shoulder. He pointed with his forefinger, brushing up against her back as he leaned closer to trace the faint outline. "Some say the ghost is strangling her for exploiting the child. She was only four. A lovely girl yet hauntingly troubled."

The rich leather scent of his cologne robbed her of the ability to concentrate on the photo. If she turned her face a few inches, her lips might graze his cheek. Was his skin soft or rough? She had never kissed a man, had never wished to. Until now. Why him? She swallowed, her body trembling. Maybe because he was a mystery in and of himself.

Arthur slipped passed her and leaned his back against the wall, studying her. "Are you frightened by what you see?"

"No."

His lips twitched into a wry grin. "I didn't think so. What do you make of the photo?"

"It's a brilliant ploy for enthralling visitors," she said, turning to face the séance table. "By a cunning woman. I believe Mrs. Turner didn't stand still long enough while the film developed."

Arthur claimed the empty space beside her, his shirtsleeve a hairsbreadth from hers. "Mrs. Marsh sees a ghost in the photo."

"Then she is misguided by fear."

"Yes, I believe she is," he murmured. "Though I hardly blame her. The picture … according to the housekeeper, that was the only other séance Mrs. Turner ever held in this room."

She couldn't fathom what had gone wrong, having never taken part in one of the rituals herself. All she knew of séances was second-hand. Candlelight, holding hands, questions for the dead. One knock on wood for yes, two for no.

"What happened that night?" she asked.

He wrapped his hand around hers and held their joined hands in the air. "Imagine a stormy night, the crackle of thunder, and howling wind. The candlelight dances, forming shadows of past loved ones on the walls."

The melodic timbre of his voice lulled her into a trance-like state. She closed her eyes and absorbed the energy zapping between them.

"Tension sizzles in the air, and the child asks…"

"'Mama, are you here?'" Maribeth whispered. The words flood-ed her mind, strong and true. "One sharp knock echoed in the chamber. Guests gasp and—"

Arthur dropped her hand and sighed. "A damn shame that you've heard the story already. This one is my favorite."

Why ruin his fun? She wished to know how the story ended, since she'd never heard the tale in the whole of her life, and his outburst stunted the vision blooming in her mind.

"Please, go on," she said, studying the intricate letters and num-bers etched into the center of the round séance table. "Your retelling is most entertaining. I do believe you've missed your calling as an actor."

Lowering himself onto one of the chairs, Arthur leaned his head back and crossed his legs. "The ghost answered with one knock, and the guests gasped." His right hand covered his heart in a dramatic gesture and his mouth dropped into a wide O. "'Please don't make me do this,' the child cried. A gust of wind surged out of thin air and doused all six candles. Pandemonium reigned and the guests fled, stumbling over each other in their haste to escape."

He was an exceptional storyteller.

"Yes, that rendition feels like an accurate conclusion to the story. But do you believe it, Arthur?"

"Based on the photograph, I believe the girl was an unwilling participant, as well as scared and sad."

"What happened to her?" Maribeth asked.

"Nobody can say for sure," he replied, holding her gaze. "That was before my time as steward of the estate. Most speculate the girl was abducted from the premises shortly thereafter, never to be seen again. Was there foul play? Or did Madame Brown answer her daughter's plea and save her from the wicked hands of Mrs. Turner? We may never know the truth."

Another mystery to solve?

"How old would the girl be now?" she asked.

Arthur tipped his head and his eyes narrowed in thought. "Perhaps twenty or thereabouts. I've often wondered if she might return some day and seek revenge."

"Revenge for what?"

"From what I hear, Mrs. Turner and the child didn't get on very well. And after the séance…" He formed a steeple with his fingers under his chin. "What if the lady of the house arranged for the child to go missing? Now *there* is good reason for murder."

And Edith believed Maribeth's imagination was twisted? The child had only been four years old when she disappeared. "You're grasping at straws, Arthur. Surely the child cannot recall memories from such a young age, let alone those vivid enough to inspire revenge."

"Don't you?" he asked. "We all remember the things we most despise about our childhoods and, more importantly, how they made us feel."

"What did you hate?" she asked.

He shoved his hands into his pockets and his jaw tightened. "The last day in every town, when we packed away all of our belongings and moved on with the circus. Not having roots, starting new in every city, leaving my friends behind. Earning a living off of the lies of fortune-tellers."

A small window to his soul. His parents had been frauds, and that embarrassed him. No wonder he found Maribeth's work distasteful. Oh, he did a good job of hiding the truth, but there were little signs.

"I'm afraid I have no such memories." **Her childhood memories were forever elusive, hovering outside her grasp. Little of her past stuck with her, except how she'd felt. Cold and scared in the dark bowels of the coal mine. Or the stinging pain from the slash of the whip across her skin. The crooning lilt of her mama's voice, the silky texture of her hair when she bent to kiss her forehead.**[28]

She shook the melancholy thoughts away. Why was Arthur traveling this path? Unless he suspected the child had grown up and was among them, a murderess in hiding.

"Has anyone ever visited and claimed to be the girl?"

"More than I can count on one hand," Arthur said. "But they've all proven to be imposters in the end." His eyes suddenly widened and he sprang from his seat, walking to the photograph, where he inspected the child with great interest. "Yet there is one woman who has these blonde curls and is about the right age…"

Blonde curls, twenty years old … Maribeth's heart clattered in her chest. Was he insinuating that *she* was the daughter of Madame Brown, come to seek revenge? He would blame her for the crime. The bloody scoundrel!

"I am not—"

---

[28] A little more insight into the heroine's past and why she doesn't fit into her social class (i.e. motivation). Who whipped her? She remembers her mother fondly but never remarks on her father. Why?

"Gabriel's wife—"

They stared at each other in shocked silence for a moment and then his lips spread into a wide grin.

"You thought I invited you here so I could pin the murder on you? Do not fret, Maribeth. I bear you no ill will."

She exhaled, swallowing past the lump building in her throat. Perhaps her imagination was a bit overactive. Just as his appeared to be.

"What of Gabriel's wife?" she asked.

"Judith has the look of the girl, though it is difficult to say for sure. The photograph is old and the girl was so young at the time."

"You're serious?" She rubbed her arms, warding off a sudden fit of chills. What an absurd notion. "You believe Judith could be Madame Brown's long-lost daughter?"

"They came for a visit on the morning of Mrs. Turner's death." Arthur snapped his finger. "And she was raised by her aunt and uncle. I will dig into her past or pass along the information to the chief inspector. Perhaps that will shed some light."

Inquiring into Judith's heritage could take weeks. There must be a better way to establish the likelihood that she was the girl from the photograph. Such as … such as …

"Is there a portrait of Madame Brown somewhere in the chateau so we might compare the two women?" she asked, warming to the idea. "At twenty, the daughter is much more likely to have the look of her mother than of the child in that picture."

Arthur shook his head. "No, I'm afraid not."

"Why haven't you mentioned your suspicions about Judith to the coroner or the police?"

"Because it didn't strike me until I saw the picture again." He glanced over his shoulder, surveying the séance room. "Could be mere coincidence. This place is messing with my head."

"Well, we cannot leave yet," Maribeth said, taking a seat on the throne. She spread her arms out and laid the backs of her hands on the table, palms facing up. "I haven't attempted to communicate with the dead. Give me a few moments of absolute silence."

"I'll be here," he said, standing behind her chair, "should you need me."

His gruff voice brought a ghost of a smile to her lips. He could leave whenever he so chose, but he stayed nearby instead. For her, to ensure her safety.

She closed her eyes and regulated her breathing, focusing on the rhythmic ebb and flow of air in her lungs. Her mind drifted on a sea of tranquility. Here she unlocked the mysteries of the unknown and embraced the hopes and fears of those clinging to that sphere between heaven and earth.

She was suddenly a little girl, terrified and alone, with all these strangers staring at her. Dark shadows danced on the walls, creatures of the damned hovering, waiting to claim their prey. Tingles erupted along her spine.

Why do you show me this, Lord? Was the terrified little girl connected with the murder of Caroline Turner? *Dig deeper, seek justice.* All her life, Maribeth had been labeled impetuous. Her instincts drove her actions, no matter the cost. Trouble often found her. Still, her intuition could not be denied. Maybe the child wasn't abducted at all but was murdered, too. Her head screamed for her to seek out Mrs. Turner's ghost, but her heart demanded she open herself to the scared, little girl in the photo.

Thank you, Lord, for the gift of sight. I humbly pray for your guidance. Blinding white light grew from the edges of her mind, obliterating all thoughts and fears. *His* purity and goodness filled her soul and cleansed her heart. With the power of God vibrating through her core, she opened her eyes.

A shadowy figure hovered on the opposite side of the table. The elegant woman was dressed in a royal blue gown and wore her red tresses high atop her head. Caroline Turner's spirit stood proud and fierce.

Can you tell me who killed you, Mrs. Turner?

The ghost nodded, her hands clasped serenely at her waist. *"My husband shoved me over the balcony. He was enraged by my betrayal, far beyond the reach of reason."*

Adultery, pregnancy. So Mr. Turner did not wish for another man's child in his home, inheriting his fortune.

Is there any evidence?

"Yes." The spirit drifted closer through the table, her lower half disappearing beneath the wood. *"Search for the letters in my bedchamber. There is a secret drawer in the back of my jewelry box. I informed my husband of my delicate condition while he was overseas. Stanley swore he'd kill me before he'd let any bastard child of mine inherit his wealth. Find the letters. Bring justice to my husband's doorstep."*

The visage of the ghost faded, and Maribeth slumped forward, resting her forearms on the table, pillowing her head. Her energy was spent. Did Arthur know of the damning letters? He was keeping secrets. She'd sensed that from the onset. And she didn't like it one bit. Gathering what little strength she possessed, she stood and faced him. He stared at her beneath hooded eyes.

"Mrs. Turner swears her husband shoved her over the ledge of the balcony, and yet you deny having seen anything. Are you lying to me?"

The tick in the left side of his jaw flared to life, but he said nothing. What possible reason could he have for lying? She could stare him down for an eternity.

After a few moments, he glanced away. "I said I don't know what I saw on that dark, stormy afternoon. Would you have me speculate when a man's life is at risk? Someone argued with Mrs. Turner on that balcony to be sure, but there's no solid proof against my employer."

"That's where you're wrong."

His gaze snapped back to hers. "What do you mean?"

"There are letters," she declared, hands on her hips. "And I will find them. We must return to Mrs. Turner's bedchamber at once."

Arthur might play games with the authorities, but Maribeth would not allow a crime to go unpunished. Could she trust him to be honest with her and protect her from harm should they stumble upon evidence?

She bit her lip. Ghosts could lie, too. Caroline Turner might seek to punish her husband from beyond the grave. But Stanley Turner was a man of means, with the lives of all his servants at his mercy. If he truly killed his wife, he was a potential threat to others. So why did Arthur shield the man from his fate?

Chapter Eight

Arthur leaned his head against the back of his desk chair and gazed upon the flickering flames within the hearth. The way the fire danced and crackled mesmerized him, much like Miss Maribeth Sommerset did.

He blew out a shaky breath. She knew of the letters and their exact location. But how? He had found them in a quick sweep of Mrs. Turner's bedroom before the police arrived.

The medium was a trickster. There could be no doubt on that score. Perhaps she made an educated guess? Letters between a husband and wife were common enough, and a lady's jewelry box held her most prized possessions. Stanley had been away on business before the accident, and Maribeth read the newspapers. Yes, she was deuced lucky or dangerously sly.

But not sly enough to outwit him. One day had passed since their visit to the séance chamber and she'd yet to discover the whereabouts of the letters. Nor would she ever. The contents were too damning. Arthur lifted the worst of the lot and perused once more.

December 13, 1888
Boston, Massachusetts

My dearest wife Caroline,

I am weary to the bone. Over the years, I have tolerated countless house parties and secret lovers. Discretion was my only demand. And even that appears too much for you. You're pregnant with his child?

This cannot be! You are stark raving mad if you believe I will acknowledge the child as mine. The timing alone makes such a claim impossible. I cannot—no, I will not—call you wife any longer.

Prepare yourself, madam, for when I return from my travels, I will file for a divorce.

I swear, I'd rather see you dead than surrender my vast fortune to your disgusting greed. My daughter will inherit the Turner fortune, not the by-blow of your seedy lover. Yes, Bella is my legitimate daughter, the joyous and welcome product of my deep and abiding love for her mother, Arabella. I thought to shield my little girl from the world by concealing her true identity. But you always suspected the truth, did you not?

I will find her.

So help me God, do not think to stand in my way. For if you do, I will post every letter of yours to the newspapers, full of your rantings of Madame Brown haunting your every waking hour. The doctors will come for you, and I will not stop them. Not this time.

Your ever-faithful husband,
Stanley Turner

Arthur folded the letter and tossed it onto his desk. If only he could give one of the other letters to Chief Inspector Marsh as evidence of the housekeeper's claim of the ghost's guilt. Mrs. Turner believed whole-heartedly that she was being haunted, and after reading this, so would her sister, the chief's wife. But he could not risk this letter falling into the hands of the police. At least his employer would be smart enough to destroy all evidence of their correspondence.

Arthur glanced at the fireplace. Maybe he should burn the letters even though they proved Mrs. Turner was crazy and feared Madame Brown's ghost. A sharp knock sounded at the study door and Webber entered.

"Have a care," Arthur said, snatching the letters from his desk and shoving them into the top drawer. "How many times must I tell you to wait for permission to enter?"

The butler narrowed his gaze on the desk. "You are up to something no good. Whatever you're hiding, I'll figure it out. Mr. Turner is guilty, and nothing can save his neck from the hangman's noose.

No matter how many questions your private investigator asks, the end result will still be the same."

To hell with you! Webber was a nuisance, a bloody thorn in Arthur's side. "What do you want, Webber?"

"Mr. and Mrs. Young's houseguests will arrive this afternoon. I thought you would wish to know."

And no doubt chomping at the bit for inside news on the deliciously scandalous affair. How could he have forgotten they were to arrive for the funeral at week's end? He must remind Maribeth that whatever she unearthed was highly confidential information.

"Thank you."

The butler's gaze moved to the large package leaning against the far wall. "What is that, if I might ask?"

Arthur drummed his fingers on the desk. Webber, being the nosey sort of fellow that he was, would stoop to pick the lock of the study if his curiosity wasn't quelled.

"Mr. Turner commissioned a portrait months ago. Do not presume to open the package, Webber. When the master of the house is well again, he will deal with it."

"Is the portrait of Caroline?"

"You mean Mrs. Turner?" he asked. An impertinent man, the butler was forever forgetting his station.

Webber snorted. "Yes, of course."

"That's none of your business," Arthur said, standing. "Off with you now."

Webber exited without another word, but the tight set of his jaw foretold of trouble yet to come. Before the door closed, however, another figure slipped through.

"Mr. Young, good afternoon," Arthur said with as much cordiality as he could muster. "What can I do for you?"

"Our guests arrive today, and my wife is at sixes and sevens. She isn't one for melancholy affairs. The funeral isn't for a week. Mrs. Young has her heart set on holding a treasure hunt tonight, by the light of the moon. Haunted houses and all that. This will keep our guests entertained and out of the way of the ongoing investigation."

Arthur struggled not to roll his eyes. "I appreciate the sentiment. I'm sure your guests will be highly entertained by the prospect. Do you require lanterns? Mrs. Hawkins can arrange for—"

"No," Mr. Young said, holding up a hand. "As steward of the property, you know these grounds better than most. My wife would be grateful if you would suggest hiding places for the clues. She fears her choices would bore our guests to tears."

Damnation! Assisting spoiled misses in their pursuit of fun, and while the master of the house was suffering, was not within the sphere of his duties. Especially with Judith being a suspect. He ought to refuse outright, on principle. But burning the bridge between himself and Mr. Young would not be wise.

"How many locations do you seek?"

"Five will suffice."

Arthur sat and scribbled notes onto a sheet of parchment, including a crude map outlining where his suggested locations could be found on the property. "The first bench within the maze, so the guests do not become lost. A hen's box within the chick coup; Mildred is the only pure white hen. The playhouse in the thicket, a hidden treasure in itself. The fountain of Aphrodite within the garden, commissioned from the great Bertel Thorvaldsen, and the wine cellar. Your wife may choose any bottle as her ultimate prize, except those in the red section, which are Mr. Turner's private stock." He glanced up from his writing. "Will those do?"

"Splendid," Mr. Young said. "You've missed your calling."

Arthur stood and handed over the list. "I am multitalented, it would seem. Mr. Turner is a gracious host, so I'm sure he would beg my aid in this matter. Especially since he is unable at present to assist you himself."

The rebuff was petty, perhaps. The truth of the matter was, the owner of the estate would encourage his cousin in indulging his wife's whims. A treasure hunt was an innocent diversion. Much preferable to other, less desirable amusements. And Mr. and Mrs. Young were never close to Mrs. Turner.

"You disapprove?" Mr. Young asked, his gaze riveted on the list.

Voicing his opinion wouldn't sway the end result, so Arthur held his derisive smile in check. "What I think does not matter. Is there anything else I can assist with? I must attend to other pressing matters."

"This will do. Thank you." Mr. Turner's cousin turned on his heel and closed the door quietly behind him.

Finally! Grabbing the thin stack of letters from the top drawer, Arthur shoved them in the inner pocket of his jacket. Best he burn these in his house, away from prying eyes. If Maribeth discovered he had these in his possession, she would … he didn't rightly know what course of action she would take, but he didn't wish to find out. She was key to disproving Mrs. Marsh's suspicions over Stanley's guilt. He would head home and dispose of the letters as soon as he spoke with the gardener about trimming the hedges in the maze.

Chapter Nine

A beam of sunlight warmed Maribeth's face, and she sat up in bed. The curtains were pulled back, and on the windowsill sat a doll. She rubbed her eyes and stood, yawning. Hadn't she closed the drapes last night before seeking her bed?

The doll was exquisitely crafted, with long, blonde curls and green eyes. She wore a yellow silk dress with tiny rosebuds, and it bore an inscription across the chest: Bella. Biting her bottom lip, Maribeth traced her finger over the fancy script. Yes, this was the child's name. It felt right. She had been named after her mother, Arabella. Who put the doll here?

She scurried to the bedroom door and turned the knob. Still locked. That was odd. Her stomach quivered as she walked to the adjoining bedroom door. Her fingers rested on the door handle, and she blew out a breath. *Turn the knob.* She did. Locked from the other side. Or hadn't Arthur said the door was sealed?

Had someone entered her bedroom while she slept? But who and why? Arthur was testing her skills, so he wasn't the culprit. Or was the ghost of Mrs. Turner or Madame Brown coming to her aid?

A burst of cold air whooshed through her and she gasped, unable to breathe for a moment. Maribeth spun around, seeking the source. The doll suddenly fell off the windowsill, and the head shattered against the wood floor.

"Bella is dead!"

Hello, Mrs. Turner, is that you?

Remnants of dark despair blanketed the room, but no one answered her call. Was that Caroline Turner? It was difficult to say. *Madame Brown?* Maribeth stayed very still for a minute, but only silence greeted her.

Side-stepping the broken doll, she peered outside the window. There were no ghostly figures hovering nearby, and the powerful spark in the air had dissipated. She glanced down and looked into a pair of sightless green eyes.

Her throat constricted, and she blew out a breath. The child was dead. A shiver coursed through her. What had happened to the poor, little girl? From this vantage point, Maribeth surveyed the maze of hedges on the northeast corner of the property. Her heart pattered out a staccato rhythm. Had the child succumbed to the lure of the beautiful, winding paths, where someone snatched her?

Stop! She must focus on the mystery at hand. Did someone murder Mrs. Turner? She still hadn't a clue where to find the missing letters. A search of Mrs. Turner's jewelry box came up empty. Arthur insisted that the chief inspector combed the entire room yet found nothing. But what did men know of women's secret hiding places? Perhaps the ghost had forgotten where she hid the letters.

Still, the layers between her mattresses were bare, and there were no hidden compartments in her bureau. Nor did Maribeth find anything stored among her undergarments. Had Mr. Turner disposed of the evidence before the police arrived or moved the letters? Where would he stash them? In his own bedroom?

A key rattled in the door to her chamber, and Maribeth glanced over her shoulder.

"Begging your pardon," the housemaid said with a bob. "I thought you must have taken yourself to the kitchen for breakfast. The sheets need changing, but I can come back later."

"You can stay, Pearl. I was about to leave." Maribeth grabbed a shawl off the end of the bed, and an idea percolated in her mind. Housemaids enjoyed intimate knowledge of the manor and its inhabitants. "By the by, I'm in need of writing supplies for a letter to my family. Would you happen to know where I might find pen and paper?"

Pearl went about her work, peeling the coverlet off the bed. "A small writing desk in the parlor. Mrs. Turner was mighty fond of writing letters in her fancy script. She drove Webber mad with her constant correspondence."

An image of the cranky butler flittered through Maribeth's mind's eye, and she grinned. "I'm sure he found posting letters a mundane task. But then, Mr. Turner often traveled, or so I've heard. So his wife had cause to write often."

"Oh, indeed." The maid tossed the soiled sheets on the ground and wiped her forehead, her cheeks flushed from exertion. "Rich folk are strange, though. The pair scarce spoke a word in each other's company, but the mistress sent the master endless letters."

"Maybe she wrote about the ghost of Chateau Swansea to her husband," Maribeth said. "Have you ever encountered the ghost of Madame Brown on the premises?"

Pearl flapped open clean linens. "Of course, but then who in the household hasn't? She's harmless. Walks the halls, like she still owns the place. Sits in the parlor for tea. Even enjoys a stroll in the maze from time to time."

"So you're not of the opinion that the ghost murdered Mrs. Turner?"

"Goodness no," the maid said with a snort. "Wasn't poor Mr. Turner what done it either, if you ask me. He wouldn't hurt a fly; he is kind and gentle. The police are bloody imbeciles if they don't have a list of suspects as long as the River Tawe."

Maribeth grabbed one end of the sheet, tucking the material under the mattress. One ought never to dismiss the opinion of a servant, especially one in a low station with little to gain or lose.

"Mrs. Turner wasn't well liked then?"

"The lady of the house enjoyed drama."

"Like what?" Maribeth asked, more out of curiosity than the belief the conversation would lead her anywhere in the investigation.

"She threatened to toss Cook onto the street without a reference. Said her savory meals thickened the mistress's waistline. Wasn't the food expanding her belly!" Smug satisfaction twinkled in Pearl's eyes. A snort escaped the housemaid and she covered her mouth, eyes widening. "Forgive me, I forget myself. Spreading vile rumors that might hurt Mr. Turner isn't right. He is a saint, tolerant ... always looking the other way."

Fear of losing one's job was certainly a motive for murdering the lady of the house.

<u>"Are you saying Mrs. Pickering belongs on the list of suspects?"</u>

Mrs. Turner fell from the balcony, but Arthur claimed he saw no one push her. Had the lady of the house grown ill and fallen? The cook prepared every meal. A little poison in the mistress's afternoon tart and the deed would have been done. Still, Maribeth struggled with the idea. Why risk so much over a job? Murder was a serious offense if you were caught in the act.

Pearl shrugged. <u>"Cook has five young ones. Food and clothing aren't cheap. Fine houses are few and far between in these parts. All I'm saying is, there are others who won't be sad when they bury the mistress ten feet under."</u>

Something to think on at the very least, but now she had other pressing business in the parlor. Namely, finding the missing letters. She excused herself and walked down the hallway with a modicum of decorum. Outside the parlor, she placed her ear to the door. The hour was too early for visitors, and based on their brief encounter the day before, Mrs. Young seemed to be the sort of woman who took breakfast in her bedroom.

Maribeth slipped through the doorway. Inside, she froze. The ghostly outline of a blonde woman dressed in an elegant emerald silk gown sat on the settee. Holding her breath, Maribeth treaded softly over the carpet. *Hello, Madame Brown? May I speak with you?*

"*Noooooo!*" the ghost snarled, standing abruptly. Her nostrils flared, and she dashed across the room, halting near a writing desk on the far wall. The hem of Maribeth's dress fluttered, and she swallowed hard as cold air assailed her lungs. A swirl of energy, frigid and intense, nearly formed crystals in the air around her.

"I'm sorry," Maribeth whispered. She shivered but made no move to rub warmth back into her arms. Anything could set off a malevolent spirit. "Have I done something to upset you?"

"*You are Caroline's puppet!*" The lady pointed one accusatory finger at Maribeth, her eyes sparking. <u>*"Stanley didn't kill that little tart. She's the murdering bitch."*</u>

The temperature dropped, and Maribeth winced. She couldn't make out the nearly transparent facial features of the ghost from across the room, yet she had no doubt this was the infamous clairvoyant. Perhaps Mrs. Hawkins's testimony was spot on. Madame Brown was certainly no friend of Caroline Turner.

"I seek only the truth," Maribeth said, keeping utterly still. "Help me, please."

"You seek the letter Stanley wrote? It proves nothing! But the one in Caroline's desk tells another story." The apparition beckoned with one finger. *"Which side are you on? Justice or vengeance?"* Madame Brown lifted her chin and swirled around, walking out through the wall.

"Wait," Maribeth shouted. *I have more questions.* Her teeth chattered, and she rubbed life back into her arms. What were these letters Madame Brown spoke of?

She rushed to the writing desk, an elegant piece, with curved legs and three drawers decorated with gold filigree. A quick perusal showed the center drawer held paper, pencils, and a fountain pen. In the left drawer, she found envelopes, wax, and a stamp bearing the likeness of Chateau Swansea. A low growl reverberated in her throat and she yanked the final drawer open.

A neat stack of letters lined the inside. Her gaze flashed to the parlor door. *Oh, goodness, quickly now.* Fingers trembling, she tugged the first note out of the envelope and read. The page was full of mindless discourse with Mrs. Turner's sister. Tossing it aside, she read through the remaining three notes. Pure drivel; talk of apple cobbler and special deliveries, all which took place ages ago. Why the woman even kept the correspondence was a mystery.

Maribeth touched the wall where the ghost had disappeared. *What are you trying to tell me, Arabella? I don't understand.* The other room, beyond this wall. What was it? She must find Madame Brown and question her further. Maribeth was no puppet, but she couldn't read minds. Perhaps the ghost would shed light on the events leading up to Mrs. Turner's death.

She stored the letters in the drawer once again and exited the parlor. Creeping along the hallway, she came to the adjacent room's door. Her pulse pounded in her ears. Being an investigator certainly had its thrilling moments. If anyone caught her snooping in places where she didn't belong, she'd feign ignorance and say she was lost. Her hand fastened on the handle—

"Mr. Dunn does not appreciate being disturbed in his study," the butler admonished with cold distain from behind.

Her heart clambered up her throat. This room was the steward's study. Did he have the letters stowed somewhere inside? She could confront him outright, but he would probably lie to her face. No, best that she sneak back again later. In the dead of night.

"Pardon me," Maribeth said, turning around. "I didn't realize this was Mr. Dunn's study. I'm not acquainted with the layout of the chateau. Might you direct me to the kitchen?"

The butler's pinched eyebrows said he didn't believe her innocent act. "Mr. Dunn provided a tour yesterday. I'm afraid your memory is quite poor." He pointed down the hallway. "Past the stairwell, left, and to the end of the corridor."

"Thank you." She scurried away and allowed herself a slight grin only when she reached the turn. By the time she entered the kitchen, her erratic breathing had evened out. An assortment of fresh fruit, bread, and pastries covered a platter on the counter, and sprigs of mint decorated the plate. Maribeth gagged involuntarily and flicked off the leafy greens.

Cook eyed her from head to toe, hands parked on her ample hips. "What are you doing?"

Maribeth stuffed her hands into her pockets and shrugged. "I'm sorry. That was rude. **But mint is rather foul smelling, don't you think?**"[29]

"I think you're late," Mrs. Pickering snapped. "I was fixing to put everything away before it spoiled. Will this do, or should I put a few eggs on to boil?"

"A light fare is fine." Maribeth snatched a plate and selected a lemon tart along with some ripe, green melon. Her mouth fairly

---

[29] Maribeth's aversion to mint is backstory planted secretly in the current story and relates to the cozy mystery. She has no idea of the true reason why she despises the scent of mint. Stay tuned.

watered in anticipation of the sweet fruit. She sat on a stool and grinned at Cook. "Wouldn't want my waistline to thicken."

The cook slapped a wad of dough onto the counter and har-rumphed. "The scullery maid has been flapping her jaws again, I see. Pay her ridiculous notions no mind." She sprinkled flour on the dough and massaged it in. "Mrs. Turner enjoyed teasing me and would never have given me the boot. Loved me and my fancy fare. Can't say as much for the butler."

There was a story aching to be told, but the cook's voice trailed off. Another suspect for the ever-growing list?

"Your tarts are divine," Maribeth said through a mouthful. "I wouldn't toss you out on the road either. As for Webber, well, the jury is out for deliberation. Did he often butt heads with Mrs. Turner?"

Mrs. Pickering pushed and pulled on the dough, kneading with rigor. "They tolerated each other well enough until the day before she died. That's when the lady of the house finally gave that uppity butler an earful. Told Webber he was forgetting his station in life. 'Bout time, too." The cook paused, wiping her nose with the back of her hand, leaving a flour stain. "That one is always thinking himself better than the rest of us. If the missus was on the verge of turning out anyone—"

"I beg your pardon!" a man growled from the entrance.

Maribeth whirled around on her seat. Webber stood in the doorway, a scowl forming deep creases in his brow.

"What vile rumors do you spread?" he asked. "I was the humble and faithful servant of Mrs. Turner. The lady of the house was not sour with me. I daresay she respected me until the day she died. Her ire rose from the unexpected visit of the master's cousin, Mr. Young. I merely pointed out that the timing was consistent with his annual visit to check on his inheritance."

Cook lifted her eyebrows to Maribeth and resumed kneading the dough. "Well, there's a motive for murder. If Mr. Turner didn't kill his wife for her infidelity, Mr. Young might've murdered her if he knew of her delicate condition. He's been waiting patiently for his inheritance for more than a decade. Thought he had it in the bag."

"That much is true," Webber said. <u>"Knowing Mrs. Turner's dislike of the man, she may have goaded him with news of her pregnancy. They argued fiercely in the breakfast parlor on the morning of her death."</u>[30] He swallowed hard and glanced away.

The butler almost looked sad. Did he have a heart after all? While he stopped short of speaking fondly of the former mistress of the chateau, he also did not speak poorly of her.

Mr. Young moved higher on Maribeth's list of potential suspects.

"Did Mr. Young know of the pregnancy?" she asked. Surely that was an important fact with wide-reaching implications.

The butler turned up his nose. "I do not spread rumors. <u>However, the housekeeper was a direct witness to the argument. You might impose on her to satisfy your curiosity.</u>" He turned his attention on the cook. "The house party will arrive as scheduled today, shortly after three. I've already informed Mr. Dunn. All is ready with the menu, I presume?"

"Yes, sir," the cook said, shaking her head. "A shameful business though, I might add. Entertaining guests when the missus isn't even in the grave and the master is upstairs, locked up in his suite. I'll never understand these high and mighty folk."

Webber nodded his agreement and stormed out. It was only half past nine in the morning and Maribeth was already exhausted. Tucking an apple into her pocket, she waved goodbye to the cook and headed for the back entrance of the house. A walk through the maze would do her good.

Thankfully, the layout of the chateau was simple to navigate, and she reached the terrace leading to the garden in short order. Mrs. Hawkins, the housekeeper, stood at the top of the stairs, her gaze fixed on the horizon.

---

[30] Notice that a lot of the backstory in a mystery comes to light through dialogue as the protagonist interrogates witnesses. In this story, some of the past is revealed through the hero because he is privy to certain information the heroine is not aware of. This is fun because the reader is the only one with the whole picture.

"Good morning," Maribeth said. "We haven't had much opportunity to speak since my arrival. Since you're here, I wonder if I might have a moment of your time."

Mrs. Hawkins eyed her warily. "So you can gather evidence against my master? I think not. I'm compelled to speak with the chief inspector, but I'll be damned if I give you anything to bury Mr. Turner. He didn't kill his wife!"

The housekeeper stalked away.

"Wait," Maribeth said, running to catch up with the woman. She moved swiftly for someone her age. "Webber said you witnessed an argument between Mrs. Turner and Mr. Young. Is that true?"

"And what of it?"

"Perhaps you will shed light on other potential suspects. What was the subject of their disagreement?"

"Mr. Young wanted money from the master, an advance on his inheritance per se."

Maribeth nodded. "Go on."

"Mrs. Turner chastised her husband's cousin for his greed, and the young man threatened to turn Mrs. Turner out without a single shilling as soon as Mr. Turner died. But she planted a facer on the upstart. Announced she was pregnant with the heir of the Turner estates."

"That must've been a terrible surprise," Maribeth said. "For both men."

The housekeeper's eyes watered, and she dabbed at the corners with a handkerchief. "Poor man. There's no telling who the father is. The lady of the house was fond of companionship ... of handsome servants ... and of strolling in the maze daily in the late afternoon."

Mrs. Hawkins's gaze wandered to the grounds, where the steward stood at the far edge of the lawn, speaking with the gardener. Sunlight glistened in Arthur's sable hair and glinted off the polished surface of his black shoes. His suit was subdued but stylish. After concluding his conversation, he walked with purpose toward the entrance of the maze, never once looking their way.

"Mrs. Hawkins, what is the gardener's name?" Maribeth hadn't interviewed him yet but made a mental note to do so. Based on Mrs. Turner's unstable personality and ability to drum up mischief, everyone was a potential suspect in Maribeth's estimation.

The housekeeper's mouth screwed up in a disapproving frown. "His name is Mr. Keppler. The man doesn't know a rose from a daisy, if you ask me."

Maribeth glanced sideways at the older woman. "Then why is he the gardener?"

"Why, indeed." Mrs. Hawkins fixed her with an imperious frown.

Upon closer inspection, the gardener was in his mid-thirties with a trim physique and auburn hair; a rather handsome fellow. Perhaps Mrs. Turner had hired him for reasons other than his knowledge of horticulture. No wonder the lady of the house was fond of walking through high hedges.

"Does Mr. Dunn often stroll through the maze in the late after-noon?" Maribeth asked on a whim.

"Every day. His house is on the other side of the estate, through the maze." With that, Mrs. Hawkins excused herself.

Her parting comment left little doubt that she suspected Arthur Dunn as a candidate for Mrs. Turner's secret lover. Had Mr. Turner finally discovered his most trusted servant betrayed him with his wife? That might prove ample provocation for a murderous fit of rage.

"Arthur, wait for me!" Maribeth shouted while lifting her skirt.

She dashed across the lawn, stopping only once she caught him just inside the maze. His warm smile caught her off-guard, causing her already fluttering heart to beat harder. Who would not wish to indulge in a dalliance with this man?

"Good morning, Maribeth." His gaze devoured her, dark and delicious. "You ought to run more often. Exercise is quite becoming on you."

Men with his charm and handsome features were dangerous. Both Mr. Young and Mrs. Hawkins believed the steward was guilty of the most heinous of crimes. Her head accepted the logic of their accusations, and yet her instincts … Perhaps she shouldn't trust her instincts around this man. One longing look from his soulful brown eyes sent her mind astray from her task.

"What troubles your heart and causes those grooves to gather in your brow? No, let me guess. Still no luck in finding the letters?"

In that moment, she cared nothing about those. Only one thing occupied her thoughts, invaded her peace of mind. And if she were being honest with herself, the reason had nothing to do with the investigation at hand.

"Tell me the truth, once and for all. Were you having an affair with Mrs. Turner?"

Chapter Ten

He would not quarrel over ridiculous accusations. Either Maribeth chose to believe him or she did not. In this case, the latter seemed to be true.

"<u>If my memory serves me, I've answered that question once before,</u>" Arthur said, heading farther into the maze.

"Wait one minute!"

He rounded the first corner in the maze and took the path on his right. She must give chase if she wished to pester him further, and by the sound of her rustling skirts, she was closing in fast, a tenacious viper nipping on his heels.

Her hand fastened on his forearm, and she yanked him to a stop. "You deny any and all allegations of relations with her?"

His gaze fell first upon her heaving bosom, then traveled upward to her flashing green eyes. Why was she so angry? He told her before that he hadn't tupped the mistress of the house. Who wagged their tongue this time? Gossip of every sort was an abhorrence, especially when it involved him. Except, in this particular instance, the thought of him bedding another woman aroused a passionate response in Maribeth. He could not deny how much that pleased him, and still her continued questioning rankled.

"If you believe I was Mrs. Turner's secret lover, you're the worst investigator I've ever had the misfortune to hire! Mrs. Turner was a bitter, spoiled debutante who dug the hole for her own grave. You want to believe Mr. Young? He is a heartless son of a bitch who only visits annually to keep tabs on his inheritance."

How dare she accuse him of swiving his employer's wife? **The man was more of a father figure to him than his own father had ever been. Stanley gave him a respectable job and gifted**

him a house near the estate.[31] He would never repay the man that way.

"I don't put stock in Mr. Young's rantings," Maribeth said, chewing on her bottom lip. "But Mrs. Hawkins has been a dedicated servant in this household far longer than anyone else on the estate. She implied … I had the sense…"

"I swear on my honor that I never desired Caroline Turner," he said, closing the gap between their bodies.

Her penetrating gaze touched his soul, seeking the naked truth. This wasn't about the investigation, though she hid behind that guise. He shouldn't care if she thought him a lecher. A servant's dealings behind bedroom doors didn't merit scrutiny from a lady.

Yet, I care what she thinks of me.

A great deal, in fact. She was candid, sincere, and courageous. What must her peers think of her forging a career as a psychic investigator? She didn't care about societal dictates. His heart thudded hard in his ears. He didn't look away but offered himself up on a platter. Although he might be crass, he was forever loyal to those he loved and respected.

A mischievous glint sparkled in Maribeth's eyes. "Nor did she fancy you."

He laced his fingers through hers and squeezed. "How can you possibly know whether or not the late mistress of the house fancied me? Your cold observation wounds my manly pride."

"She told me so just now, and quite vehemently, I might add."

He held her gaze, entranced by the rich timbre of her voice and her confidence. How did she manage such sincerity? Guileless, so genuine.

"Of course she would deny as much," he whispered in Maribeth's ear. "Yet you know she lies, do you not?"

"Self-righteous bastard." Her voice quivered. "She demanded you come to her bed, but you refused."

---

[31] For the first time, we get concrete details on what Stanley has done for Arthur. He gifted him a house on the estate. This further supports the hero's motivation.

He froze, suspended for a moment between the past and present. *You would deny me, the lady of the house? Self-righteous bastard.* **His encounter with Mrs. Turner was utterly private and so long ago.**[32] How could Maribeth possibly know this?

His heart skipped a beat. God, he wanted to believe in her. What magic did she weave around him? The lemony scent of her perfume wafted over him, luring him in. Pure, innocent. He held himself rigid, resisting the temptation to nuzzle his cheek against her soft curls. He wanted to taste her rosebud mouth, feel the gentle curve of her hips, and elicit moans of pleasure from her lips.

"Why did you refuse her, Arthur? She was a beautiful woman."

"On the outside, perhaps." How could he have betrayed Stanley and lived with himself? "I did not desire *her*. Not the way I crave—"

"The map says we must turn right at the juncture." The sound of Mrs. Young's feminine lilt penetrated through the shrubbery.

Arthur held one finger to his lips. Grabbing hold of Maribeth's hand, he pulled her deeper into the maze, past the first bench and farther still. Turn after turn, they ran in silence until, finally, the maze emptied into the front garden of his property.

"Oh, my," she said, a bit breathless. "Your house is absolutely charming. Straight out of the pages of a fairytale!"

The two-story structure with pale yellow siding and blue shutters might be called whimsical, but he cherished quiet evenings on the back terrace. He often sat there, entranced by the rugged cliffs and untamed waters of the ocean. Even on stormy nights, he enjoyed the magnificent view from the bay window of his bedroom. Here, for the first time in his life, he had lain down roots.

"A gentleman's house is not charming," Arthur said, folding his arms. "Might we settle on appealing or pleasing to the eye?"

"No, no." She tapped one finger to her lips, deep in thought. "What of impressive, grand, or splendid?"

---

[32] This backstory is critical to the romance conflict. Arthur finally has evidence that Maribeth may be a legitimate medium. She has revealed something known only to Arthur. But notice how I've tied this in naturally to the current storyline. Maribeth is interrogating Arthur about the former mistress as part of the investigation about the killer because she worries he may be a prime suspect.

"Impressive," he said with a nod. "Though dull in comparison to Devil's Cove Manor, I'm sure."

"Please, don't say that." She closed her eyes, breathed in fresh air, and smiled as the sound of waves crashing against the cliffs penetrated the air. "Anyone who wouldn't love to live here belongs in a madhouse."

Would she truly be happy living here, even with him?

He grinned and jogged up the four stairs to the porch. "Would you care for a drink while you peruse the inside of my impressive house? There is something I wish to speak with you about."

She turned her face skyward and frowned. "I fear a storm is coming. I can't stay long."

"All the more reason to come inside." He held out his hand in invitation. "Or do you still harbor the notion that I might be Mrs. Turner's killer?"

"I haven't accused you yet," she said, sweeping past him to enter the house.

He did not miss the *yet* in her sassy response. Her sass brought a smile to his lips. She did not allow others to trample on her or intimidate her.

Taking a seat in the rocking chair nearest the hearth, she met his gaze. "We may have established that you were not lovers, but no one has been crossed off my list of suspects yet. Despite Mrs. Turner's insistence that her husband killed her, my list of suspects grows daily."

He bent on one knee and lit a match beneath the kindling. "You doubt what the ghost told you of her husband's guilt?"

Maribeth hesitated. "Madame Brown paid me a visit earlier. She was quite angry, called me Caroline's puppet. Until I find the letters, I cannot know for certain. Ghosts can be liars, too, and from what I've learned of the mistress of the house, she isn't trustworthy."

He paused and looked up. This was an interesting development. "Did the ghost come to your bedroom?"

"No," she said, suddenly taking interest in a fleck of dirt on her skirt. "I went to the parlor in search of pen and paper."

"And Madame Brown simply appeared and accosted you?"

179

Maribeth sighed. "She was sitting in the parlor when I walked in. I'm sorry, I shouldn't snoop where I don't belong."

His brow lifted. "A moment ago you were seeking pen and paper. Listen, Maribeth. I gave you free rein of the estate. Did you think I was joking? If anyone questions you, send them to me. <u>What else did Madame Brown have to say?</u>"

<u>"That Caroline is the killer, not Stanley."</u> Maribeth rocked in her chair. <u>"What do you think she meant?"</u>

<u>"I haven't a clue."</u> But he would ponder over it more later.

The flame from his match caught hold of the dry bits of tree bark and grew under the fanning of his gentle breaths. Yet again, the woman he'd hired on a whim proved to be astute. The more time he spent with Maribeth, flickers of hope grew in his heart, tremulous and unsteady as the fire. Would they catch hold and spread, or wither and wane?

"Who else is on your list of suspects?" he asked, claiming the chair opposite her. An instant later, his cat bounded from under the sofa and jumped on his lap, purring.

"Oh," Maribeth said, leaning closer. "He's a beauty. What is his name?"

"She," he corrected, scratching behind the feline's ears. "I call her Cleopatra. She struts around this place like a queen and demands my attention at her whim. Please, you must excuse her rudeness. <u>Your list of suspects?</u>"

<u>Maribeth turned her fixed gaze to the budding flames in the fireplace. "The cook and the cousin. Did you know Mrs. Turner threatened to fire Mrs. Pickering? Or that she had a vicious confrontation with Mr. Young on the morning of her death?"</u>

<u>"Yes to the first, no to the second. Mrs.</u> Turner was always issuing threats. The cook's job wasn't in jeopardy. Hiring and firing servants rests exclusively with Mr. Turner these days; otherwise, the

staff would turn over weekly, **as was the case when the mistress of the house oversaw that duty.**"[33]

Maribeth retrieved a small notebook and pencil from her pocket and scribbled a few words. "Well, I have one less suspect. And what do you make of Mr. Young?"

"As I told you before, his motive is the strongest."

"Or equally as strong as Mr. Turner's," she said.

He chose to ignore her observation. Arguing over that point would get them nowhere. "Do you have any idea what Mrs. Turner and Mr. Young argued over?"

"She admonished him for seeking an advance on his inheritance. He threatened to turn her out of the house as soon as Mr. Turner died. She didn't appreciate his threats and goaded him with her pregnancy, of a rightful heir."

"So he knew before the news article was printed," Arthur said, leaning forward. This was monumental, irrefutable evidence of a motive. And Mr. Young's gambling debts were well known. "You've been quite busy over the past twenty-four hours."

"While you dealt with the estate's business and plans for Mrs. Turner's funeral, I was earning my fifty pounds." She folded one leg over the other and stroked the quilt hanging on the armrest of the rocker. "Your home pulses with tranquil energy," she said, turning toward him. "I sense love and peace, yet there are no family paintings. Are you all alone?"

"Quite so." And more than happy. Years on the road as a youth had soured his gut toward his family. An occasional letter requesting financial assistance was all he could look forward to these days. He jumped out of his seat and headed for the sideboard. "Care for a drink?"

"Yes, please." She strolled up beside him and watched as he poured sherry into two glasses. "I'm sorry if I've stumbled onto a sore topic."

---

[33] This is backstory secretly planted here to give a clue as to who the killer might be. Much like the example I gave in chapter eight for *Blackburn Castle*, I imagine readers come back to this and have an aha moment. Remember, our villains have backstories too.

He handed her one tumbler and downed his drink in a single gulp before pouring a second. The liquid warmed his throat and stomach instantly. *Not so hasty, boy! There's more where that came from.* Stanley's chiding voice echoed in his ears, and he took another drink, this time a sip. He rolled the sherry over his tongue, savoring the bouquet.

"As I said before, we moved from town to town. My parents never stayed in one place long enough for paintings, and they're a nuisance to transport," he said, leaning his hip against the sideboard. "They are fortune-tellers by trade and make their living on the road."

"Are they talented?"

"Oh, indeed!" A bitter laugh escaped, and he bit back the rest of his scathing retort. "My mother has a knack for reading body language and probing her subjects in a way that reveals their deepest wishes. Then she spins tales from threads of gold and silver, all of which glitter brightly in her crystal ball.[34] I've yet to meet another storyteller of her caliber. Until you."

Maribeth sighed heavily. "All of my stories are grounded in truth and come from my heart."

His gaze met hers, and he sipped once more from the heady wine. In some ways, she was far more talented than the fortune-teller who raised him. Maribeth's stories burrowed into your soul and wove through the fabric of your beliefs.

---

[34] We dig a bit deeper into how Arthur feels about his parents and his upbringing. This is backstory that further highlights why he and Maribeth would never suit (i.e. the romance conflict). Yet at the same time, Arthur is realizing that the heroine really isn't like his mother or father. She is genuine. Just as his disdain for her is crumbling, his past smacks him in the face and offers a strong dose of reality. Arthur comes from an entirely different class than Maribeth and can never hope to have her as his own wife even though he desires her.

"So how did you become steward of Chateau Swansea?" she asked, raising her glass to her lips.

"A stroke of luck," he said. "The circus came to Swansea ten years ago, and when I learned of a position to be understudy to the steward of this great estate, I immediately applied for the job."

"With no credentials to speak of?" She lifted one impertinent eyebrow. "Why did Mr. Turner hire you?"

"Perhaps he took pity on me, as I did you." He winked at her. "As I recall, you didn't offer a single experience to recommend yourself as a psychic investigator."

A snort escaped her lips, and he grinned inside. Nettling her was far more entertaining than elephants lifting their hind legs during a show.

"He hired me because I'm gifted in identifying crooks, thieves, and liars. My parents are the best, and I *am* their son.[35] Mr. Turner wishes to locate his lost charge, the daughter of Madame Brown. Her name is—"

"Bella," she said with a smirk. "I found one of her dolls on my windowsill this morning. Her name was embroidered on the dress."

Impossible! All of the child's belongings were packed away in a hidden location. Unless Maribeth had discovered it. But how could she?

He walked to the nearby window and glanced outside, where fat droplets of rain had begun falling. The police weren't getting any closer to solving Mrs. Turner's death. Soon, the chief inspector would be knocking on the door again, questioning Stanley's involvement. Something had to be done to drag his employer back to the here and now so he could defend himself. Turning, Arthur leaned his backside against the windowsill.

"That's what I wish to speak to you about, the child. I interview young ladies who show promise of 'the sight,' because Mr. Turner

---

[35] The little nugget reveals that the hero considers himself a crook / thief / liar (i.e. the romance conflict). By revealing this backstory to the heroine, the hero incriminates himself and casts doubt about his trustworthiness (i.e. the hero's conflict). But he needs to tell her the truth about why Mr. Turner hired him, so he can get her to join in his search for Bella.

believes such gifts to be hereditary. I screen every candidate who comes knocking on the door. Sometimes I seek out viable young ladies when I read news of their peculiar talents. In fact, I traveled to Devil's Cove directly after the incident at the ball to interview Lady Covington but discovered she was too old to be Bella. Pity I didn't know about you at the time."

Maribeth stared at him over the rim of her glass, preparing to sip her drink. "That was before I knew of my talent anyway. Besides, I had a loving mother and it wasn't Madame Brown. Were any of the young ladies you interviewed legitimate?"

"Not a single one," he said. "They were all tricksters, as are most who claim to possess such skills. But the inducement to lie in this particular instance is great. Should she ever be found, Bella stands to inherit Chateau Swansea and a sizable dowry."

"Left by her mother?"

"One would think so, but no. The girl is Mr. Turner's legitimate daughter. Stanley married Arabella only days before she gave birth to their child."

Her gaze narrowed. "Why are you telling me this now?"

"So you can help me find her."

Maribeth's eyes flared wide and she set down her glass. "What game do you play with me, Arthur? You hired me to investigate a murder. Or was that a ruse?"

He glanced into the amber liquid pooling at the bottom of his tumbler. "Not entirely."

"Did you truly see Mrs. Turner fall from the balcony?" she barked.

"Yes."

Her head tilted. "But you didn't see Mr. Turner shove her over the edge?"

"No."

She advanced until she stood before him, poking her index finger in his chest. "Do you know who Mrs. Turner was having an affair with?"

Any response he offered would not satisfy her, because he had no hard proof. He walked to his nearby desk and deposited the incriminating letters between the Turners into the top drawer, all the while shielding his actions with his body. Once the evidence was safely tucked away, he turned to face her.

"Why do you hesitate in your response?" she asked, her stare bold.

He sighed. <u>"Everyone suspected she was having an affair with one of the servants, but the news of her pregnancy was unexpected. As I cannot say who the father is with certainty, I'd rather not speculate. People's lives hang in the balance. Let the police conduct their investigation into that matter. Your focus should be on digging up information inaccessible to the chief inspector. In the meanwhile, will you help me find Bella? You can do both."</u>

Her eyebrows knitted together and she folded her arms over her chest. "No, that isn't my specialty. I communicate with the dead, not the living. Unlike Madame Brown, I'm not clairvoyant."

"I beg to disagree," he said, strolling toward her. "I've watched you closely since your arrival, bore witness to your reactions."

She bit her bottom lip and glanced away. "I don't know what you mean."

Liar. Others of her ilk would proudly lay claim to such abilities. Why did she shrink away like a frightened rabbit?

"I think you do. Let us begin with your odd behavior in the foyer when you arrived. Did you speak with the housekeeper yet about the chink in the tile?"

Her head wobbled back and forth.

"I was curious," he said. "A fascinating story, to be sure. You see, Bella broke one of Mrs. Turner's favorite vases, an Italian masterpiece, in the foyer. Her punishment was harsh and swift. But you're already aware of that. You told me you sensed a frightened child. What was her punishment? Quickly, tell me."

Her lips parted and her breathing quickened. "A stinging slap on the hand."

Precisely. A sudden chill raced down his spine. He'd ignored the facts for too long.

"And the smile on your face when you read the child's book in your bedroom? That was more than you recalling cherished memories of your guardian reading to you. What did you sense?"

She licked her lips. "I heard peals of laughter, felt happiness."

What thoughts must careen through her mind in those unguarded moments? His imagination did not extend that far. Truly fascinating.

"One more point, and you must be honest with me, Maribeth. Had you ever heard the story behind the picture in the séance room before you sat on the throne?"

"No," she whispered.

"Yet you quoted, 'Mama, are you here?' I cannot deny these truths any longer." He pointed to the rocker she'd recently vacated. "Stanley often rocked his daughter in that very chair. Everything you've touched ... all that you hear ... those are all things Bella touched or said as a child while she lived here. You've sensed her presence; I know you have. Let me take you somewhere special in the morning. You are clairvoyant."

"I am not!" Her gaze flittered to the door, out the window, away from him. "Why do you place your trust in me? By your own admission, my kind are conniving charlatans. I could be lying through my teeth and you would not know."

Crooks, liars, and thieves. She was none of those. He would know.

"Only Mrs. Turner knew about the letters."

She stepped back with a skittish gleam in her eyes. "Which we haven't found. Do they even exist?"

He lifted an eyebrow. "For Mr. Turner's sake, I certainly hope not."

"I could've made an educated guess," she said, backing up another step.

"But you didn't," he murmured. He caged her in, one hand braced on each side of her head against the wall. She was now well and truly caught. "Moreover, you've been here two days and yet you haven't pretended to communicate with the ghost of Madame Brown in my presence. I think you genuinely possess supernatural skills. You knew that Mrs. Turner demanded I come to her bed."

"You said as much."

He shook his head. "No, I did not. I said I never desired her. The rest you divined on your own with alarming accuracy. Self-righteous bastard. Those were *her* precise words."

"Maybe I heard the tale from one of the servants."

"I think not," he said, lowering his lips to her ear. "Mrs. Turner was a proud sort. She would never divulge the truth that I spurned her advances. And I never spoke a word to another soul, which can mean only one thing."

Her breath hitched, and he met her gaze. "I speak with the dead."

So it would seem. He stared into her steadfast gaze and allowed himself to believe; just this once, in this moment of time. **With her God-given gifts, they had a chance, however slight it might be, at attaining the one goal his employer had placed on him so many years ago.**[36]

"We must find Bella before the authorities declare Stanley guilty of killing his wife. If his daughter is alive, I'm hopeful she will snap my employer out of his nightmarish daze. I owe him this much. Please, help me find her."

Her eyes misted. "I can't. She's dead."

His stomach dropped. "Why do you say that?"

"Shortly after I found the doll on my windowsill, it fell to the ground and shattered. I heard a ghostly whisper. 'Bella is dead!'" She licked her lips. "I'm not sure, but I think it was Mrs. Turner. You once speculated that she arranged for the kidnapping. If so, she would know the child's fate. Perhaps that's what Madame Brown meant when she said Caroline is the killer."

"Lies, all lies!" He tightened his fists, then released them. "Caroline said this on purpose, meddling even in death. She knows how much Stanley wants to find his daughter, knows how this would

---

[36] Ah, we finally get to the crux of the matter. Arthur wants to protect his employer from going to jail (i.e. the hero's goal) long enough to fulfill the one task he was originally hired ten years ago to complete. Arthur must locate Stanley's daughter, Bella, because she is the rightful heir of the Turner fortune.

devastate Arabella. I don't believe a single word! If the child were dead, I would sense it. Help me find her."

Her gaze flittered from side to side, and she squirmed. "Maybe you're right. But what if I can't? I've never attempted anything like this. I wouldn't even know where to start."

"Leave that to me." He placed her trembling hand between his, offering her his reassurance. "Say you'll try. I'll fetch you first thing tomorrow morning. I want you well rested."

She pulled free from his hold and nearly ran to the door. Looking back over her shoulder, she met his gaze. Fear and doubt warred in her expressive eyes, so unlike her usual bold nature. "Rein in your hopes. I'll go with you in the morning, but I cannot promise anything."

Her petite figure slipped through a crack in the doorway, but she lingered in his mind and soul long after. He did not require promises, only her acquiescence.

Tomorrow, they would turn a new leaf in the investigation.

Chapter Eleven

A yawn escaped Maribeth's lips as she exited her bedroom. Sleep had eluded her the night before. Was she truly clairvoyant, able to divine the past, present, and future? She certainly *felt* different since her arrival at the estate. With those awesome powers, she would be sought-after by many. She might unlock the secrets of her own childhood.

Her mouth went dry. Did she want to peek into the dark corners of her past? Some skeletons were best laid to rest. But her parents ... were probably long dead. And Arthur was grasping at straws.

If she were clairvoyant, why hadn't she gleaned anything from reading the letters she'd found in Mrs. Turner's desk? There were no whispers of secret lovers or howls of murderous ghosts. No, the letters were a waste of time, without a jot of useful information scribbled on the pages.

She gazed down the hallway toward the mistress's abandoned bedchamber. Perhaps she could search the room once more, without Arthur's unnerving stare glued to her every step. Walking briskly past the stairwell, Maribeth focused on the last door on the right. The housekeeper kept the door locked, but Maribeth was handy with a hairpin. Reaching into her coiffure, she plucked one out, heart pounding.

Stop being a ninny. The east wing of the chateau was quiet at this early hour, the guests having enjoyed the treasure hunt until the wee hours of the night, and Arthur wasn't meeting her in the kitchen for another half hour. She took a deep breath.

The door behind her clicked open. Maribeth squealed and whirled around, hiding her hands behind her back. Mr. Turner's nurse cocked her head sideways, gaping at her. What was her name, again? Bagley. Bentley.

"Mrs. Bartley! Good morning," she finally managed to choke out. Her erratic heartbeat pulsed loudly in her ears and would be visible at the base of her neck, if not for the high collar of her gown. Slipping her right hand into her pocket, she deposited the hairpin inside. "You startled me."

The nurse glanced down the hallway. "I thought I heard something out here. Where is Pearl with Mr. Turner's breakfast tray? She's late again! The master will wake soon. He's been restless all night. Barely slept a wink. And now he is to go hungry as well?"

"I haven't seen her this morning," Maribeth said, catching a glimpse of Mr. Turner over the nurse's shoulder. Were the letters hidden in his drawers? Not that she'd ever have an opportunity to search. Arthur said she had free reign of the estate, but he was protective of Mr. Turner and would be cross with her if he found out she searched there. Unless he never found out...

"Would you like me to stay with your patient while you collect his breakfast from the kitchen? A short break might do you good."

A wave of relief flittered over Mrs. Bartley's drawn face. "That's very kind of you to offer. He's resting at the moment, so you needn't do anything but sit beside him or read quietly. I won't be gone long."

Maribeth entered the bedchamber and watched the older woman scurry away. She closed the door gently. Mr. Turner lay flat on his back in bed, looking no different than he had on their first encounter except that his eyes were closed this time.

"Good morning," she said, tentatively.

He didn't react to her presence in any noticeable way. Her gaze fell upon his bedside table and the wide drawer with a simple brass handle. The perfect place for keepsakes. Or letters. Sifting through his belongings felt abominably wrong, but how could she ignore such an opportunity? Well, if Arthur wanted his employer to wake, perhaps a stranger scouring through his personal belongings would do the trick.

She glanced sidelong at the door as she walked to his bedside table. No one ever said being an investigator was easy work.

The brass drawer handle was cool to the touch, and the drawer slid open easily. Lying in the center was *The Owl and the Pussycat*. She frowned and lifted the edge of the book. How had this gotten here? Little else cluttered the space—a pocket watch, an emerald cravat pin, and a few other trinkets. But no letters.

She made quick work of rummaging through his chest and wardrobe, which also did not contain anything of interest. Crouching on all fours, she peered under the massive bed. A tortured groan filled the room and Maribeth leapt to her feet, a gasp caught in her throat.

"Bugger me!" she hissed.

Mr. Turner thrashed in his sleep, his arms hindered by the blanket pulled up to his chin. Were these nightmares of murdering his wife or images of his long-lost daughter's abduction? Vengeful husband or loving father?

Whoever he was, he certainly didn't have the look of an evil man. This gentleman inspired loyalty from his servants. She sat gingerly on the edge of the bed and smoothed the hair away from his forehead. The neatly trimmed brown locks were sprinkled with gray along the edges. At her touch, he quieted once more.

She studied his facial features, drawn to the wrinkles around his mouth. Ah, someone who still knew how to smile. Or had at one time in his life; the grooves in his forehead hinted at deeper troubles.

"What are you doing in here?"

Maribeth stood abruptly, meeting Arthur's curious gaze from across the room. She licked her lips. How long had he observed her in silence—long enough to hear her curse aloud? She must pay more attention to her surroundings.

"I'm watching over Mr. Turner while Mrs. Bartley fetches his breakfast. Are you stalking me?"

The corner of his mouth curled up. "Not at all. I'm merely checking in on Stanley. I stop by every morning when I arrive and every evening before I head home."

He cut a fine figure in his long, black coat, unbuttoned to reveal a starched white shirt and dark gray suit. His appearance was impeccable except for a few splotches of red on his jawline.

"Are you bleeding?" she asked, peering closer.

His fingers grazed the angry, inflamed skin, and he winced. "Only a minor scratch. Cleopatra didn't mind her claws this morning when she woke me for her vittles."

"Miss Sommerset, thank you." The nurse paused in the doorway with a full tray resting on her hip. Her warm gaze settled on Arthur. "Oh, Mr. Dunn, you're early. Will you be staying this morning to feed Mr. Turner? Though he doesn't say a word, I do believe he enjoys your company."

Maribeth looked from the nurse to Arthur, her brow rising with interest. So his visits were more than just "stopping by." How many stewards willingly took on the task of feeding an invalid? He truly did care for his employer, or he wished to give the appearance of doing so.

Arthur tapped his gloves against his hat and shook his head. "Thank you for asking, but no. I have other pressing matters to attend to this morning. Miss Sommerset, shall we?"

They left the nurse to her duties and made a quick detour to Maribeth's chamber for her jacket, bonnet, and gloves. Her stomach grumbled as they descended the stairs.

"There are fresh cranberry-orange muffins in the kitchen if you'd care to grab one on our way out." Arthur peered sideways at her. "I can't have you perish from hunger while under my care."

With a grateful nod, she conceded to her rebellious stomach. They each snatched one of the still-warm confections from the platter on the kitchen counter. She nibbled the fare as they walked along a path on the west side of the estate. The morning air was brisk, nipping at her cheeks.

She had just popped the last bite of her muffin into her mouth when they came upon a crude stone stairway at the edge of the forest. The stairs led to a narrow path carved through a gnarled thicket, the growth so dense and entwined that not a single stream of sunlight lit the way.

<u>Tingles cascaded over her skin, and she swallowed against the tightening in her throat. She wanted to run toward whatever lie beyond the dark hole of the entrance, and flee as fast and hard as her legs could carry her away.</u>

"Bella's presence is strong. Come, all will be well." Arthur paused two steps up and glanced back, holding out his hand.

"Where does the path lead?" Her feet refused to move. *Silly girl.* Whatever awaited her beyond the dark path could not harm her. Arthur would ground her and keep her safe.

"Somewhere very special to the little girl."

My haven, my hideaway. The thought burst through her consciousness, and she closed her eyes, grasping for the wispy thread of connection to Bella.

From whom must you hide?

Maribeth freed her mind of all other thoughts, filtered out the chirping birds, the leaves rustling in the wind, and Arthur's gentle breathing. She prayed for God's guidance and accepted the warmth of His love, giving herself over to her gift.

Where are you, Bella? Show me where I might find you. Befriend me. We are so alike, you and I. You're loved and wanted at Chateau Swansea. Come home, dear girl, come home.

Yet all was quiet in her mind.

Her eyes flittered open, and she reached for Arthur's hand. "Please, don't leave me. I need you."

His gentle squeeze was reassurance enough. He would be her rock, her steadfast connection to this earth. Light tremors still pulsed through her, but she breathed easy and let him guide her up the stairs. He ducked his head at the entrance of the thicket and she followed suit. Cool, damp air cloyed around her and everything went black for a few seconds until her eyes adjusted to the dim light seeping in from above. The tunnel was no longer than a stone's throw, and when they emerged on the other side, Maribeth stood, awestruck.

<u>"My playhouse," she whispered, the foreign words materializing out of the depths of her soul.</u> Tears welled in her eyes, her throat

clogged, and she burst into tears, the droplets forming rivulets down her cheeks.

She couldn't do this. Didn't want to do this. To feel this connection to someone else, to divine her thoughts yet be unable to control the flow of conversation.

"Where are you, Bella?" she shouted to the treetops, whirling around in circles. "Tell me! Dammit. Where are you?"

Arthur encircled her in his embrace, pressing her cheek to his chest. "Shhh. You can do this. Listen to your heart. I have faith in you."

"Oh, God. She's within me. Here." Maribeth pushed away and pounded on her heart. "I feel her so strongly, hear her voice, sense her pain. But I cannot communicate with her." She swiped at her tears, wiped her nose. "How am I supposed to communicate with her if she isn't dead, isn't *here*? Spirits, I understand. This ... this voice in my head ... these random thoughts ... I ... I am lost."

Adrift in a dinghy on the high seas in the midst of a raging storm. She couldn't find her bearings, felt assaulted from all angles by the cold, vicious waves. Without her mentor's guidance, she was helpless, useless. *I am not clairvoyant. I am not!*

"Consult your internal compass," Arthur said, his voice gentle, so full of compassion. He slid the backs of his fingers along her jawline in a gentle caress. "You will find your way."

She clasped his hand, pressed her cheek in his warm palm. Why could she not share in his conviction? She wanted to believe, wished desperately to help him find his employer's daughter. Dedicating one's life to a cause and coming so close without success ... that she understood. His frustration must be tenfold. Yet he was patient and kind.

He lifted her chin, met her gaze with intense longing. His mouth lowered to hers, brushing against her lips. The sensation was exquisite, like the gentle caress of a silky rose petal. She closed her eyes, savoring the tingles washing over her. So this was what Edith meant about the joys of kissing.

"Better?" he asked.

She nodded, swallowing hard.

"Would you care to explore?" he asked with an amused tone. She met his unwavering stare despite the blush heating her cheeks. His eyes were so beautiful from this vantage point, so dark and rich in color. She'd never stood so close to a man, felt the heat of his body. Her gaze wandered to his plump, supple lower lip. Now that she had tasted him, she would gladly practice the art of kissing a bit more.

He cleared his throat. "Perhaps you'll discover an even stronger connection within."

A stronger connection within his mouth? She met his mischievous gaze. The playhouse. That's what he meant. He wished to explore the playhouse with her.

"Heaven help me," she muttered, lifting her skirt. "The link binding me to Bella is seemingly cast from steel."

Inside, she met with a charming scene. A kitchenette comprised of a mini wood stove and icebox filled one corner of the room, and a table for two was nestled near the window. She could imagine a delicate china tea service with pink roses sitting on the table, awaiting its guests. Books and dolls would've been strewn on a bear rug in the other corner, filling the house with warmth and love. Yet despite the playhouse's undeniable charm, a repugnant vibe pulsed from the walls.

"This is where Bella was abducted," she said, wrapping her arms around her waist, warding off the sudden chill filling her from within. "That's why you brought me here."

Arthur leaned his shoulder against the doorframe and glanced around the room. "You are far more talented than I ever imagined possible. The things you say ... the look in your eyes when providence strikes. You give me chills."

A slow smile crept over her lips. "Sometimes I give myself chills."

"You must be clairvoyant," he said, his words a declaration of fact. "Say you'll help me find Bella before it's too late."

An army of ants skittered up her legs, but she shook off the foreboding sense of doom. Arthur needed her help. "I will try."

"Excellent!" He stepped aside, giving her space to pass by him. "Let's return to the chateau and discuss our next steps. I'm sure we'll find a handful of resources in the library to consult. Madame Brown was a voracious reader."

"Very well," Maribeth said. They must start somewhere. Writing for advice from her mentor would take days. "Is there anything else here you wish me to see?"

"Only a swing around back."

She followed him outside and rounded the corner. A simple wooden slat suspended by two weathered ropes hung from a tree branch. How Bella must have laughed and shouted with delight as her papa pushed her higher and higher, until she leapt off the seat and flew through the air. Maribeth followed the path of the trajectory, felt the wind rush past her ears and the crushing blow of the ground meeting her feet at the edge of the forest. Her palms stung from the landing, pitching forward to break her fall. Maribeth's gaze settled on the worn patch of dirt where Bella must've landed time and time again.

Something black and brown poked out of the bushes.

"What is that?" she asked, peering closer. "Are those a pair of shoes?"

Arthur spanned the length of the play area in a few strides and crouched to inspect the base of the bush in question. She hurried after him.

He held out his hand in protest. "Stop, please, turn away!"

But she was already peering over his shoulder, at the sightless eyes of Gabriel Young. A river of dried blood trailed from the back of his head to the ground, where it had amassed in a small pool. Beside the cold, dead remains of the man lay a rock as big as Arthur's fist, covered in blood.

The muffin in Maribeth's stomach roiled and she stumbled backward, gasping for air. "He was bludgeoned to death."

"So it would seem," Arthur said, rubbing the back of his neck. "And by the scuff marks on the ground and blood under his fingernails, I'd say he put up a fight."

She ventured another glance at the motionless form. "Do you suppose whoever killed Mrs. Turner has struck again?"

"Who would wish both of them dead?"

The question swirled around them, teasing and plucking at the edges of Maribeth's wit. If Mr. Turner was the killer, what reason would he have to murder his cousin as well? *Oh, goodness.* The answer struck her in a flash.

"What if everyone was wrong and Mr. Young, not a servant, was Mrs. Turner's secret lover? That would be a strong motive for murder," she blurted.

"That's ridiculous." Arthur stood and glowered down at her. "You're accusing Stanley of this? He is comatose in his bedroom. You saw him this morning! He didn't kill Mr. Young. How can you even think that?"

"No, you're right," she said, nibbling on her thumbnail. "Mrs. Bartley said he hadn't slept well last night. She was by his side, or at least I assume as much. We can verify this with her."

"The police will gather the facts." Arthur rubbed his eyes, looking rather weary. "I will have to send for them immediately. We must stay focused on finding Bella. It's our only hope when the constable jumps to the same conclusion as you did."

"Who did this, then?" She posed the question as much to herself as him.

"I don't know." His brows furrowed and he shook his head. "There must be a connection between the murders, although I don't know what that might be."

"Are they connected?" she asked.

He nodded. "Otherwise we're dealing with two killers, not one."

She hadn't granted herself permission to ponder that vein of thought. *Two killers, not one.*

"Why didn't his wife report him missing this morning?" she asked.

Arthur shrugged. "They sleep in separate bedchambers."

Maribeth glanced at the latest victim and the gaping wound on his forehead. One thing was certain: Mr. Young's killer was human and mostly likely a man.

"A ghost may have shoved Mrs. Turner over the edge of a balcony with a spurt of vindictive energy," she said, "but even the most malevolent of spirits couldn't bludgeon a man with a rock and leave traces of blood under his fingernails. The chief will be searching for someone with vicious scratches hidden beneath—"

Vicious scratches. Maribeth homed in on Arthur's profile, where claw-like abrasions marred his jawline and raised blood to the surface. He turned, catching her wide-eyed stare at his wounds before she could look away. Her knees wobbled for a moment, but she shook her head.

"Maribeth, you don't think—"

"No, I don't." She gripped his forearm, steadying herself. "So please don't speak it aloud."

Arthur did not kill Mr. Young in cold blood. Not him, the only man who stirred desire in her body. She could never be attracted to a heartless murderer. Underneath his aloof exterior, Arthur was kind. He visited his employer daily and fed him breakfast! No, Arthur had no motive.

But then who? *Mr. Young, why are you not here?* She would sense his lingering soul if he were, yet she felt nothing.

"Come, we must go back," Arthur said, threading his fingers with hers.

She stared at his nails. Clean, neat. Without any bloodstains whatsoever. Yes, they must go back to Chateau Swansea and the halls where a dangerous threat lurked in the shadows.

Or was it in plain sight?

Chapter Twelve

A tap on the door pulled Arthur's attention from the paperwork strewn over his desk. He sighed, but there was no use pretending that a single word on the pages registered in his brain. How could he concentrate when the chief was conducting interviews in the parlor? Only a thin wall separated him from the ongoing investigation.

"Enter," he said, leaning back in his leather chair.

Maribeth poked her head inside the door, and he waved her in. She fiddled with the lace ruffle of her three-quarter length sleeves. The pale green and white stripes of her muslin gown accentuated her slim waist and set off the extraordinary hue of her eyes.

He stood and gestured to one of the chairs opposite his desk. "You've completed your interview, I presume?"

She sat primly on the edge of the seat, glancing around the room. "Chief Inspector Marsh is quite efficient. We spent little more than a quarter hour together. He'll see you next, after he's finished with Webber. You have the pleasure of being the last on his list."

Arthur snorted and opted for the seat next to her. "I doubt there will be much pleasure to be had in that quarter."

"Well, maybe his patience has worn thin and he'll go easy on you." Her gaze fixed on a spot over his shoulder, and she gestured with the flick of her chin. "Is that the package you retrieved from Chapman Brothers last Thursday?"

He folded his legs and nodded. "Were you stalking me, Maribeth?"

"Don't be ridiculous." She looked him square in the eyes. "But I did wonder at your standing in the pouring rain, weathering a storm over a silly portrait or landscape. Why does it sit there, unwrapped, after all that trouble?"

Her curiosity was getting the better of her. She nearly vibrated in her seat.

"Mr. Turner commissioned the portrait while he was away on business in America," Arthur said. "He took ill before he had an opportunity to unveil the piece."

Leaning in closer, she whispered, "Do you suppose it's a likeness of Mrs. Turner?"

"Indeed, I do." His employer had intimated as much.

"How very awkward." Maribeth clasped her dainty hands around one knee and wrinkled her forehead. "I've been meaning to ask you whether or not you found Mrs. Turner's letters to her husband. Surely, you've searched among his belongings?"

Damn and blast. The woman kept her nose to the grindstone. He didn't want to lie directly to her face. Still, for Stanley's sake, no one could know of their existence.

"The letters can hardly matter now." He stood and walked to the sideboard, where he poured himself a glass of brandy. "After today's events, the chief cannot suspect Mr. Turner of being the killer." Lifting an empty glass, he gestured toward her. "Would you care for one?"

"No, thank you," she said, waving off his offer like a pesky fly. "Of course the letters still matter! Mrs. Turner might have revealed the identity of her lover within the pages. What if Mr. Young *was* her lover? That would shine a negative light on Mr. Turner."

"You still think he had a hand in this?" Arthur asked. They'd been over this before. His employer lay unresponsive in his bed. How could he possibly have been involved in the most recent murder?

Maribeth stood and threw up her hands. "I don't know what to think. People kill in the heat of passion or as a means of revenge. The chances of two unrelated murders occurring on the estate are remote. Yet how are the deaths connected?" She rubbed her fingertips against her temples before facing him head on. Her eyes pleaded for understanding. "The only connection I can make is that they were lovers, and Mr. Turner ... planned ahead. Perhaps hired someone to attack Mr. Young?"

"Premeditated murder?" Arthur stormed toward the door, unable to stand another moment in her presence. "Keep your voice down. Better yet, don't say anything at all."

Angling across the room, she cut him off at the door. Her hand rested on his forearm. "I'm sorry if I've offended you, but who else would want Gabriel Young dead?"

With one heated glare from him, she stepped away. "That, madam, is the material question!"

He exited the study without a backward glance. His blood boiled and his mind raced. Who was behind these horrid acts? By God, he would figure it out, with or without the assistance of an amateur sleuth.

★★★

The study door slammed shut in Maribeth's face, and she winced. He had called her *madam*! Was her train of thought out of line, or was Arthur incapable of being objective under the circumstances?

She blew out a breath and paced the length of the plush throw rug. Did a serial killer roam the halls of Chateau Swansea? Or were these misfortunes unrelated? More, now than ever, she needed Mrs. Turner's letters.

Lifting her skirt, Maribeth hurried to the desk and pulled out the center drawer. She had fifteen minutes to conduct a thorough search of this room, an opportunity she had never dreamed possible. The drawer did not reveal any hidden notes. Nor did she find anything in the remaining compartments.

The bookshelves were the second-most likely spot for concealing the letters. Maribeth scanned the books, seeking any volumes that appeared out of place. Running her fingers over the tops, she felt for indications of a letter stuffed between the pages. But there was no evidence of what she sought.

She banged her forehead against the binding of the closest book. *Where are the letters, Caroline?* The bookshelf creaked and shifted, startling her. She stumbled backward and gaped as the bookshelf parted in two halves.

A secret corridor? Maribeth stuck her head inside and a musty odor immediately accosted her. Cobwebs strung from ceiling to floor, and stuffy air seeped out. A muted hum drifted eerily from the black void. Were those men's voices? She stepped into the narrow passage, ducking to avoid the sticky spiderwebs. A shudder rippled through her, but she inched farther inside, lured by the muffled voices.

The parlor shared a wall with the study, did it not? With each step, the words took on clarity. A calm baritone penetrated the thin wall. But there was another as well. The interview with Chief Inspector Marsh! What were they saying?

A shaft of light poked through a peephole at eye level, teasing her. Who had placed it there? A former mistress of the house who secretly observed her guests in the parlor or a mistrustful master? The height of the peephole favored a woman. Maribeth ought to turn around, but she was assigned as an investigator on the case, was she not?

Just one peek. Placing her eye at the hole, she looked and Webber came into focus as a knock sounded on the door.

Chapter Thirteen

Arthur rapped his knuckles three times on the parlor door and burst through. Webber's head snapped in his direction, his expression bland.

"Your timing is impeccable, Mr. Dunn." The butler stood and tugged on the lapels of his jacket. "I just finished telling Chief Inspector Marsh about last evening. After having enjoyed a snifter of brandy over a game of chess"—Webber glanced at the chief— "which I won, of course, we then retired at one o'clock in the morning. We arose with the rooster's crow, ate breakfast, a rasher of bacon with two eggs each, and walked here together to begin our duties. Anything to add, my dear boy?"

Arthur reined in his shock, assuming the same bored expression. What the deuce was the addlebrained man prattling about? Webber couldn't discern a rook from a pawn. His fabricated alibi was equal parts obvious and ridiculous. Though, admittedly, the chief didn't know if either of the men fancied the game of chess. Should he play along or call the man's bluff?

Chief Inspector Marsh lifted a brow, and a cold sweat suddenly broke out over Arthur's neck. Why was Webber offering an alibi that exonerated both of them? The look in the butler's eyes said, "You owe me." Why did the pompous fool suppose Arthur was indebted to him? Until he knew more, however, he would be wise to play along.

"Exactly as you say." Arthur nodded curtly.

The chief pursed his lips, his gaze shifting from one to the other. "You may go, Webber, but I may have more questions for you later, so do not stray too far."

An interesting turn of events. Was Webber's alibi for his own benefit or Arthur's? Taking the chair that afforded him the best view of the door, Arthur sat and folded his hands on his lap. Chief Inspector Marsh set aside his notepad, giving his full attention. Today, with dark shadows under his eyes and his mouth pulled down in a frown, he looked ten years older than thirty-eight years.

"Does Webber stay over often?" the chief asked.

Never. "A worthy chess opponent is difficult to find, and Webber is fond of his brandy. After a few glasses, he is in no condition to walk back to the chateau."

If the officer noticed that Arthur evaded a direct response, he did not say as much. Instead, he asked, "Mr. Turner plays chess, though, does he not?"

"He is indisposed at present, I'm afraid." But enough of the small talk. Arthur was here to offer his testimony. "Makes your job damned difficult! From what I could tell this morning, there was little evidence at the scene of the crime. With both Mr. Turner and his cousin crossed off the list of suspects, you must be in a quandary."

"I might have been, were it not for this letter from Mr. Turner's solicitor." The chief inspector placed a pair of spectacles on the bridge of his nose. He lifted a piece of paper that lay beside him on the sofa and perused the contents. **"Were you aware, Mr. Dunn, that your employer recently amended his power of authority should he become ill?"**

A knot formed in the pit of his stomach, but he responded with calm dignity. "Indeed, since I was present when Mr. Turner signed the paperwork, along with his doctor to verify that he was of sound mind."

Chief Inspector Marsh set the letter aside and leaned forward. "Dr. Sanders declared Mr. Turner of unsound mind yesterday. *You* are now the executor of the estate and all medical decisions while Stanley Turner is incapacitated. Should he be imprisoned for the crime of killing his wife and cousin, you will manage his vast fortune and estates in perpetuity. Unless, of course, his lawyer locates Mr. Turner's

legitimate daughter from his first marriage. In that case, she stands to inherit her fortune immediately."[37]

A faint sound echoed in the room, peculiarly akin to a gasp, and the chief swiveled in his seat.

"Did you hear that, Mr. Dunn?"

Arthur shook his head. "Could be critters in the walls. Or perhaps we're disturbing Madame Brown's afternoon tea."

"Don't be cute!"

How could he joke? A noose was being tightened around his neck, cutting off his ability to breathe. The chief was an intelligent man. Did he know the full extent of the changes to Stanley's will or only what they were currently discussing?

Chief Inspector Marsh lit a cigar and puffed diligently on the end until he was rewarded with a cloud of smoke. "May I ask what immediate plans you have for Mr. Turner? Commit him to an asylum or retire him to another of his properties, perhaps? You are suddenly a powerful man with a great deal of resources at your fingertips."

"I beg your pardon!" Arthur shot to his feet and stalked to the hearth, gripping the mantle lest he plant the chief a facer. "How dare you insinuate that I would abuse the trust my employer placed in me!"

"Man is predisposed to sin. Wealth of this magnitude may inspire the worst behavior, even in the best of men," the chief said drolly. "I cannot ignore this material fact. Count yourself among the primary suspects. However, I promise a thorough investigation and consideration of *all* the relevant facts."

---

[37] Unfortunately for the hero, this backstory incriminates him as the potential killer (i.e. the heroine's and the hero's conflict) and dampens the romance burgeoning between Maribeth and Arthur (i.e. the romance conflict). When I was plotting this story, I needed several facts that would incriminate my hero so I brainstormed and came up with some backstory (e.g. the power of authority) as well as some things in the current storyline (e.g. the cat scratching his chin). I wanted to make sure the tension between my H/h stayed high. They were getting pretty cozy in the last couple of chapters.

Had the chief investigator built a case against Arthur in the course of the afternoon? Any evidence he'd gathered from other witnesses could only be conjecture and circumstantial.

"According to my sources," the chief continued, "you suggested the locations for the midnight treasure hunt hosted by Mr. and Mrs. Young for their guests, one of which was the playhouse in the thicket. The killer attacked his victim there between the hours of one o'clock and five o'clock in the morning."

Arthur gritted his teeth. He didn't care for this train of thought. "Unfortunately, there are neighboring estates, and Chateau Swansea attracts undesirables from time to time. The gardener, Mr. Keppler, knows these grounds as well as anyone. He can also verify that vagabonds roam the forest near the cliff."

"You believe this morning's incident is unrelated to my sister-in-law's death?"

Biting back a quick retort, Arthur instead weighed his words. "Without all the facts, I can only speculate, but given what I know, a connection between the two tragedies seems remote."

"My initial inclination, as well," Chief Inspector Marsh said. Then he tilted his head. "But then I asked myself, who benefits with Caroline Turner and Gabriel Young out of the way? Besides you, that is?"

The thinly veiled accusation struck him like a powerful blow to the gut. "I am not your man! As Webber said, he spent the evening with me. We were in bed by one o'clock and awoke at dawn. The gardener can verify the time we arrived at the chateau this morning."

Chief blew a few rings of smoke and narrowed his gaze on Arthur. "But either of you could've slipped out for a quick jaunt without the other any wiser."

"In theory, yes." The alibi Webber had concocted wasn't air-tight; he would concede as much. "However, there is no evidence to support that theory."

"That, my dear boy, is for me to disprove," the chief said.

Arthur clamped his mouth shut. Perhaps now was the time to ask for his solicitor. The chief plied him with question after question, all in a similar vein yet phrased a little different. *Good grief!* Did the chief believe he was a halfwit?

He swiped one hand through his hair, and despite his better judgment, fought back. "Be reasonable, Chief Inspector Marsh! Why would I lead Miss Sommerset to the playhouse if I killed Gabriel Young? That makes no sense."

"A ploy to give the impression of innocence?"

He suppressed a snort. This was not a laughing matter, but his patience had worn thin after hearing the same question posed ten different ways. Others may fall victim to such tactics and contradict themselves, but Arthur would not. "Are you done questioning me?"

"Almost." The chief pointed his cigar in Arthur's direction. "Where did you acquire the scratch on your chin? Come a bit closer. I'd say it's rather fresh and deep."

Arthur probed the sensitive spot with tentative fingers and smirked. "My temperamental cat's claws, not the unkempt nails of a dandy fighting for his life. Would you care to match the length and breadth of Cleopatra's claws with my wound?" He regretted the outburst before the last word passed his lips, but this past week would try the patience of a saint. "My apologies. I'm tired and distraught by Mr. Turner's diagnosis."

Chief Inspector Marsh accepted his apology with a curt nod. "Though poorly delivered, you raise a valid point. Best we leave no stones unturned. I'll wait here while you send for the cat."

Finally, he could escape the incessant questions. Arthur strode to the door, his posture stiff. "I'll retrieve Cleopatra myself. And Chief? Please be advised that I will relinquish all decisions regarding Mr. Turner's welfare to the housekeeper, Mrs. Hawkins, until I am fully exonerated."

"I always knew you to be a wise fellow. <u>Mr. Turner had a mind as sharp as a steel trap, too. So I ask myself this question: Why did he send for his solicitor on the morning of his wife's murder? Perhaps he learned who sired his wife's child and wished to revoke your power of authority.</u>"

"<u>Or mayhap he sought to file for divorce,</u>" Arthur bit out.

"A possibility, to be sure," Chief said. "One last thing. We discovered a single gray hair near the scene of the crime. Would you be willing to submit a sample? You have a few, do you not?"

Arthur gritted his teeth. "I discovered the body. If my hair is found to be a match, that doesn't prove anything. But, yes, to demonstrate my complete cooperation, you may have a sample."

With a noose tightening around his neck, he would need his wits to escape this mess. Why in the hell had he agreed to Stanley's wishes to alter his last will and testament in the first place?

Chapter Fourteen

Tarnation! Maribeth cursed the damned hedge maze. She was hopelessly lost. Her heartbeat thudded crazily in her chest. Why hadn't Arthur told her about the power of authority? He said he wanted her assistance in locating Bella, but to what end? Reunite father and daughter or kill her, too? Bella stood between him and wealth beyond measure.

What else was he hiding? *Mrs. Turner's letters to Mr. Turner.* Arthur had stashed something in his desk drawer during her visit to his home. A cold-blooded murderer might flaunt the evidence under her nose, derive a thrill from flirting with discovery. Beneath his austere exterior, was he a calculating killer?

If Arthur lied to her, then she must find Bella and warn her of the danger.

What was she thinking? Arthur genuinely respected the master of Chateau Swansea. She would sense an evil undercurrent, and Mrs. Turner's ghost would've ratted him out. But the pieces didn't fit. Something was off.

Twenty, maybe thirty minutes. That's all she had to search through Arthur's house while the chief grilled him, if she could find her way through the maze! She stopped to catch her breath, hands on hips. The day was overcast, leaving the path shrouded in dark shadows. The damp air weighed heavily on her shoulders, and she shuddered. *Left or right up ahead?* Closing her eyes, she listened for the sound of waves crashing on the cliffs. A twig snapped, and her stomach clenched.

"Hello, is anyone there?" she asked, turning around. Why would anyone stroll through the maze on a bleak day? Except, maybe the gardener or a skunk. *Or the killer.* Leaves rustled in the hedges, and she suppressed a squeal.

Get out of here! She had heard the rush of water to the right. Lifting her skirt, she ran as fast as she could, scraping her arms when rounding the corners. Footsteps thudded in the grass behind her. *Oh, god.* Who was chasing her?

Left, left, right, left. She chose the paths by sheer instinct, guided by fear alone. Her breathing became labored. A minute later, she stumbled out of the maze, in front of Arthur's house. She charged up the front porch steps. If only she could get inside, she would be safe. The doorknob rattled under the pressure of her grip but did not turn. Why was it locked? On her last visit, she had swept by him and opened the door with ease. He lived in the middle of nowhere!

Retrieving the hairpin from her pocket, the one she planned to use on Mrs. Turner's bedchamber door, she went to work on the task. Her hands shook violently, wind howled in her ears, and sweat trickled down the cleft of her bosom.

A black crow cawed from somewhere above. A warning of her assailant's approach? Maribeth shot one glance over her shoulder but saw nothing.

The lock unclicked. She stepped inside and immediately barred the door. Sagging against it, she wiped her brow. Her chest heaved in and out. Was someone outside watching her? On wobbly knees, she tiptoed to the window and peered outside. *Where are you hiding?* She searched the hedges and the garden but found no signs of life. Whoever had given chase was gone.

Now to find the letters. She crept down the main corridor to the parlor entrance. Her skin prickled, the uncomfortable sensation intensifying with every step. Invading Arthur's privacy felt unpardonably wrong.

But two people were dead. Did she trust her instincts enough to risk another life? She rushed over the threshold, her eyes on the prize. The desk was rather plain, with a neat stack of paper in the center and an assortment of pencils and ink pens in a jar at the head.

Her fingers trembled as she took hold of the knob and tugged. An envelope lay tucked inside. She quickly removed the note and devoured the contents which read, *Snooping into another's affairs isn't wise.*

"Did you find what you seek, my little dove?"

Maribeth sucked in a breath, suppressing a scream. Arthur's lips skimmed over her neck, his breath deliciously warm, his body perilously close. She was trapped in his embrace.

"Christ, you scared me!" she said, her voice trembling. Had he been the one giving chase in the maze to teach her a lesson?

"I never pegged you as a snoop or thief. Your skills with a hairpin are impressive."

She met his gaze over her shoulder. *Dirty rat!* That was him earlier. She gritted her teeth. How could she be angry with him when she was in the wrong? This was *his* house, and she'd broken inside. "And yet, from the onset, I knew you for the liar that you are. Only I never imagined the extent of your lies. What did you do with Mrs. Turner's letters?"

He sighed into her hair, nuzzling his cheek against the curls. "I burned them. Stanley wrote a few careless words in a moment of anger. He would never kill a soul. But why risk someone finding them?"

She stiffened. The heat of his breath on her ear stole her ability to think. Probably by design. That wasn't well done of him. "What did the letters say?"

"Caroline wanted Stanley to acknowledge her bastard child as his heir. Of course, given the timing, that was impossible. He said he'd rather see her dead than give in to her request. A poor choice of words, surely, but without any real intent behind them. Stanley believes Bella is alive, and she is the rightful heir."

Arthur believed the girl lived still, too. "Will you kill Bella if I help you find her?"

He smoothed the hair away from her face and kissed her cheek. "You heard everything from my interview with Chief Inspector Marsh? I didn't kill Caroline or Gabriel. You must believe me."

"Why must I?" She snorted. He had been withholding important information from her, albeit to protect his employer's neck.

"Because I need you." He snaked one arm around her waist, pulled her back flush with his chest as his other hand rested in the center of her bosom. "Because you know in your heart that I could never do those things."

Her throat pulsed and ached. She wanted to believe he spoke the truth. But he had been lying to her since the onset. "Why didn't you tell me about the power of authority?"

"It's irrelevant," he said, turning her around to face him. "**Stanley Turner believed in a young man who had lost all faith in himself. Without him, I would be nothing.**[38] My greatest wish is to reunite him with his daughter. Will you abandon his dream or help me fulfill it? She will bring him back to the living. He may know enough to solve the case."

Reunite a loving father with his long-lost daughter? Tears welled in her eyes, blurring her sight. There was a time when she wished the same for herself. "We have other pressing matters to attend. A killer walks among us. What's to say he will not strike again?"

"The police will deal with the killer." He nuzzled her ear. "Please, help me find Bella."

There was such warmth and sincerity in his countenance. He was a master manipulator. She ought to refuse him on that principle alone. But helping Arthur would end in her snagging an awesome résumé piece. Either that, or she'd live out her days at Devil's Cove Manor as an old maid.

---

[38] A little snippet here to remind the readers that Arthur is doing everything thus far to protect his employer (i.e. hero's motivation).

Chapter Fifteen

Maribeth knelt beside the entrance to the crawl space in Bella's bedroom and shoved her lantern as far inside as she could manage. The flickering flames illuminated a six-foot radius within the space but failed to reach the far corners.

"All of the child's belongings can be found inside here, stored in chests," Arthur said.

She sat utterly still, perched on her knees with her skirts bunched around her legs, a bit lightheaded. The area hidden on the other side of the bedroom wall was dark, musty, and cramped. From what little she could see, there was limited space for her or Arthur to fit inside. But they must retrieve something personal of Bella's, more than just a book or a doll, if Maribeth hoped to find a deep connection to her.

He rolled up his sleeves. "Dresses, jewelry, dolls. Everything that ever meant anything to Bella is in there. Come, let's see what treasures we discover."

Her body vibrated with the blood rushing through her veins. She hadn't been inside such a confined space since she was a little girl. Inhaling slowly, she shut out all thoughts of the coal mine. She was a grown woman, and Arthur would be nearby the entire time.

"You go first," she said, scrambling to the side.

He got on all fours, mindful of his head. As he inched forward on the small path, he pushed the lantern farther in, eventually setting it on one of the chests. He sat and crossed his legs. "Maribeth, where are you? Don't tell me you're afraid. You snuck into an ancient corridor by yourself, without the benefit of a lantern."

She poked her head inside and looked around, biting her bottom lip. "That was different. I don't care for confined chambers where I cannot stand and escape quickly. Even a mouse wouldn't claim this place as its home. There is no air! How am I to breathe?"

A smile tugged at the corner of his mouth. "I daresay you will survive. The sooner we begin, the sooner we will finish."

She scowled at him but scrambled in and settled beside him, again perched on her knees. "Hurry, let's get this over with."

Maribeth lifted the first lid and rifled through a pile of pastel-colored dresses in every hue known to mankind. "I've never seen so many clothes for a child. Mr. Turner must've loved his little girl very much."

Her fingers moved reverently over the superfine cloth. She held the yellow dress close to her chest, nuzzled the fabric with her cheek.

"I don't feel anything," she said. She closed the chest and met Arthur's gaze. "Next?"

Arthur opened the one farthest from him. He pulled out a stuffed dog, a red spinning top, and, finally, a delicate porcelain doll. "There's a china tea set as well, decorated with pink roses. The craftsmanship is excellent. It must have cost a fortune."

"She took inordinate good care of her toys," Maribeth said, stroking the doll's silky hair. "But I want something more personal. Jewelry, perhaps. Or a hairbrush."

"Try that one," Arthur suggested, pointing to a smaller box nestled among the larger ones.

Maribeth peered inside and squealed. "Ribbons with a brush and comb set. There's even a matching mirror."

The lantern suddenly wavered, grew dangerously dim, flickered to life again, and then sputtered out. Blackness engulfed them so thoroughly, she could not see Arthur's outline, despite the fact that she could hear his breathing.

"Turn on the light," she whimpered.

He shook the canister. "I think the oil is spent."

"Don't tease me! Turn on the light." Her voice shook and she choked back a sob. A deep chill permeated her clothes. Every muscle in her body trembled from the cold. She rubbed her arms vigorously. "Now, Arthur. Turn on the light. Turn on the light."

"Maribeth? We'll be fine. Crawl outside. I'm right behind you."

"Turn on the light, turn on the light," she chanted in a strained whisper. Curling into a ball, she rocked back and forth. **If she closed her eyes, she could pretend she was asleep, block out the sound of rats scurrying past her legs or the heavy, methodical thud of picks on coal.** *Clank, clank, clank.*[39] "Turn on the light. Please, oh, please. Turn on the light."

Something brushed her back and she jerked, slapping frantically. *Rats!* Sobs tore out of her, wracking her body. She curled tighter around her legs. Squeezed tight so they couldn't get to her face.

"Maribeth! Listen to me," Arthur said, shaking her shoulders. We're getting out of here now. You must crawl toward the light. As much as I'd like to, I cannot carry you. There isn't enough head-room."

Arthur. He was here. Her rocking ceased as he rubbed her back.

"Come, my sweet. Crawl. Let's get out of here together."

Her sobs subsided and he nudged her toward the exit. She scrambled away, though her skirts hindered her progress.

★★★

When Arthur finally gained his feet again, Maribeth stood in the farthest corner of the room, her forehead propped against her forearms on the wall.

"Is there anything I can do for you?" he asked, inching closer.

She spun around with wild eyes, her face as pale as the sheets on her bed. Ragged breaths heaved in and out of her body. Glancing around, she took stock of her surroundings. Her tongue darted out, wetting her lips.

---

[39] This is backstory purposely planted here to throw the reader off the scent of Maribeth's true identity. In her POV, she reacts to her memories of the coal mine. Later, when Arthur suggests she is experiencing another clairvoyant moment related to an incident with Bella locked in the same space, the reader is convinced Maribeth knows nothing of that event in Bella's life. As you will learn later, Arthur already suspects at this point that Maribeth may be Bella. The reader may be wondering the same thing, but I've planted enough seeds to make them doubt the truth.

"What's happening, Maribeth? Tell me what you're feeling." Based on stories he had heard from his employer, Arthur could almost guess, but he wanted to hear everything from her perspective.

"I don't wish to speak of it," she murmured with her gaze squarely fixed on the floor.

Where was the confident young medium? This wilting wallflower was sad to behold. Hopefully, a few moments of quiet reflection was all she needed to collect herself.

"Very well," he said, keeping his voice calm. "Will you please wait here while I retrieve the chest of Bella's personal items? Or I can stay a few more minutes. Until you're feeling more yourself."

She lifted her tortured eyes to his. Rivulets of tears stained her cheeks, but he did not look away. He focused his energy on staying rooted to his spot when all he wanted was to pull her into his arms and demolish the crippling fear hidden in the depths of her soul. Did clairvoyants relive the pain of their subjects in excruciating detail? One look at Maribeth and the answer seemed obvious: without a doubt.

"I'll wait here for you. Please, hurry. The thought of you alone in that cramped, dark…" A shudder rippled through her, visible to anyone watching her as intently as he was.

"I'll be quicker than a flash of lightning," he said, wiping away the streaks of tears from her face with the pads of his thumbs. In this moment, she seemed as fragile as the porcelain tea set. "I have no skirts to impede my progress," he said on a whim. "Though I daresay you managed far better than I would have in your place."

A smile tugged on her lips. "You wearing a dress? That, I cannot envision."

"Thank God," he said, grateful for the warmth radiating in her stare. "Close your eyes, take a few deep breaths, and when you open them again, I'll be waiting by the bed with our prize."

The moment her eyelids fluttered down, he lit a candle from her bedside table and set to his task. After finding the ornate box again, he set it on the bed and brushed off the dust coating his knees. He cleared his throat. "Come, Maribeth, open your eyes."

"I've watched turtles move faster than you," she said.

His playful, witty minx was back.

"I concede defeat. Perhaps lightning was a poor analogy."

She eyed the box on the bed warily but took a seat next to it. "Come sit with me."

He sat opposite her with the chest centered between them. He turned the brush over in his hands, but he felt nothing other than the superfine bristles delicate enough not to mangle a young girl's curly tresses.

"May I?" Maribeth asked, holding out her hand.

She stroked the brush through the ends of her own blonde curls while gazing into the matching mirror. A dreamy smile curved her lips up. What was she thinking? Did Bella's thoughts flood her mind? **"My mama used to brush my hair every night," she suddenly said. "Only the bristles were coarse and she often cursed the tangles in my hair. I was jealous of my mama's hair, a rich coffee brown and straight as an arrow. But so incredibly soft."**[40]

Arthur caught a lock of her hair between his fingers. "You're an ungrateful wench, then. This shade of blonde is rare, and the curls are an untamed beauty like no other."

Her gaze shifted sideways, avoiding his. "I've always thought the curls make me look childish."

"You are no child," he said, tugging on the curl until she met his stare. "You're all fiery woman beneath your petticoats."

"When you first saw me on the stairs at the Inn at Oxwich, you gawked at—"

"Your beauty," he said. "The way your eyes lit up when you teased your friend, the unconscious sway of your hips as you walked through the lobby arm in arm, how your lips puckered into a smirk when you found the conversation amusing."

Her lips parted in an O and she blinked several times. "You were ... you were watching me before I ran up the stairs?"

---

[40] At this point, I really needed to highlight the fact that Maribeth has memories of a childhood and her mother. Some of her childhood memories were good, some bad (i.e. the heroine's conflict). I want the reader to share in Maribeth's shock that she is actually Bella when it comes out later.

"From the second you entered the lobby from the café."

Eyes widening, she cried, "But you were unkind later that day when I offered you my trade card."

He snorted and rubbed his eyes. Good God, but he'd behaved like an ass. "I'm sorry. I admired your spunk in setting me down for stealing your carriage. Then you gave me that damned trade card." A groan worked its way up his throat. "You destroyed my fantasy woman with a harsh dose of reality. A psychic investigator? Really, Maribeth, if anyone was unkind, I say it was you."

Her rosebud mouth gathered in a smirk. He leaned over and claimed her lips, threading his fingers through her curly tresses. She opened to him, and he probed, tasting her silken tongue. Her pulse raced under the pad of his thumb. Was he her first? He wanted to be her last. She pulled back and sighed, her eyes sparkling. They had strayed far from their initial task, and he must bring them back on point before he laid her across the bed and explored beneath her skirts.

"Do you sense anything of Bella?" he asked, gesturing to the brush still within her grip.

She wrinkled her nose. "I'm afraid I don't sense her in the least. What if she's truly dead, Arthur? Maybe I can only connect with her past because that's all there is."

A depressing thought, one he might be forced to acknowledge. "I don't want to believe that here," he said, pounding on his chest. "But perhaps I must. All these years wasted, chasing a dream." The clues all pointed to one conclusion. Bella was dead, and there was nothing he could do to bring her back.

Maribeth rubbed his cheek. "We haven't consulted any of Madame Brown's books in the library on this topic yet. There might be something I'm doing wrong."

A thread of hope. He stood, unable to contain his restlessness. "By God, you had a violent reaction only minutes ago. I thought we were so close to finding her."

"I hate to disappoint you," Maribeth said, "but my fear of dark, confined spaces stems from *my* past, not Bella's."

"You're certain?" He scraped a hand over his chin. "Stanley once told me that his daughter's governess locked Bella in the crawl space without a lantern all afternoon as punishment for not learning her letters. I thought perhaps ... Why were you afraid?"

Maribeth stared at her fingertips, brushing the pad of her thumb absently over the skin. "My mama was poor, and we needed food for our bellies. Have you ever felt the aching grind of an empty stomach? The gnawing pain of hunger is the worst. One day we begged on the corner not far from where we lived, and a man offered us a crust of bread, told my mama he would pay a schilling per month for me. As a trapper girl."[41]

An image of Maribeth crawling through the damp, crowded tunnels filled his head. Trappers sat all alone for hours, often with little to eat and in total darkness.

"The coal mines are no place for a child," Arthur said, "let alone a little girl. That's against the law."

"And yet we needed to eat. Laws are broken every day. I'm so sorry I haven't been more useful."

So there was no connection between her reaction to the crawl space and Bella Turner? He blew out a breath. "All hope of finding Stanley's daughter is lost."

She stood and rubbed his arm. "Don't say that, Arthur. Do you have anything that belonged to Madame Brown? I can seek her out. That's my strength. She was a renowned clairvoyant. Some ghosts carry their skills with them beyond the grave. Maybe Arabella jumped to conclusions and believed Caroline's lies that her daughter was dead without first trying to connect with Bella's soul."

---

[41] Even though this backstory had been revealed to the reader, Arthur wasn't aware of this part of Maribeth's history. This is a critical piece of data for him to chew on, as this fact makes Maribeth more "accessible" to him for a relationship (i.e. the romance conflict). We're more than halfway through the book, and the reader needs hope that these two are going to end up together.

What other choice did they have? Their options were growing thin, and she hadn't encountered the ghost since that one time in the parlor.

"Leave it to me," Arthur said, heading for the door. "Stay and rest. Today has been a trying day. You must be exhausted. Meet me in the study in the morning for breakfast and we can discuss our next steps."

Chapter Sixteen

The first rays of sunlight cast an orange glow over the horizon when Arthur entered Chateau Swansea. He took the stairs at a clipped pace. Most of the household would still be lying in their beds on the verge of wakefulness. Even Mrs. Bartley.

He consulted his pocket watch as he strode down the hallway. Quarter of six. Breakfast was served between seven and eight, so he had at least an hour to retrieve the wedding ring Stanley gave Arabella. But he only needed thirty seconds. **The ruby ring was kept hidden in the decorative base of the lamp on the bedside table. In a rare display of nostalgia after Stanley's recent return from America, his employer had shown Arthur the ring and shared favorite stories of his first wife and daughter.**[42]

In hindsight, Arthur should've noticed the subtle change in Stanley's behavior. The scathing banter between the master and mistress of the house, once reserved for private moments, was laid out for all to witness. His disdainful looks and lack of patience in her presence. They all made sense now in light of her pregnancy and blatant infidelity.

Slipping into the bedroom, Arthur peered down the corridor to ensure he was alone before closing the door.

"You're visiting rather early, Mr. Dunn."

His heart pounded in his ears as he whirled around. The housekeeper sat in a chair by the hearth, staring at him with interest. Her

---

[42] The ruby ring plays an important role in the aftermath section of the story, so I wanted the ring to appear a couple times before its true meaning was revealed. But all backstory must be relevant to the current storyline! So I came up with the idea that Arthur would retrieve the ring so Maribeth could connect with Arabella's ghost to assist in their continued search for Bella.

knitting needles clanked with swift movements, but she kept her attention rooted on him.

"Finding sleep difficult?" she asked, her lips thinning.

Did she secretly wonder at his guilt? They had enjoyed a cordial relationship since the first day of his duties. Of all the servants, she knew him best. He shook his head and assumed his usual seat beside Stanley's bed.

"Who among us at the chateau can sleep these days? Something foul is afoot, and I fear for Stanley's life."

"As do I," Mrs. Hawkins said. She set her needlework aside and came to the foot of the bed. "Forgive me for being so bold, but I cannot leave him alone with you during your visits."

So all the servants were chattering over his probable guilt. No doubt they marveled at his cunning. Who signed over power of authority for their livelihood to a mere steward? Sorcery, black magic. He could hear their whispers in his head. Had Arthur orchestrated every step in the Turner family's tragic demise?

He gripped the arms of the chair. His parents were the circus performers, not he. "I relinquished his care to you for the time being, Mrs. Hawkins. You must do as you see fit. But there are limits. Do not ask me to cease all visits."

The housekeeper harrumphed. "This is for *your* safety. Should anything happen to him during one of your visits, you will have no defense. Do you believe me a foolish old woman? Stanley loves you like a son. He's stubborn as a bull and quick as a whip. If he entrusted you with his life, then he trusted you implicitly."

Tears misted Arthur's eyes, and he focused on his clasped hands until he felt capable of speaking again. "Thank you."

"There's another matter I wish to speak with you on," Mrs. Hawkins said gruffly. "Perhaps you will consider hiring guards for Mr. Turner's protection; one for each door to his chamber."

A sound suggestion. Why hadn't he thought of it himself? "Please, make the arrangements. Any and all decisions impacting Stanley are under your purview."

"Very well." She sat once again near the hearth, this time shifting her body away to afford him privacy during his visit.

He studied the easy rise and fall of Stanley's chest. At least one of them was sleeping restfully. Lord knew his employer had struggled through his share of nightmares.

"Good morning," he said, sandwiching the older man's hand between his own. "Now, more than ever, I could use your advice, old friend."

Why has your mind deserted you? The answer eluded Arthur. Infidelity, though repugnant, was not shocking in this case. Stanley was fully aware of his wife's extramarital activities.

Was this lapse in mental stability caused by the man who sired the babe? A stable lad or footman wouldn't faze his employer. Who among the staff would Caroline target as a means of punishing her husband? Besides Arthur, that was.

His stomach clenched. Had she spun a fantastical tale of seduction and convinced Stanley that Arthur had betrayed his master and fell for her?

Why did you call for your solicitor without my knowledge?

"Everything seems to be spiraling out of control," he murmured. "Come back to us, Stanley. I fear only you can set things right."

Raking his hands through his hair, he slumped into the chair. Could anyone piece together his employer's broken mind? He glanced at the housekeeper, who sat quietly, pulling on the skein of yarn, paying him no mind.

The time to act was now. He leaned forward and slid the secret compartment of the lamp's base open. Inside, the ruby ring sat on a folded piece of paper. A note? He snatched both items and shut the drawer. Slipping his hand into his waistcoat, he deposited the goods.

"Today Miss Sommerset will attempt the impossible and speak with Arabella," he informed Stanley. "Pray your first wife takes pity on us." Standing, he cleared his throat. "A good day to you, Mrs. Hawkins. Send word when you've arranged for the guards and I'll see to their compensation."

Outside the bedroom, Arthur fished in his pocket for the note. Stanley wasn't one for keeping correspondence with his wife, yet the swirly "Mr. Turner" script on top belonged, undoubtedly, to Caroline.

Tucked inside was a brief note as well as a clipping out of the *South Wales Herald* dated April 4, 1874. Arthur read the headline twice: No survivors found after Wheal Turner explosion. Why did Stanley keep a news article about a disaster in one of his coal mines from fifteen years ago? Accidents were a regular occurrence in the coal mining industry. Depositing the clipping into his waistcoat pocket, he read the note.

January 7, 1889
Swansea, England

My dearest husband Stanley,

You are deliciously passionate when driven to the brink of insanity! If you showed this fiery proclivity in our union, I wouldn't seek entertainment elsewhere. In the beginning, there was only ever you. But I cannot compete with a ghost and thought to rid myself of all traces of her existence long ago. In that, it seems, I failed miserably.

Why do you persist in your futile efforts to find Bella? Your precious little girl is lost forever. Did you truly believe she was abducted in plain sight? I am mistress of Chateau Swansea, and nothing happens on these grounds without my permission or knowledge.

I, too, grow weary of our constant fighting. Perhaps we may come to a suitable compromise. Acknowledge my child as the Turner heir and I shall divulge your daughter's fate.

Your ever devoted wife,
Caroline Turner

Bugger me! Arthur folded the note and shoved it into his pants pocket. Bracing one hand against the wall, he rubbed his eyes with the other. Even he had not allowed for the mistress of the house to be this evil. *What did you do with the girl, Caroline?* Maybe Stanley killed his wife in a fit of rage, after all. But then who killed his cousin? Stanley was catatonic. Wasn't he?

Or is he getting away with murder by faking his condition? Would I kill the person who arranged for the disappearance of my child and lied to me for years? Maybe. Depending on the child's fate. Had Bella been sent to live out her life happily with a family of means, or was she dropped off with an orphanage or worse?

An image of Stanley's haunted face surfaced. *Or worse.* His employer had agreed to acknowledge the whelp as his heir in exchange for news on his daughter's fate, and in doing so, lost his mind. Had Caroline sent Bella to work in Wheal Turner? The timing of the explosion was within a year of the child's abduction.

Bella is dead! Or so Caroline's ghost claimed. She would say anything to destroy Stanley's happiness. But if his daughter had worked and died in his own coal mine... *Dear God.* His employer may never recover from that shock. Caroline was pure evil. Did Gabriel Young play a part in Bella's disappearance to secure his future as the Turner heir?

Maribeth believed the girl dead. He fingered the ruby ring in his waistcoat and closed his eyes. Madame Brown was the key to solving the mystery, but not her ghost. There were too many signs for him to ignore any longer.

Storming down the corridor, he took inventory of every conversation he'd had with his employer since his return from America. His hatred of Caroline had been palpable, and his love for Arabella ever present.

Arthur raced down the stairwell and pushed through his study door. His gaze landed on the wrapped package, leaning against the wall in the corner. Why hadn't he realized the truth days ago? Stanley never would have commissioned a portrait of the *second* Mrs. Turner. No, the portrait was of his first wife, Arabella Brown.

In five swift strides, he stood before the package and tore through the brown paper casing, revealing a provocative portrait of the renowned clairvoyant sprawled on a chaise longue. Clothed in a forest-green silk gown, Arabella was stunning. The artist had captured the perfection of Arabella's sultry green eyes and enticing rosebud mouth. A special gift for her lover.

His knees buckled, and he sank to the floor. *Heaven help me!* The world spun, and he felt ill. Bella was not dead, but she may soon be if he did not discover the killer. No one could see this painting!

Standing, he carefully turned the portrait around so the back, still wrapped in packaging, faced the room.

A sharp knock set his blood pumping through his veins. He blew out a breath and turned just as Maribeth slipped through the doorway. She glanced around the room until her gaze settled on him in the corner. Her lips parted, as though poised to ask him a question, until she glanced at the portrait behind him, a curious glint in her eyes.

He walked toward her, commanding her full attention. "Thank you for coming so quickly. I have news."

"Did you find the wedding ring?" she asked, her voice hitching with excitement.

"No, I'm afraid not." The lie tasted bitter on his tongue and, for once, he wished he weren't so damned good at deception. She deserved the truth, just not from him. But when the truth finally came out, she would despise him for withholding what he knew. His throat worked with the need to tell her everything.

Her eyebrows knitted.

"But I found this," he said, offering her the note from his pants pocket.

"The letter?" she asked, snatching it from his hand.

He waved her on. She nearly ripped the paper in her haste to open it. Lowering herself to the edge of one of the wing-backed chairs, she devoured the contents.

"Acknowledge my child as the Turner heir, and I shall divulge your daughter's fate," she finished aloud. Her mouth dropped, and she looked up. "Do you think Stanley accepted Caroline's terms?"

He shrugged and sat on the corner of the desk, crossing his arms. "Maybe. If the truth of his daughter's fate was intolerable, this may account for his deteriorating health."

But there was one other possible cause for Stanley's mental breakdown, one that Arthur had not truly believed possible until this moment.

"Or he killed Caroline, and his conscience couldn't live with the consequences."

Maribeth speared him with a look of utter betrayal. "But you swore you didn't see him shove his wife over the ledge."

"And I stand by what I said. Caroline rushed at Stanley in a raging fit, screaming profanities best suited for the gutters of London Street. He stepped aside and she fell to her death." Arthur squeezed the edges of the desk in a white-knuckled grip. "But what if he stuck out his foot, tripping her? He most definitely made no move to save her."

"You think he later regretted his involvement?" Maribeth whispered. She shook her head. "We cannot know what he did or thought in that moment. Arthur, no one else knows of this letter. Why didn't you tell the constable exactly what you witnessed? Evading Caroline's attack was self-defense, not murder."

He groaned and shoved off the desk, pacing the length of the room. "Mrs. Marsh is grieving and wants a scapegoat. She will never rest until someone rots for her sister's death, whether guilty or not. I let the old bat feed her inner fears after Mrs. Hawkins's testimony." He threw up his hands. "Why not blame the ghost of Chateau Swansea? At the time, I truly believed the incident to be a terrible accident."

"And now?" Maribeth lifted her brow.

"I'm no longer certain of anything. Mrs. Marsh was adamant that Stanley killed Caroline. What if she knew her sister was behind Bella's disappearance and that she'd offered Stanley a truce? The sisters were close to one another. Close enough that Caroline may have divulged her pregnancy."

Maribeth nodded. "Mrs. Marsh may know the identity of her sister's lover as well."

"That puts her in grave danger. The chief isn't an imbecile. He'll close this case as soon as possible." Arthur scrubbed his face, struggling to discern fact from fiction. "My plan to protect Stanley was a grand success. As it stands today, I'm the only person with a motive to kill both victims."

"Only because Marsh knew of your power of authority." Maribeth drummed her fingers on the arm of the chair. "Curious, don't you think? Everyone knew Gabriel Young was the heir of the

Turner estate. So why did the chief inquire with Mr. Turner's lawyer *before* Mr. Young's death?"

Good Lord, but she was right. The chief inspector arrived within an hour of being notified of Gabriel's death. There was no reason to suspect Arthur up until that point. Unless his wife told him to dig deeper.

"Do you think Caroline told her sister that I was her lover? And the chief started investigating me from the onset?" He was beginning to lose the plot line entirely. "Why would Caroline lie to her sister?"

"To besmirch your reputation? Knock you off your pedestal. Get you turned out?" At his incredulous grunt, she shrugged. "Caroline was a woman scorned, and by your own admission, she was an entitled brat."

"What do we do next?" he asked.

Maribeth chewed on her lower lip. "Stanley Turner may be the only one who knows the identity of his wife's lover. You know him best. How can we get through to him?"

The only suggestion he could offer wouldn't appeal to her, but they had to try. He held his hands out to her and she stood, laying her palms over his.

"Pretend you're Bella, finally come home." He twined a strand of her hair around his index finger and stroked his thumb over the silken threads. "Stanley often spoke of his daughter's golden curls, the lovely shade of green of her eyes and her mischievous nature. I believe she was much like you. Read to him from *The Owl and the Pussycat. That was their story.*"

She pressed her lips together and looked away. "I hate the deception, using something so special to him under false pretenses. I feel like an interloper. I don't even know why he read that particular story to his daughter."

Beneath Maribeth's no-nonsense exterior lay a beautiful and honest soul. Arthur squeezed her hands. "I once asked him that very question. An owl and a pussycat are an unlikely pair, much like Arabella and Stanley were. She was vibrant and deeply spiritual, while he was reserved and highly skeptical. And yet, they fell in love."

Just as the steward fell in love with the psychic. Only he was a frog and not a prince. Would an heiress ever desire the love of a fortune-teller's son?

"Let us be married; too long have we tarried," Maribeth said, quoting from the fairy tale. A spark of recognition ignited in her eyes. "He regretted waiting so long to marry his one true love."

"Yes, he did," Arthur said.

"Can't you think of another way to get through to him?"

He would scale the highest mountains to spare her this anxiety. But, in this case, the grand gesture would be futile.

"Don't you believe I've tried everything else within my power?"

Her shoulders straightened with resolve. "You truly believe this will work?"

His gaze strayed to the portrait hidden from view and he nodded. In fact, he would stake his life on it.

Chapter Seventeen

Maribeth knitted her fingers together and waited by the door of Mr. Turner's bedroom. Near the hearth, Arthur spoke quietly with Mrs. Hawkins. Pretending to be the long-lost daughter of a sickly man was bad enough, but to have an audience … her stomach clenched. The housekeeper must think her unbearably cruel, yet Arthur's logic was sound.

"Excuse me." One of the guards poked his head inside the doorway. His breath reeked of mint.

Maribeth stepped aside, briefly pressing the back of her hand to her nose. The fresh lemon scent of her hand soap filled her nostrils.

The giant of a man stood next to her, his shoulders straight and arms at his sides, alert. "Don't mind me. Mrs. Hawkins looks busy at the moment. I'll wait here with you."

She offered him a weak smile. Talking would only encourage conversation and more of his disgusting breath. She suppressed a shiver. *Oh, stop being judgmental.* He could chew on all the mint he wanted to, so long as he kept Mr. Turner safe.

Arthur caught Maribeth's gaze from across the room and nodded for her to proceed. *Lord give me strength.* What did one say to a beloved parent after sixteen years apart? A pasty film covered her tongue. She imagined herself sitting at her own father's bedside, formulating her greeting. Swallowing, she took the first steps toward his bed.

Butterflies took flight in her belly, flittering to her breast and back again, trapped inside an unyielding cage. *Was my father a kind man?* She couldn't remember a single feature from his face or any of his unique personality traits. Sitting on the edge of a chair beside Mr.

Turner, she concentrated on the lovely hue of his kind eyes, like a gorgeous cloudless day in May.

"Hello, Papa," she said with a slight tremor, "it's me, Bella. I've finally come home to Chateau Swansea, to you. Please, won't you say hello?"

Mr. Turner stared sightlessly into the bedroom. She laid her hand over his cold, lifeless one and squeezed. Did he feel the warmth of her fingers beneath the block of ice shielding his mind from the reality of the world around him? Her gaze drifted to Arthur, and he nodded encouragingly.

He expected too much of her! She wasn't a magician. Nor did she know the first thing about a loving relationship between a father and his daughter. What would a father wish to hear from his abducted daughter? That she was safe, happy, and had lived a blessed life, despite all that had happened.

Could she lie and raise his hopes, only to bring them crashing down once he regained his faculties? But if she didn't carry through, Arthur might hang for two murders he didn't commit.

"You needn't worry anymore, Papa. Arthur found me in Devil's Cove and brought me back to you. All is well, truly." She cupped Stanley's chin and gently turned his face to hers. "Come, look. See the truth for yourself."

Dead eyes stared through her.

"This is futile," she whispered.

A book was thrust into her hands.

"Read to him," Arthur said, sitting on the edge of the bed.

She held the storybook high enough for Stanley to see the cover. "Do you remember *The Owl and the Pussycat*? You read to me every night before bed. Shall I read for you?" Turning to the first page, she read aloud, "The Owl and the Pussycat went to sea in a beautiful pea-green boat." She flipped the page. "They took some honey, and plenty of money wrapped up in a five-pound note."

An unbidden, silly smile curled her lips up. The illustrations were delightful. "Do you see the goldfish in a bowl beside the pussycat?" she asked, pointing it out. "Is the fish a pet or lunch, do you suppose?"

She looked up, hopeful for a reaction, but Stanley wasn't even focusing on the pages. Why bother holding up the book for him when she knew the words by heart? Tossing the book aside, she closed her eyes and recited the verses from memory.

"The owl looked up to the stars above, and sang to a small guitar. O lovely pussy, O pussy, my love. What a beautiful pussy you are, you are, you are! What a beautiful pussy you are! *Hoot, hoot.*"

The playful baritone hooting like an owl echoed in her mind as surely as she was breathing. A cavernous hole swallowed up her heart, even as a deep, abiding sense of love swept through her. Was this yet another footprint of Bella's memories on the book?

Arthur nudged her shoulder and whispered, "Don't stop."

She opened her eyes and goose bumps pebbled over her arms. Stanley was staring *at* her, not through her. Oh, goodness. What were the next lines of the story? They sat on the tip of her tongue. *Quick, quick.*

"Pussy said to the owl, 'You elegant fowl, how charmingly sweet you sing! Oh! Let us be married; too long have we tarried. But what shall we do for a ring?'"

She paused and Stanley squinted at her with his head tilted. She caught her breath, sat utterly still.

"Arabella…" he croaked. "Am I dead then?"

A vice clamped around her heart, and she pulled his hand to her lips. He saw his dead wife in Maribeth's blonde curls and green eyes… "No, no. You're not dead. You are very much alive. So am I, your daughter, Bella."

A tear trickled down his left cheek and he closed his eyes, curling into a ball away from her. "My daughter is dead. My sweet merry Bella is dead. My daughter is dead."

Pressure suddenly weighed on her chest, and the high neckline of her gown constricted her airflow. *Merry, Mary.* His voice grew fainter and fainter as he chanted, until it died altogether. Maribeth sprang to her feet and shuffled backward, putting distance between herself and the bed. She could scarce draw a breath, couldn't think of anything but the kind man with the sad blue eyes.

Mary. <u>Her own father had called her Mary! He also had beautiful, sad blue eyes.</u> Tremors wracked her body, stole every bit of strength she possessed until she nearly crumpled onto the floor. *Oh, God*. She remembered the color of her father's eyes, her nickname, spoken so lovingly from his lips. Grabbing hold of the back of the chair, she supported her trembling legs.

"She isn't dead," Arthur said, dispersing the haze in Maribeth's mind. He rubbed Mr. Turner's back in soothing circles. "Please, listen. Stanley, this is Arthur. Listen to me. Your daughter is very much alive."

But his pleas fell on deaf ears. The master of the house was lost once again, hiding in the rose-colored world he'd created in his mind.

"Read more of the story," Arthur suddenly demanded with a desperate glance over his shoulder. "Now, goddammit."

Maribeth heaved in a breath of air and, walking to his side, placed her hand on Arthur's shoulder. "He's gone. There was a moment when he was with us, I grant you. But I did something wrong. Missed a beat in the story or one of their little nuances. Give me the book. I'll read more and we can try again tomorrow. Let's talk in privacy in the study."

"Not the study!" Arthur snapped. He pressed his lips together. "We can retire to the parlor."

But they always conversed in the study. Perhaps his office reminded him too much of his employer. He truly cared about Mr. Turner, or he was a talented showman. Something had felt off ever since their earlier meeting.

She retraced every second of their earlier encounter in her mind's eye, from the moment she rushed inside his study and found him standing in the corner by the portrait to... Were the walls closing in on a killer, causing him to lose his temper?

No, she mustn't let her imagination run away from her as she was wont to do. Arthur was her partner in finding the murderer. Wasn't he? Mrs. Hawkins trusted him, so had Mr. Turner. She must trust him as well. For now.

Meow!

Maribeth shot upright in her bed. Of course, that was it! The pussycat purred after her verse. Mr. Turner was listening for his daughter's meow. She must read to him from the book again.

The wall clock showed five minutes before ten o'clock in the evening. Far too late for a visit. She flopped onto her back again. Where had the time gone? She had been so focused on the book that she'd missed the evening meal. With her mind no longer preoccupied, her stomach rumbled.

Perhaps Mrs. Pickering had left her a plate from the evening meal on the counter. Or she could scrounge for a slice of bread with fruit in the pantry. She was light on her feet and quiet as a mouse. No one would be the wiser if she snuck down the servants' staircase. The route was far quicker than the main staircase and passed by the study where the portrait of Mrs. Turner lay in waiting. Something wasn't quite right about the whole affair, wriggled under her skin like an earthworm in the mud, slow and steady. She must view the portrait.

Lighting a candle, she poked her head inside the narrow stairwell and lifted the candleholder toward the third floor. The flame flickered dimly against the whitewashed walls and illuminated the better part of two and a half stairs.

Utter silence greeted her. The chateau was asleep, the staff all abed for the night.

Anyone could lurk beyond the flame's golden glow. A clandestine meeting of secret lovers or a murderer lying in wait. *Don't be a ninny.* Whoever killed Gabriel had no reason to harm her.

She swallowed and slipped into the dark passageway. Bracing one hand on the wall, she took a tentative step down, then another and another. Her slippers were soundless on the broad steps, but her heartbeat thumped in her ears. *Stupid. Stupid. Stupid, girl.*

The floorboards suddenly whined, and she halted. Was that the stair underneath her foot creaking or one from above?

"Hello, is anyone there?" she asked.

Pivoting, she lifted the candle higher. She saw nothing beyond the flickering shadow of the flame. A field mouse suddenly scurried across the step and squeezed through a tiny hole in the wall. Maribeth squealed and jerked backward, almost losing her footing. Her stomach dropped to the floor, and she struggled to gain her balance.

Oh, dear God, get out of here!

Turning, she lifted her skirt and rushed down the stairs. Candle-light danced on the walls, casting eerie shadows. She rounded a corner and pitched forward, propelled by a vicious shove to her middle back. A scream hurled through her. She lost her grip on the candle and tumbled down the black stairwell.

Searing pain exploded in her shoulder, hip, and back. One. Two. Three. She lost count of the steps before her forehead finally smacked against the concrete floor with a sickening thud.

Groaning, she rolled onto her back and stared into the black void, unable to assemble a coherent thought. Every muscle in her body ached and throbbed. She heard heavy breathing. A feverish chill cascaded over her in waves.

Dagger. She kept a dagger strapped to her calf. Bending one knee, she dug beneath her skirt just as a blinding light materialized. Her breath caught in her throat, and she instinctively shielded her eyes from the glare. She was going to die.

Chapter Eighteen

"Maribeth, is that you? Oh, bloody hell! What happened? I heard you scream."

Arthur knelt beside her and shrugged out of his jacket, placing it under her head. Where had he come from? A headache pulsed at her temples, and she wanted to retch, but she drew her dagger and pointed it directly at him.

"Someone pushed me," she rasped, scrambling away. The pulsing in her head intensified, robbed her of breath. "How did you get here so fast?"

He lifted his hands up and backed away. "Easy, now. I was in the kitchen preparing a plate for you. You missed supper, and I thought to bring you a bite to eat. Are you sure you didn't trip?"

"Yes, I'm sure." Her gaze darted up the stairs. She'd fled from the mouse and rounded the corner. Did the momentum of her flight pitch her forward? In her frightened state, had she imagined being shoved? "I believe so, but … Everything happened so fast. There was a mouse."

He glanced toward the empty stairwell. "I don't want to leave you here alone. Did you hear anything else? See anyone?"

Harsh breathing, her own? She shook her head and immediately regretted the gesture. Whoever did this either stood before her, had fled the scene, or was a figment of her overactive imagination. With tentative fingers, she probed the knot forming on her right temple near the hairline.

Arthur crouched and held out his hand, still several feet away. "Come, let me help you into the kitchen, then I'll call for the doctor."

A wave of dizziness assailed her. Bile rose in her throat and she turned, coughing up the acrid spittle. She couldn't defend herself against him in this moment even if he were the killer. If he wanted her dead, he need only knock her unconscious and drag her limp body into the forest. Her cries hadn't awakened anyone else.

Wiping her mouth on a handkerchief, she came to her knees. Her limbs shook and she paused, reaching for him. "Help me to the kitchen," she said, "but no doctor. My injuries are superficial."

"Someone quite possibly tried to kill you and make it appear as an accident," he said. "We will have to inform Chief Inspector Marsh. I'd feel better if we sent for the doctor as well."

"Please, no." She took his hand and stood. The floor seemed to shift underfoot. She clasped his arm and moaned. "I'm embarrassed enough without others learning of my silly accident. I was frightened by a mouse and ran down an unfamiliar stairwell with only a single candle to light my way. There is no evidence of foul play. Even I cannot say with certainty whether I tripped or was pushed."

He guided her into the kitchen and assisted her onto a stool before lighting several lamps. While Arthur gathered supplies, she took inventory of her injuries. The merciless pounding in her head was the worst, but the searing pain radiating across her back also merited attention. She trailed her fingers over her satin gown until she met with a jagged piece of cloth. A sticky wetness covered her fingers.

"You're bleeding," Arthur said, placing a bowl of water on the counter. "There are rusty nails protruding from the stairs. I've asked Webber to take care of them more than once. Lazy blighter! You need a doctor, Maribeth."

"No doctor!" She held out her blood-stained fingers. "There isn't much blood. I don't want anyone…"

Her mouth suddenly felt as dry as cotton. She couldn't tell him the truth. Didn't wish for the others within the household or community to know of her past. Secrets even her best friend, Edith, did not know. They would judge her, judge her guardian. Could she cleanse the wound herself?

Arthur cupped her chin, turning her gaze to his. "You don't what anyone to *what*? The doctor is discrete and trustworthy. We can wake Mrs. Hawkins to observe while he administers to your wounds if the idea of being alone with a man makes you squeamish."

"I'll tend to the cut myself," she said, grinding her teeth.

"You can't reach that far." He folded his arms over his chest and leaned against the counter, his inscrutable gaze fixed on her. "At least let me help you. Come, you know me well enough by now. Whatever you're hiding, I'll take with me to the grave. I am neither judge nor jury."

He was a fiercely private man who trusted few. That much she knew to be true. What choice did she have? Allowing the cut to become infected because of her pride would be folly, especially in the midst of their investigation.

"All right," she said, meeting his stare. "But don't you dare look on me with pity when you're done."

His eyebrows arched as she unbuttoned the front of her gown and peeled the material off her shoulders, exposing her upper back. Heat flooded her cheeks, and she dipped her chin. As a young girl, she'd boasted of her strength in defying a fierce pirate. But she wasn't a child anymore and society frowned upon those who did not fit into their perfect little mold.

What would Arthur think of her now?

★★★

A dozen or so flesh-colored welts crisscrossed Maribeth's back, a grotesque landscape on an otherwise flawless canvas of creamy white skin. He clamped his jaw tight, cutting off the curses leaping on his tongue. A full minute passed before he could control himself enough to speak in a semi-calm voice.

"Who whipped you like a savage animal?"

She shook her head. Did she fear retribution? The scars were old, yet she was no more than twenty. *Dear God.* What kind of monster beat a child? Perhaps a notorious pirate known as the Devil. Had he kidnapped Maribeth and tortured her for his own perverse pleasure? *Fucking bastard!*

"Your guardian should be hanged for his abominable treatment of you! He lives among the gentry and they sing his praises. Disgusting pig."

She whirled around, her eyes flared wide. **"Dominick saved my life! Lord Covington has been nothing but kind and loving from the day he found me. You promised you would not judge!"**

How could he not when faced with something as heart-wrenchingly cruel as this? But she was right. He promised her neutrality, and he would honor his word, though he must know the truth.

"This happened in the coal mine?" Arthur whispered. "That's why you trembled in the crawl space. They beat you into submission."

Her bottom lip quivered for a moment before her forest-green eyes turned hard. "No, Dominick found me in the hull of a slave ship bound for South Africa. The coal mine foreman sold me to the highest bidder. My mother..." Her voice cracked, and she paused. "I never saw my mother again, though my guardian spent years trying to locate her before he adopted me. So, you see, you're terribly wrong. Dominick provided a loving home. He intends to settle a dowry on me as well."[43] She turned her back to him again, her head downcast. "I leave for London after we solve this case," she said in a near whisper. "My coming out ball is in a few weeks."

The tension in his shoulders eased fractionally. After all the pain she'd endured, she'd found a loving caregiver. A coming out ball ... Men of the highest ranks would vie for Maribeth's hand by month's

---

[43] The painful truth of Maribeth's childhood finally comes out in full (i.e. the heroine's motivation). The heroine is opening herself up to ridicule by the hero, but he sees her inner beauty. Knowing the extent of Maribeth's sordid past gives the reader hope that she will chose the hero over her place in society (i.e. the romance conflict). Notice how this revelation was worked naturally into the current storyline. Maribeth was set upon by the killer and fell, which caused an injury that she could not attend herself, forcing her to place her trust in the hero. By bringing up the dowry as well, the hero is slapped in the face with the reality of their situations in life. So even as we hope they can be together, we despair that it will never be.

end. He hadn't thought that far into the future. Didn't wish to think on it now, not with the scars of her past laid before him and his heart crushed beneath a boulder. Yet he must acknowledge her, somehow.

"With Lord Covington as your guardian, I'm sure you'll be embraced by London society."

She stiffened. "All of London will spurn me. I cannot wear the latest fashions without exposing … my past. No, I will never fit in, despite my guardian's well-laid plans. What gentleman would ever want a lady with hideous scars?"

He could tell her she was terribly wrong, but she wouldn't listen. Somehow, he must show her instead. "Why did the captain order the whipping?" he asked, tracing one particularly thick welt with the tip of his index finger.

She met his gaze over her shoulder briefly. "I stole a hunk of cheese from the larder. My hunger was greater than my fear of the punishment."

"Oh, Maribeth." His voice cracked with his heart. He kissed the delicate curve at the nape of her neck, and gooseflesh erupted across her beautiful skin. The events of her past surpassed anything he'd ever been forced to endure. In comparison, his had been a life of ease and excess.

"That was a long time ago," she said, resolved. "I'm alive and happy. I don't need a ball or a husband. All I want is the chance to help others."

Liar. She craved a family, only she didn't believe she could ever have one. In that belief, she was wrong. He wanted her desperately for himself—others would, too.

Arthur dipped a cloth into the bowl and dabbed at her back. A fine line of fresh blood seeped out of the gash. With a little whisky to cleanse the wound and a bit of pressure, the bleeding would stop.

"Wait here," he said, heading into the pantry, where he found a bottle of spirits along with bandages and tape. "Brace yourself, this is going to burn."

An impish grin lifted her lips. "Not nearly as bad as the bite of a whip, I'd wager."

A mental image of her tied to a post popped into his head and he sucked in a breath. The whip crackled and slashed through the air. He shook his head, dispelling the picture before the first lash broke through her delicate skin. How could she jest about such a terrifying experience? She had been little more than a babe at the time.

"Please, don't jest," he murmured. "The pain you must've endured..."

She braced her hands on the counter and bowed her head. "But I prefer laughter over tears."

He couldn't laugh at anything in the moment.

"Then talk to me to keep your mind off the pain," he said, drizzling the spirits on the cut.

Her shoulders tensed and she grunted. "I figured out what I did wrong earlier today when I read the book."

The first smile of the evening tugged at the corner of his mouth. "Of course you did. What was the issue?"

"Bella always said me-OW! Bloody hell, that hurts like a mother!" She glared over her shoulder when he splashed more of the alcohol on her back. Air hissed through her teeth and she continued, "After the verse with the ring. Mr. Turner played the role of the owl, Bella the role of the cat."

"I'm sure you're right." He wiped away the excess liquid and taped a bandage over the cut. With extreme care, he pulled the dress over her shoulders. "All done. Turn around after you're decent again and let me see the goose egg growing on your forehead."

A cute little snort filled the kitchen, and she boldly faced him with her chemise still exposed. He cleared his throat. Maybe fastening the buttons was too painful. He took over the task. She was his patient tonight. He must pay absolute attention to her wounds, not the citrusy scent on her skin or the way her curls framed her face.

"You, sir, have never seen a goose egg. This is no bigger than—"

"A third eye?"

"Black and blue, no doubt." She winced when he touched the surface of the bump. "Do you think the staff will believe I brawled in the Red Fox?"

Pushing the hair back from her forehead, he leaned closer to inspect the damage. "If anyone can pull off such a bald-faced lie, it is you."

"Or you."

He met her impertinent gaze, mere inches away. "We do share a talent for storytelling. But I will inform Mrs. Hawkins and Mrs. Pickering that you've taken ill and require bedrest all day tomorrow. I'll send you an icepack. The swelling will be gone by mid-day, and if you wear your hair down, no one will be the wiser."

He stepped back and braced his hands on the counter.

"Suffered a few shiners yourself, Arthur?"

"One or two. You must have a terrible headache." He entered the pantry again and set about collecting the ingredients for a headache remedy. Living alone had taught him to be proficient in nursing light ailments, cooking, and fixing odds and ends. But he drew the line at laundering his own clothes.

After she had drunk the bitter medicine, he escorted her to her bedroom, where he proceeded to check under the bed and inside the crawl space for any unwanted visitors. He inspected the lock on the adjoining bedroom door for good measure, then peeked behind the window dressings.

"There are no goblins hiding in my room," Maribeth said with a smirk.

Perhaps not, but he couldn't say as much for the rest of the chateau.

"Lock the door behind me and stay in bed tomorrow." He used his sternest tone.

She sat on the foot of the bed and began unlacing her boots. "But I have to read the book to Mr. Turner again."

"That can wait."

Her head snapped up. "Why? We're so close to the truth."

"Mrs. Hawkins informed me at supper that Stanley isn't doing well. He took a turn for the worse after our earlier visit. She has forbidden any guests tomorrow. I must defer to her judgment. Good night, Maribeth."

She stood and planted her hands on her hips. "That's a terrible mistake. We're making progress. I want to read the book again first thing in the morning. Stanley will come around. I know he will!"

"Obstinate woman," he hissed. "You fell down a flight of stairs and need to rest!" His body shook uncontrollably.

"Arthur," she said.

He took a calming breath. "What?"

"Why are you shaking?" She walked to his side and touched his arm.

He pulled her into his embrace. His pulse raced, and his vision blurred. "I almost lost you today without..." The words clogged in his throat. He stared into her big, green eyes, wide with curiosity.

"Without what?"

He clamped his mouth shut. She was a gentleman's daughter; he was a steward. In less than one month, she would meet a titled man who would give her a family, fulfill all the dreams she never dared to believe in.

"Nothing," he said, kissing her forehead.

She wrapped his arms around her waist and pressed closer. "You're a terrible liar or a coward. Which is it?"

"A coward," he murmured in her ear.

"Please, tell me." Her lips brushed against his, a brief and tempting contact. "You almost lost me today without what?"

"Without telling you how much I adore you." He claimed her rosy mouth. Her lips were pliant and molded beautifully to his. He smiled and trailed kisses along her chin, all the way to her ear. "All of you."

"Even the stubborn bits?" she asked with a cheeky grin.

"Especially those."

He nibbled down her neck and made quick work of the first three buttons of her gown before he knew what he was about. Blowing out a breath, he stepped back and relinquished his hold. What was he doing? She must be sore and tired. He was overstepping the boundary.

"You should get out of this tattered dress and into your nightgown. I should go now. A good night's sleep is all you need."

She led his fingers back to the fourth button on her gown. "Stay with me. Help me undress." Though her voice trembled, she held his hands in place.

"Maribeth…" His voice cracked. He wanted her, but he could not have her. "As much as I wish to claim you, I cannot. One day soon you'll find a man worthy of your love, someone who can provide you with the life you deserve."

"I want you."

He shook his head. "I'm a steward."

"You're steadfast," she said, kissing his palm. "Unfailingly loyal." She pressed her lips to his cheek. "And, unlike any other man of my acquaintance, you make my knees wobble." A grin spread across her lips. "Do not tell me who I can or cannot desire. I want you."

He unfastened another button and another. "You simply haven't met enough men yet. After your coming out ball, you'll forget I ever existed. As you should."

"I will never forget you." Heat flared in her emerald eyes.

After peeling the shredded gown off her shoulders, he trailed kisses to the hem of her chemise. She sucked in a breath, and he tugged the flimsy fabric down to reveal one perfectly pebbled nipple. He suckled, hard and long until she buried her hands in his hair.

"Arthur," she mewled.

He pushed her gown over her hips, and it tumbled in a heap at her feet. She stepped out of the pile, her eyes hooded. Her fingers threaded through his, and she pulled him toward the fireplace. Within seconds, he stoked the coals into a blazing fire.

"Let's get you out of these clothes," she said, pulling off his jacket.

"We can't," he said again.

A saucy smile curved her lips as she tugged the shirt out of his pants and pushed it over his head. "Yes, we can." Her gaze devoured his bare chest, warming him from within.

Before he could protest, she unlaced her chemise and let it fall to the ground. She stood still and proud in her nudity. His groin tightened, became unbearably hard, and pushed against his trousers.

She knelt, pulled off his boots and socks, and then lay on the plush rug beside the fireplace. "Take off your trousers, Arthur, and come to me."

He wanted her, but she would regret this in a month. But he could worship her body without ruining her prospects. He would give himself this gift. A token to remember her by.

"I will hold you, kiss you," he said, stretching out beside her. "But don't ask me for more."

"Arthur—"

He held one finger to her lips. "Promise me you'll attend your coming out ball. You owe this to yourself and your guardian. Afterward, if you still feel the same, then…"

She nodded solemnly. "Kiss me."

"Everywhere," he murmured, pulling her into his arms. He trailed his tongue over her supple skin, tasted her sweet mouth, and memorized the contours of her delectable body. Her moans of pleasure filled him with an unbearable need. But he controlled his urges.

She snuggled on his chest, and he rubbed her back in soothing circles. Soon, her breathing evened out and he carried her to bed, tucking the blanket under her chin. A sigh escaped her lips, and he smiled.

"Good night, sweet Maribeth."

Closing the door, he set off in the direction of the study. He had avoided that damned room all day, when he should've rewrapped the portrait and ordered the footmen to transport it to his house posthaste.

The carpet runner absorbed the clipped pang of his heels as he barreled down the stairs with one hand on the banister and the other holding the lantern high. Maribeth couldn't definitively say whether or not she had been pushed down the stairwell. But Arthur would have the answer in a matter of seconds. He crossed the threshold into the study, and all the blood drained from his face.

Over the fireplace mantle, the painting of Madame Brown hung in all its glory, only the killer of Chateau Swansea had left a message in the form of a knife protruding from Arabella's heart—or was that through the middle of her back?

Chapter Nineteen

Early the next morning, Arthur tethered his horse on a post outside the police station. He shoved through the main door and pounded his fist on the counter, startling the little pup napping while on duty. The officer nearly toppled out of his chair.

"Bloody—"

"Spare me the blistering setdown," Arthur said, tossing a folded note on the desk. "Chief Inspector Marsh summoned me here. Eight o'clock sharp."

The officer read the missive and glanced at the clock on the wall. He jumped to his feet. "Who gave you this? I wasn't informed and nothing happens around here without me know—"

"Johnson!" The chief's deep growl reverberated down the hallway. "Send Mr. Dunn back the moment he arrives."

Arthur lifted an eyebrow. "You were saying?"

"You heard him"—Johnson pointed to the hallway—"go!"

Tucking his hat under his arm, Arthur walked at a clip until he came to the last door, with the chief's nameplate. He pounded one fist against the glass insert.

"Enter," the chief inspector yelled.

Arthur stood at the precipice. "Good morning, Chief Inspector. I came as soon as I received your missive. Eight o'clock is rather early for a morning call. What can I do for you?"

Chief Inspector Marsh sat back in his chair and waved him in. "Shut the door behind you and take a seat. This isn't a social call. I heard there was another incident at the chateau and would like a full report."

"Indeed," Arthur said, setting his hat on an empty chair before taking the seat opposite the chief. "I meant to write to you first thing this morning. But with such an excellent informant, I'm surprised you summoned me at all. Who sent you word of the incident, and what, pray tell, did the informant say?"

Chief Investigator Marsh flipped a small envelope over and over in his fingers. "I don't know who sent the note."

"May I see it?" Arthur held out his hand. "Perhaps I will recognize the handwriting."

"I'm afraid not," the chief said, puckering his lips. He tossed the note across the desk. "She used news clippings to write her brief message."

"She?" Arthur asked, perusing the note.

A young woman was accosted in the stairwell and almost fell to her death. Arthur Dunn must be apprehended before another dead body is found.

"Purely speculation." Chief Inspector Marsh leaned forward. "You see, I've asked myself why someone would take care in hiding their identity."

"Because he's wanted for murder?" Arthur suggested.

Chief Inspector Marsh grinned and slapped his hand on the desk. "Don't think I didn't consider that possibility. But why would the killer out himself? No, that doesn't make any sense whatsoever. The note was sent by a woman afraid for her life. A logical conclusion, don't you think?"

Only one woman was aware of what had occurred last night. Did Maribeth truly suspect Arthur as the killer? No, no. He didn't believe that. She could've screamed for help or taken up his offer to call for the doctor. The note came from a manipulative mastermind, a man intent on removing the one deterrent to his plans to murder his next victim.

Arthur set the note back on the desk and said, "I'm sure the killer hoped you would draw that conclusion."

The chief waggled his finger at Arthur. "You are an intelligent man. Let's assume for a minute that you're right. Why would the killer want you detained?"

"Because I'm getting too close to the truth, to discovering his identity."

"Are you?" the chief asked, sitting on the edge of the desk.

Hell, yes! But did he want to share what he'd found thus far with the police? They were in a better position to dig deeper into the past and find the answers Arthur sought. Who were all of Caroline's past lovers? Yet he couldn't ignore the family ties between Caroline Turner and the chief's wife. Was the man sitting across from him independent?

Could Arthur afford not to trust him?

"Yes, I believe I am."

"Tell me what happened and I will reserve my final judgment until I have all the facts."

Arthur nodded briskly. "Miss Sommerset lost her footing in the servants' stairwell and took an unfortunate fall."

"At what time?"

"Around ten o'clock. I don't recall the exact time."

"Who found her?"

"I did."

"Why were you at the chateau so late?" Chief Inspector Marsh stood and came around the desk, looming over Arthur. "You live off the property in a comfortable home."

"Mr. Turner wasn't feeling well, and I was concerned," Arthur said, meeting the chief's direct stare. "Mrs. Hawkins requested that I stay overnight in case he grew worse and the doctor should be called."

"Was the lady injured?"

"Yes, but her wounds were superficial. I suggested we call for the doctor, but she refused the offer. She believes the incident was an accident."

The chief narrowed his gaze. "And you don't?"

"No, sir." Arthur pointed to the note. "He wants me out of the way. The killer failed in eliminating his target last night because I arrived to Miss Sommerset's rescue before he could finish the deed."

"The psychic investigator?" the chief asked. "My apologies, but I don't follow. Why would anyone want to kill her?"

"Because the killer believes she is Bella Turner," Arthur said, fishing the correspondence between the Turners from his pocket. "Please read this."

Chief Inspector Marsh perused the note and his eyebrows furrowed. "What are you saying?"

"Whoever killed Caroline and Gabriel is the same man who kidnapped Bella Turner all those years ago. I believe he blackmailed Caroline into becoming his lover, and she became pregnant with his child. But when he discovered her plans to reveal Bella's fate to Stanley, the killer got cold feet. Once the truth came out, his identity would soon follow."

"That's a lot to surmise from one letter," the chief said. "Conjecture, as you like to say."

"True, but the facts fit. I call them as I see them." The only people who could confirm his theory were Stanley and the killer.

"Armed with the information of his daughter's fate, Stanley would hunt the man down," the chief said, mulling over the plot.

Arthur nodded. "Except Stanley lost his mind when he learned the truth. He believes his daughter is dead."

Chief Inspector Marsh rubbed his chin. "And what of Gabriel Young?"

"Gabriel might have stumbled on the truth. I haven't pieced that together yet. But the killer believes the medium is Bella Turner. And if she is, it's only a matter of time until she remembers everything, including him."

The chief's mouth gaped, but no words came out. He stood and locked the door before resuming his seat behind the desk. "Why do you think that? I thought the girl must be dead."

"I can't say for sure," Arthur answered honestly. "Her resemblance to Arabella Brown is striking, and I believe she is a legitimate medium. Did she inherit the ability from her mother? Maybe. Her age is spot on as well."

"Why do you hesitate, then?"

A fair question. Arthur had mulled over the dilemma since opening the portrait.

"Miss Sommerset has vivid memories of a woman she called mother as well as working in the coal mines, yet she cannot recall ever having been to Chateau Swansea. Did Caroline send her stepdaughter to live with a poor family who convinced the child she

249

was theirs? Bella was only four when she was abducted, so it's possible."

"Trauma messes with one's mind," the chief confirmed. "The child might have suppressed the memories."

There was that factor as well. Could they ever prove her identity for sure? Probably not, unless she remembered her childhood. Either way, Stanley would adore everything about Maribeth and welcome her with open arms. She was the very image of Arabella, mischievous, and talented beyond measure. Bella Turner, heiress of Chateau Swansea and the vast Turner estate, had finally come home. Everyone in Swansea's high society would welcome her when she assumed her rightful place.

Arthur swallowed and braced his hands on the chair. One day soon, he would serve Bella faithfully, just as he served her father, ever loyal to the ones he loved. *If I get out of this mess, that is.*

"Well, Chief, do you believe me?"

"I do," the officer said, standing. He stormed toward the door and yanked it open. "Johnson! Bates! Come here and bring the handcuffs."

"You're coming back to the chateau with me?" Arthur asked, coming to his feet. "But we don't know who the killer is yet. I need your help in identifying and locating all of Caroline's past lovers."

The two constables entered the room; one held a set of restraints.

"Escort Mr. Dunn to cell number one for now," the chief ordered.

Arthur stared, dumbfounded, as one constable slapped the cuffs on his wrists while the other held his arms behind his back. "What are you doing? I'm innocent. You said you believe me."

"And I do," Chief Inspector Marsh said. "But I can't have you riding back to Chateau Swansea and warning Miss Sommerset of my grand plan. We will wait in the shadows and snatch the killer when he makes his move. If I set you free, he might flee."

Arthur struggled to break free, but the cuffs held strong. "You're going to use an innocent woman as bait? Goddammit! Don't do this, Chief Inspector. She'll remember the past, or Stanley will recover.

He had a lucid moment yesterday when Miss Sommerset read to him. We'll find the killer in due time. Let me go!"

"Trust me, Mr. Dunn. We will apprehend the culprit before he claims any more victims. I have a brilliant plan to lure him out this afternoon."

Bloody hell. He should've kept his mouth shut.

Run, Maribeth, run.

Chapter Twenty

A beam of sunlight inched across the wall in Maribeth's bedchamber. She tucked her hands under her cheek and marveled at the way the light exposed the intricacies of the fairytale scene painted on the wall. She smiled, still naked under the covers, and snuggled deeper into her pillow.

Her life had taken a wondrous, fairytale-like turn. Arthur Dunn adored her! Kissed her, held her close. Soothed her with his gentle touch and warm lips. Wanted her, despite her sketchy past.

All that stood between them and "happily ever after" was her coming out ball. In a couple of weeks, Arthur would be hers. *Forever.* She must write to Eveline and secure an invitation for him. If she was to dance with other men, then Arthur must come and claim the first set. Fair was fair.

What would Dominick and Eveline think of Arthur? Her guardians wouldn't judge him by his occupation or his family ties, but rather, his character. Her heart swelled to near bursting. Edith would squeal with delight when she heard the news!

Her gaze roved over the mural once again. Oh, to be loved as deeply as the owl loved the pussycat. There were so many forms of love. A man for a woman, two girlfriends, and a guardian for his ward. Mr. Turner had loved his daughter so dearly, too. Was she truly dead? He thought so, but why?

He must've caved to his wife's proposal and obtained information about Bella's fate in exchange for acknowledging a bastard as his child. There was no other logical explanation for his condition.

But what was she missing? So much had happened from the moment she entered Arthur's study until he escorted her back to her bedroom after her tumble down the stairs.

Pretend you're Bella, finally come home.

Arthur's suggestion had borne fruit, startling his employer out of his trance for a brief moment. A queasy ache snaked throughout Maribeth's body. There was something in the way Arthur had shuttered his eyes and looked away, as though he harbored a secret. She rubbed her temples and winced. The goose egg was little more than the size of a nut but still hurt like the dickens.

What was Arthur keeping from her? Her accident had kept her from sneaking into his private domain for a peek at the portrait of Mrs. Turner. She had to try again. Why would Mr. Turner commission a portrait of his wife when he detested her? Unless...

'Arabella ... am I dead then?'

Was the portrait of his first wife? Oh, good Lord. She hopped out of bed and hastily dressed, ignoring her protesting muscles. How could she lie about in bed when someone might very well wish her dead?

My sweet merry Bella is dead.

She isn't dead.

Why was Arthur adamant that Bella Turner was alive? Her head suddenly felt light. She inhaled deep and pulled on her slippers. The answer could be found in his study and, this time, no one would keep her from reaching her destination.

Maribeth threw open her door and crashed into the maid, unsettling the pile of clean linens in her arms.

"I'm so sorry, Pearl," she said, side-stepping the mess. She ran down the corridor but slowed her pace on the stairs. After the tumble she took last night, she had no wish for a repeat performance.

On the main floor, she opted for a brisk walk. The corridor stretched on for miles, but the study was within her sights. A door creaked and the butler suddenly appeared in front of her.

He reared back, and she gasped.

"Miss Sommerset," he said in his haughty tone. "Pray tell, where is the fire?"

Her heart jackhammered in her breast. "I beg your pardon," she said, regulating her breathing. "Have you seen Mr. Dunn this morning? I must speak with him on an urgent matter."

Webber lifted an eyebrow. "He was called to the police station this morning."

"Oh." She chewed on her bottom lip. "Whatever for?"

"I couldn't say, miss." The butler clasped his hands behind his back. "Might I assist you in his stead?"

"No, thank you. I'll wait for Mr. Dunn in his study. Can you inform him when he returns?"

A smug grin appeared on Webber's lips. "Of course, though I cannot say when he'll be back."

With that, the butler strode away. That was odd. Although, come to think on it, most encounters with the butler were strange. Shaking off the awkward vibes, she scrambled down the hallway and slipped inside Arthur's study. Her gaze immediately went to the corner of the room where she'd last seen the portrait.

It was gone.

A quick search inside the hidden corridor revealed nothing. Where was the damned portrait? *Infuriating man!* Arthur was keeping secrets from her again, probably out of some misguided desire to protect her from … Only he knew what.

Lord, her muscles ached. She sat in the desk chair and laid her head back, preparing to wait for him, when a flash of green caught the corner of her eye. Glancing left, her gaze lifted to the wall above the hearth where a grand portrait of a stunning woman hung.

Her throat thickened, closing off her airway. She closed her eyes, but the vision of the golden-haired beauty was imprinted on her mind. *Madame Brown.* How could this be?

Her eyes fluttered open and she drew closer to the portrait, unable to look away. She studied every inch. A section of the painting had been torn in the center of the woman's chest and patched rather poorly.

So this was Arthur's secret, the reason he'd behaved so oddly yesterday? He'd asked her to pretend to be Bella knowing she bore an eerie resemblance to the girl. No, even more than that. He thought she *was* the abducted child.

Impossible.

Why didn't he tell her of the portrait?

Arthur held the power of authority over Mr. Turner's estate. Who inherited everything if Bella was never found or if she was found but mysteriously died? Like falling down a flight of dark stairs and breaking her neck?

Arthur had been by her side in a matter of seconds after she hit the floor. Or had pain warped her sense of time? He could've pushed her and later feigned innocence when his plan failed. The killer was careful and crafty. He wouldn't risk killing her after she'd screamed. Anyone could have come to investigate.

She crumpled to the floor in a heap of skirts. He wasn't capable of this. Not the gentleman who'd kissed the nape of her neck with tenderness and gently cleaned her wounds, who held her all night and spoke of a future together. But his parents had traveled with a circus. Could he perform equally as well? She had honed many skills over the years while living on a pirate ship with her guardian before he became respectable, but her heart was touched ... Was she blind to the truth?

She stared at Arabella's inviting smile and the mischievous gleam in her eyes.

"If I didn't know better, I'd say we could be sisters," Maribeth whispered to the woman on the chaise longue.

"Or mother and daughter."

Maribeth jerked around, staring wide-eyed at Mrs. Hawkins.

The housekeeper closed the study door quietly behind her. Tears shimmered in her eyes. "Bella was a lovely child. Come, do not gape at me as though I've lost all my senses. You cannot deny the resemblance. I didn't dare hope when I first saw you. But when you read the fairy tale and Stanley looked at you, I—"

"No, no," Maribeth said, shaking her head. She stood. This madness must come to an end. "I had a mother, someone else. Not her."

Mrs. Hawkins grabbed Maribeth by the shoulders. Pain shot through her body, and she winced under the assault, still sore from her fall the night before.

"Are you sure this other woman was your mother? You were so young when you disappeared. Anyone could've filled your head with lies. Think, girl, think!" She shook her hard, once, twice. "Merry Bella, Maribeth. The names could be easily confused by a little girl. Tell me you don't remember your father's kind eyes or the way he called you my sweet merry Bella."

Mary. Her father had called her Mary. Or was she remembering "merry"? They sounded identical. Her father had lovely, sad blue eyes. The exact color of Mr. Turner's eyes.

A sickening swell of bile rose up her throat. She swallowed hard and turned her back against the desperate plea in the housekeeper's eyes. As much as the woman wished for her to be Mr. Turner's long-lost daughter, she was not! Could not be!

Oh, Mama. **The memories were etched in her mind; the silken strands of her mother's dark hair, long, smooth, and straight. Her warm chocolate eyes and crooning voice.** Those were tangible, so real.

"Remember the truth," Mrs. Hawkins pleaded. "Please, you must remember."

"Stop!" Maribeth cried, shutting out the woman's pleas. "I've already told you. There is nothing for me to remember. **My name is Maribeth Sommerset, adopted daughter of Dominick Sommerset, Marquess of Covington. I had a gracious mother in my childhood who loved me and tried her best to care for me.**"[44]

A knock sounded, loud and insistent. After another knock, Mrs. Hawkins strode to the door. She cracked it open and peered outside. Her forehead crinkled. "What is it, Webber?"

"A message for Miss Sommerset." He passed a note through the slit of the door.

"Thank you," the housekeeper said, snatching the little square of paper. "Wait a moment."

She handed the missive to Maribeth.

---

[44] None of this backstory is new but is vital to reiterate here because the heroine is in full-fledged denial about her true identity, even when faced with what seems to be hard evidence, the portrait of her mother. Coming to grips with the fact that your life has been built on lies is difficult, and children bond deeply with their parents in their youth, so Maribeth should revolt against giving up "her truth."

March 13, 1889
Swansea, England

Dear Miss Sommerset,

Allow me to introduce myself. I am Mrs. Helen Marsh, sister of the recently deceased, Caroline Turner. Mr. Dunn shared your trade card with me. I am anxious for news of your psychic investigation.

I may also be of some assistance since my sister confided much in me. Please accept my invitation for tea this afternoon. I'll wait on you at three o'clock.

Respectfully,
Mrs. Helen Marsh

Folding the note, Maribeth tucked it into the pocket of her gown. She pulled the door wider and said to the butler, "I'll need a carriage this afternoon. I've been summoned by Mrs. Marsh for tea at three o'clock. Please make the arrangements."

The butler bowed his head and strode off.

"You must listen to me," Mrs. Hawkins said in a harsh whisper once Webber was out of earshot. "Be careful, my dear."

Maribeth closed the door and took a seat on the sofa. "Why do you say that?"

"Because Helen Marsh was acquainted with Madame Brown. She may notice the similarities you bear to the famous clairvoyant. Even if you don't believe you're Bella, others who knew the former owner of Chateau Swansea might." Mrs. Hawkins perched on the edge of the sofa and held Maribeth's hand. "Mr. Dunn shared Caroline's letter with me. What if she told her sister about Bella's fate? Mrs. Marsh may know who abducted the child. If the perpetrator still lives in town, he may have seen you. What if Mrs. Marsh played a role and means you harm? I fear for your life."

Although the housekeeper's logic was sound and a mite worrisome, if there was any chance Mrs. Marsh knew who abducted the little girl, Maribeth had to visit the woman and gather all the information she possibly could.

"I'll be careful," she said, standing. "Please send Pearl up at two o'clock to help me dress for tea."

★★★

Rain pattered against the window, drawing Maribeth's gaze outside. She wouldn't allow foul weather to deter her from visiting Mrs. Marsh. Leaning closer to the mirror, Maribeth lifted the curls off her hairline and dabbed powder on her "third eye" with care.

A brisk knock sounded and she called over her shoulder, "Come in."

Pearl entered with a basket full of brushes, ribbons, and curling tongs. She set her burden on the dressing table. "You're already dressed? But Mrs. Hawkins sent me to help. I don't understand."

"Clothes, I can manage on my own." Maribeth pointed to her unruly hair. "This I cannot. I'm having tea with Mrs. Marsh this afternoon and I don't wish to make a fool of myself. Can you help me, please?"

"Of course, miss," the maid said, patting her on the back. "It's my pleasure. We'll have this mass of waves in ribbons in no time."

Maribeth sucked in a breath. The laceration on her back burned fiercely from the maid's touch.

"Are you all right, miss?" Pearl asked.

She nodded and offered a weak smile. "I bumped into the corner of my dresser last night and bruised myself. That's all. My back is still a little sensitive. You couldn't have known, so please don't fret." Fingering the ribbons in the basket, Maribeth sighed. "I'm glad you're so well prepared."

The maid pulled out a long strip of gold ribbon from the basket and began working on Maribeth's hair. "Before the mistress of the house died, she let me practice on her coiffure. I'm in training to become a lady's maid."

"That was kind of Mrs. Turner." Maribeth met Pearl's gaze in the mirror. "Was she a good mistress, then?"

"Oh, that depends on who you ask," the maid said with a smirk. "Most ladies were jealous of her beauty, but the men"—her grin widened—"the male servants liked her well enough. The gardener, the butler, the stable master."

Maribeth understood her meaning all too well. But the question remained: which man was the father of Mrs. Turner's child? If they knew the answer to that, they might nab the killer. "And what of Mr. Dunn? Did he *like* the mistress of the house?"

"I don't rightly know," Pearl said, tilting her head. "But Mrs. Turner watched *him* with a keen eye whenever he was about. I think she fancied him. But then, what woman wouldn't? Should he stumble into my bedroom, I wouldn't turn him away!"

A flare of heat burned brightly in Maribeth's breast and cheeks. *Jealousy.* What else could this sensation be? The mere thought of another woman touching Arthur ... of her lying in bed with him, feeling his tender lips on her skin. She swallowed in a gulp of air.

"You're blushing," the maid said, her face gone pale. "Forgive me. I forget where I am. You're not accustomed to such talk." Pearl fumbled and dropped the brush. She groaned, "I must learn to hold my tongue, or I'll never gain a position as a lady's maid."

"Nonsense," Maribeth said, bending to retrieve the brush. Setting it on the table, she turned her head from side to side, examining the simple yet elegant updo in the mirror. "You will do wonderfully. Do you already have a position in mind?"

Pearl gathered her things and nodded. "In fact, I have an interview this afternoon at four o'clock with Mrs. Marsh so I might attend her daughter. My stomach is in knots. Mrs. Turner wrote a recommendation before she passed away." The maid bobbed a curtsey. "If you'll excuse me, I'll be on my way. The walk to town is long."

"Walk in this rain? I won't hear of it." Maribeth stood and grabbed the maid's hands, squeezing. "You must share my carriage. We'll arrive an hour before your scheduled appointment, but I'm sure you can wait in the kitchen."

"Thank you, miss, but Webber would never allow such a thing."

Maribeth eyed the raindrops running down the window and grabbed her wool cloak with a hood. "Don't be silly! You cannot walk in this dreary weather. Besides, Webber isn't my boss."

"I thank you," Pearl said with a nod. "You're a godsend. My cloak doesn't have a hood. I would've been soaked to the bone and looking like a drowned rat upon my arrival. But you needn't wait for me after. I'll be visiting my sister for supper."

"Here," Maribeth said, handing her wool cloak to the maid. "I insist you use my hooded cloak for the afternoon. I'll wear my coat and use an umbrella."

Pearl gaped at the offering and stepped back. "I couldn't!"

With a roll of her eyes, Maribeth pressed the garment in the maid's hands. "We can't have you catching a cold. Who would change my linens then? Come on, we must be off, or I'll be late for tea."

They walked down the stairwell together, and a footman opened the front door. "Your carriage awaits you."

"You needn't have worried, after all," Maribeth said, pushing open her umbrella. "The butler isn't even here."

Pearl lifted the hood over her head and they ran to the carriage, where another footman waited. He held an umbrella high over the entrance to the coach and opened the door. The ladies stepped inside and fell onto the seats opposite one another.

A second later, the conveyance lurched forward. Pearl splayed her hands over the plush, red velvet seating. "I've always wanted to take a ride in Mr. Turner's carriage," she admitted. "Once, Harry, the stable master, let me poke my head inside. But I couldn't touch anything."

They rode in companionable silence. Pearl sat on the edge of her seat and stared out the window, her eyes wide with wonder. When was the last time Maribeth had received so much pleasure from something as simple as a carriage ride?

A thunderous bang cracked through the air, and the carriage suddenly lurched. Pearl crashed to the floor as the coachman yelled, "Runaway horses. Take cover."

The coach wobbled and bounced wickedly, thrashing the occupants around. Maribeth fell to her knees beside the maid. "Are you all right?"

Pearl attempted to sit upright but failed under the bouncing and swaying of the carriage. She swiped at a dribble of blood on her forehead. "Ouch. That stings. What is happening?"

"I think that was a gunshot," Maribeth said, a bit breathless. "The horses are spooked. Hold on, and pray the coachman gains control of them."

They hit a bump, and Maribeth flew several inches into the air before landing hard again on her knees. Pain shot through her leg, and her muscles ached more and more with each passing second.

Another crack rent the air, and the coach toppled sideways at a precarious angle, tossing Maribeth like a ragdoll. Her torso slammed into Pearl's head, smooshing the poor woman against the carriage door.

"Oh, dear God!" Pearl screamed.

Maribeth wrapped her arms tightly around the maid and held on as their bodies rolled like marbles. The horses whinnied, and the wind howled outside. Rocks and other debris crunched under the wheels. One of the lanterns crashed through the window, splintering into pieces against the carriage wall, within an inch of Maribeth's head.

Shivers raced up her spine. She lost all sense of time. Seconds seemed like hours. Every minute detail was amplified. Pearl's screams of terror. The coachman's frantic shouts. Every painful bounce of her tailbone on the floor of the carriage.

The box finally came to a jolting halt.

Pearl scrambled across the floor. "Let me out. I want out of here."

"Wait," Maribeth cried. "We should stay inside."

But the maid didn't listen. Pearl pushed the door open and jumped out. Another gunshot pierced the air and the maid screamed. Maribeth crawled to the window and peered outside. The maid knelt on the ground, clutching her shoulder. Red liquid coated her fingers.

Bile lurched to Maribeth's throat. "Come back inside the coach, Pearl!" She crouched behind the door and held out her hand. "Please, come inside."

The ground suddenly rumbled, and Maribeth looked up. Horsemen, at least twenty strong, raced out of the forest, heading for the carriage. Even from this distance, she could make out the hats of the constables.

She stepped cautiously outside and glanced both ways. The coachman held a rifle on his shoulder, trained at the forest lining the side of the road. Maribeth ran to Pearl's side and knelt beside her.

"Let me see," she said, gently.

Pearl lifted her shaking hand. "I'll be fine. This is little more than a flesh wound. But why would someone shoot at us?"

Because the killer thinks I'm Bella Turner.

Maribeth bit her tongue. Everything was pure speculation at this point. Perhaps this was all a terrible accident?

Thunderous horse hooves neared, and within seconds, the horsemen surrounded them.

"Are you hurt?" Arthur asked, leaping to the ground. He ran to her and cupped her face. Rain poured from the sky, running in rivulets down her face. Lightning crackled, thunder boomed.

"No, but Pearl is." She clasped her hands over his. "Why are you here?"

In the background, Chief Inspector Marsh shouted orders. "Eight men ride east in the forest, another eight ride west. The killer is out there somewhere! I want him brought back alive. Find him! Mitchell, tend to the wounded."

Arthur ushered Maribeth away from the others, around to the back of the carriage. "Marsh set a trap to lure out the killer. It seems he succeeded, despite my harsh protests." He ran his hands over her hair and down her arms. "You're truly well? I was terrified for you. This was a horrible plan. Dangerous. It could've been deadly."

"What do you mean?" Maribeth shivered as wind and rain seep through her jacket. "I was on my way to tea with Mrs. Marsh. She has information about Caroline's lover. We must go to her."

"No," Arthur said, shaking his head. "The note was written under the chief's instructions. All part of his plan to lure you out of the house and place pressure on the killer. We should get out of here. Let me take you back to the chateau."

She shook her head. "I can't leave Pearl here alone. Someone shot her, thinking she was me."

"Why do you think that?"

"She's wearing my wool cloak." Her gaze lifted to Arthur's. "I saw the portrait in your study this morning and spoke with Mrs. Hawkins. Why didn't you confide in me? The killer thinks I'm Bella Turner."

"As do I," Arthur said with a solemn look. He stroked her chin with his thumb. "And I have proof."

Maribeth slapped his hand away and glowered. "I'm not a child to be coddled. Enough of your secrets and lies. Tell me everything you know, or so help me I'll … I'll …"

Damn him! What would she do? She looked frantically around and her gaze landed on a fallen branch. "I'll clobber you with a stick!" Rain dripped from her hair and blurred her vision as she darted for the weapon.

"Maribeth!" Arthur shouted, grabbing her by the shoulders and turning her around. "I'll tell you everything. Just not here. Let's get you inside. You're soaking wet."

A shudder wracked her body. Cold, she was so, so cold. She met his concerned gaze, and tears welled in her eyes. He was a master of his craft, a talented circus actor. But the rain had washed away the fog clouding her brain, so she could finally see *him*, the fraud beneath the steward.

He'd kept secrets again, let the chief inspector use her as bait. Arthur Dunn didn't want to build a future together; he wanted to close the door on the past. For ten years, he'd searched for Bella Turner. Now he thought he had her in his grasp.

Well, the joke was on him. She was Maribeth Sommerset, a nobody from nowhere. Regardless of his claims, he would never prove otherwise.

Chapter Twenty-One

Arthur tucked Maribeth under his arms and led her to his horse. She didn't struggle in any way. Her calm resolve sent chills coursing through him. What was she thinking? He would prefer a tongue-lashing, anything to her utter silence.

"Is she all right?" Chief Inspector Marsh asked when Arthur approached.

"Yes, just a little shocked, I think." He strode to his horse. "We'll be at Chateau Swansea. Meet us there when you've conclud-ed the search."

The chief nodded and, after Arthur found his seat, he handed Maribeth up. She weighed a pittance, even sopping wet. Cradling her body close, he turned his horse toward home and clicked his heels.

"Pearl!" She suddenly struggled against his chest.

"Is in good hands," he said. "The coachman will drive her to the doctor. Hold on, we'll be home soon."

She wrapped her arms around his waist, featherlight, as though she didn't wish to touch him. One sharp turn and she would tumble to the ground. Why didn't she burrow closer as she had last night in his arms?

His chest tightened, and he murmured in her ear, "Please, hold on tighter, lest you fall."

Only once her arms squeezed the breath out of him did he click the horse's flanks with his heels. They rode hard, and within ten minutes, Chateau Swansea came into sight. He pressed onward until they were at the front entrance. A footman ran down the stairs and took the reins.

Arthur dismounted and outstretched his arms toward Maribeth. She ignored his offer and hopped off herself. Without a backward glance, she ran up the steps and into the foyer. Inside, she peeled off her jacket. Rain dripped from her hair onto the marble floor.

"You should change into dry clothes immediately," he said, unlatching the hook of his cloak. He held the blasted garment away from himself. Where was the damned butler when you needed him? Arthur was soaked to his core as well.

Maribeth shivered, but she didn't budge. "What proof do you have that I'm Bella Turner? You cannot be serious."

"We can talk once you're dry," he said, towering over her. "I didn't save you only to have you die of a nasty cold."

"You didn't save me!" she said over her shoulder as she stomped up the steps. "You served me up on a platter to the killer. The danger had passed before you arrived. Stupid, stupid plan. Pearl could've died. How could you let the chief do this?"

He trudged after her, determined to set her straight. "I don't control the chief inspector! Obstinate woman. Do you truly believe I would go along with his ridiculous plan without a fight? He cuffed me and threw me in jail after receiving your note about the incident last evening. That wasn't well done of you."

She whirled around. "What note? I didn't send the chief any notes."

Interesting. He pushed her onward, continuing in the direction of her bedchamber. So his suspicions had been right. "That's what I told him as well. I think the killer wrote the message, pretending to be you."

"Why would he do that?" she asked with an indelicate snort.

"To get you alone. He counted on Marsh locking me up. Which, I might add, he did for a while so I couldn't ride back and warn you."

Maribeth glanced sideways at him, her brow cocked. "He truly arrested you?"

"Handcuffs and all." He folded the sleeves of his shirt and showed her the red welts on his wrists. "But when I learned the details of the plan, I convinced him the better course was to lay in wait in the forest. Thank God we did. Otherwise, you might be dead. The killer wasn't expecting us."

She entered her bedroom, and he closed the door behind him. He leaned against it and closed his eyes. *Goddammit.* She had come so close to dying, again. After a decade of searching for this woman, she was finally here and he'd almost lost her. He met her steely gaze. Or maybe she was never truly his and last night was all a dream.

"So tell me of this proof you have that I am Bella Turner. I have no memories of Chateau Swansea."

"You're wrong." He wanted to thread his fingers through her curls, pull her closer, and kiss that fierce frown off her lips. "Every one of your experiences here are your suppressed memories. The broken vase and frightened child in the foyer, sitting at the throne in the séance room and calling out to your mama, reading the story-book and hearing the *hoot, hoot* of an owl. You know these things because you experienced them."

A tear trickled from the corner of her eye, but she didn't look away. "Then why don't I remember my father or this place? How can I not know my own name? No, Arthur. As much as I want to help Stanley find his daughter, I am not she."

Her words clawed at his insides. *I want to help Stanley.* She was Arthur's partner in this investigation, had done everything in her power to help *him*. Until now. He was finally paying the price for his deception, just as he'd always known he would. Surely, this way was better. Bella Turner, heiress, could never be happy as Mrs. Dunn, her father's steward's wife. Even in fairy tales, it was the prince who wooed the poor maiden, not the other way around.

"Give it time, my sweet, and you will remember." He resisted the urge to kiss the top of her head. "Until then, your life is in danger. I'll move into the chateau until we discover the identity of the killer. In the meanwhile, get out of those wet clothes. I'll send the maid up with a hot bath. Lock the door behind me."

Evening was upon them and Chief Inspector Marsh would arrive soon to confer about the attack.

"Don't stay here on my account," Maribeth said, lifting her chin. "I'm leaving on the morning train for London. You're well on your way to capturing whoever is stalking Bella Turner. My services are no longer needed, and I have a coming out ball that requires my attention."

He pressed his lips together, holding in all the arguments for her to stay. *I love you. I want you. I need you.* She didn't long to hear those pleas, nor should he try to convince her not to leave. London was far away from the tumultuous Chateau Swansea, and her guardian would keep her safe.

"I'll inform Webber of your decision," he said with a brisk nod. "Safe travels, and thank you for your assistance. Please leave your directions with Webber, and I'll send along your letter of recommendation and wages."

He exited quickly, before he did something stupid, like fall to his knees at her feet and beg for forgiveness.

Chapter Twenty-Two

Turning the lock, Maribeth leaned her forehead against the door. He was disappointed in her decision, despite his valiant efforts to conceal his reaction. This wasn't her battle, and she hadn't solved a single mystery since her arrival at Chateau Swansea. Why had she ever imagined she would succeed as a psychic investigator?

She didn't deserve a glowing letter of reference, but her guardian wouldn't sign over her dowry without one. Either way, she hadn't lied about attending her coming out ball. Dominick and Eveline had spent a fortune on the evening. Maribeth would be there with a gracious smile on her face and endure the scrutiny of the guests.

Everyone would snigger behind her back about her high-necked gown and two left feet. She couldn't control the outrageous words that sprang from her lips. London wasn't her world, despite what Arthur thought. A gentlemen didn't want a wife who bore the scars of poverty on her back.

Perhaps a steward didn't want that sort of a wife either. She had offered herself to him freely, and he had declined. What a fool she'd been to think he desired her after he'd seen her in the flesh.

A tear trickled out of the corner of her eye. She undressed and lay in bed, staring at the ceiling. Arthur hadn't begged her to stay. No, he wished her safe travels on her journey. She punched her pillow and rolled over in bed. The moonlight faded behind a cloud, and she finally drifted into a fitful sleep: crawling through the dark tunnels of the mine, grit stuck under her fingernails, dirty, stinky bodies crammed in the hull of the ship, fever, hunger. The memories crashed in like a tidal wave, kicking up sand all around her, and through the murky water, a new scene materialized.

Maribeth stood on a busy street corner holding out a tin cup with her mama by her side. She wore her favorite dress, the green cotton with tiny butterflies around the collar and waistband.

"A halfpenny for a hungry child," Mama said to a passerby.

The gentleman stopped and held his fancy walking stick under his armpit as he dug into his waistcoat pocket. "She's a pretty little thing. I have a daughter about her age. What's your name, girl?"

"Merry Bella," she said, staring at the carved head of a bird on the end of his stick. Something stirred inside her belly and her heart fluttered. She reached out to touch the crooked beak, but her mama slapped her hand away.

"Silly child," Mama said, squeezing her cheeks affectionately. "Your name is Mary-beth." Mama turned to the stranger. "We practice every day. Perhaps I should've named her Mary instead."

The man smiled and tossed one shilling into the tin cup. "She'll learn soon enough. Bon appetite, Maribeth. That should be enough to fill your belly."

Her stomach ached but not with hunger. Instead, she felt over-full. The creamy remnants of milk coated her tongue.

"If you eat another cookie, Bella, your tummy will ache," Papa said with his crystal-blue eyes sparkling. "I'll have to tell Mrs. Hawkins no more cookies before bed."

She liked when his eyes sparkled with happiness. He was only teasing. They ate cookies every night before he read a book.

"Read to me, Papa."

He tucked her under his arm and turned to the first page. "The Owl and the Pussycat went to sea…"

His voice faded and teardrops plunked onto the picture book. She leaned on her elbow and looked around. He was gone.

"Papa, where are you?"

She was suddenly all alone in her playhouse. Sunlight cascaded over the tea table, but the world felt so dark. Papa was gone again. There was no one to take tea with her except Willow, her stuffed dog. She reached for the teapot and a hand clamped over her mouth from behind. Her body slammed against someone else's. Rough clothes scratched the back of her neck. She glanced down and shrieked. A jagged, bloody cut ran the length of the hand covering her lips.

"Keep your trap shut," a man said with a growl.

The man's breath smelled sickeningly sweet. He stuffed a cloth in Bella's mouth, and she gagged. For a few seconds she couldn't breathe. Panic swelled in her gut, and she thrashed with all her strength.

"Breathe through your nose, you stupid girl."

"Papa!" she screamed into the dirty rag over and over. Tears spilled onto her cheeks and her body wracked with the force of her screams. "Papa!"

"Shut up!" the man hissed. Grabbing hold of Bella's hair, he tugged sharply. A sack covered her face, slid over her shoulders and down her arms. She thrashed and kicked, caught in a tangled web of canvas.

"Papa!" she shouted, kicking wildly at the sheets. Cool air suddenly licked at her face and neck. Her heart hammered, and she opened her eyes. Blackness engulfed her. All she heard was her own harsh breathing. Her fingers slid over rough wool and the soft red glow of coals in the fireplace came into view.

Dreaming. She'd only been dreaming ... about her childhood.

"Bella. Oh, dear God, I remember my name," she whispered to the empty room.

Arthur was right. The broken vase in the foyer, the séance chamber, the path to the playhouse; those were all memories breaking through the locked crypt of her mind. Last night was no accident. *He* knew who Maribeth was, the man with the rough clothes and sweet breath. That voice, where had she heard that voice recently?

Crawling out of bed, Maribeth threw on her robe and slippers. The walls were closing in on the killer. Had Arthur stayed the night, or was he back at his own house? She had to warn the guards and break through her father's defenses. But when she arrived at his door, only one man stood guard. She recognized him immediately as the one who stood beside her at Stanley's door the other evening while he waited for Mrs. Hawkins to finish talking to Arthur.

"Good evening," she said, glancing farther down the corridor. Weren't there usually two men on duty? Gesturing to the bedroom, she asked. "May I?"

"No, ma'am." His brow furrowed and he consulted his pocket watch. "You can speak with Mrs. Hawkins in the morning about visiting."

His sickeningly sweet breath filled her nostrils. *Mint.* Her kidnapper's breath had reeked of mint. Spindly legs crawled up her spine. The guard's gravelly voice was deep, familiar. Her gaze strayed to his right hand, and she stared, fixated on a wicked scar running the length of his forefinger. Nausea roiled in her gut.

She looked up. His eyes locked on hers.

"Who are you?" she asked.

"Will Hawkins. The housekeeper's son."

"Oh, good." Air rushed out of her lungs. She was tired and seeing danger where there was none. "Then you must know Mr. Dunn hired me to investigate the unfortunate incident with Mrs. Turner. I must insist on visiting Stanley Turner immediately."

He folded his arms over his chest and stepped aside. "If you insist, then by all means."

She entered the bedroom and closed the door with a soft click.

Mr. Turner lay in bed awake, staring at the ceiling. Where was Mrs. Bartley? Maribeth sat on the edge of the bed and drank in every aspect of him. This was the man who had loved her above all else; searched for her for years. Her throat felt thick and tears misted her eyes.

"Hello, Papa, this is your merry Bella," she said, taking his hand in hers. "I'm sorry I don't have any cookies and milk, but it's very late and Mrs. Hawkins is already in bed. Tomorrow we'll enjoy a treat together, but I promise not to eat too many cookies and risk a tummy ache." She smiled and squeezed his arm. "I know Caroline told you I'm dead, but you must listen to me. She—"

"Lied! Just as you lied to me."

Maribeth whirled around, coming face to face with the barrel of a six-shooter held in Mrs. Hawkins's trembling hands. The housekeeper cocked the gun, and Maribeth shrank back, her heart hammering.

"You claimed you had no memories of Chateau Swansea," the housekeeper growled. "You were so convincing when you denied all connections with Bella Turner, but I knew you'd remember eventually."

Maribeth had remembered her name all right, but not her kidnapper's identity. Until five minutes ago, and even then her suspicions were pure speculation. Her instincts had been spot on.

"Where is your son?" she asked in a calm voice.

"Gone." The housekeeper's hands shook. "Far away, where no one will find him. He was only doing his mama's bidding."

"*You* told him to abduct me? Why did you betray me and my father?" Maribeth's head spun, trying to piece together a logical explanation, but she had none. Mrs. Hawkins was a faithful servant of Mr. Turner. Arthur trusted her implicitly. How could this be?

Tears rolled down the housekeeper's face. "I had no choice. Mr. Turner was away on business. His wife would've turned me out without a reference. I have a son, a daughter. My sister ... she was good to you..."

"My mama," Maribeth murmured. "She was your sister? Why are you doing this? I loved her. She did her best. I don't blame you."

Mrs. Hawkins wiped at her nose and flicked her chin toward Mr. Turner. "Liar! He will blame me if he wakes and learns the truth. You'll say anything to make me put down the gun. Only you can wake him. I can't allow that. It's better this way. If Mr. Dunn inherits the Turner estate when you die, all will go back to normal soon."

Bile rose to her throat. No, this couldn't be true. Why hadn't he told her he was the heir? Because he wanted her to be Bella Turner so badly it made the point mute or because he colluded with Mrs. Hawkins and planned to kill her all along? "Are you saying you're working together?"

"No, you fool." Mrs. Hawkins's lips formed a grim line. "Are you blind? He is in love with you. All the more reason why you must die. He can never take you as his wife. A steward marrying an heiress?" She cackled loud, even as tears trickled from the corners of her eyes. "Get up and walk to the balcony! Hands where I can see them, slowly now."

Maribeth rose to her feet and took one halting step. Her stomach twisted in a bowline knot. *Arthur loves me.* She kept her eyes on the gun. It wobbled precariously in the older lady's hands. Her finger rested on the trigger. One slip, and Maribeth would never get to know her father or tell Arthur she loved him.

"Did Mr. Turner kill his wife?"

"She killed herself." The housekeeper waved toward the balcony with the gun. "The missus was wild with rage when Mr. Turner gave her divorce papers. She burned them in the fireplace and screamed obscenities. Swore she'd sold you to the devil and you died in the explosion at Wheal Turner. A moment later, she charged at him. He stepped aside, and she plummeted to her death."

Thank God. Papa hadn't killed his wife. A crazed gleam filled the housekeeper's eyes, and she jerked the gun toward the balcony again.

"Walk, walk."

Maribeth kept the woman in sight as she backed toward the balcony. Did she plan to toss her over the ledge or force her to jump? A gunshot would wake the household.

"Who killed Gabriel Young?" she asked, sincerely perplexed. Was his death a random attack as Arthur had once speculated?

"I did," Mrs. Hawkins admitted. "Do you think I would allow the likes of *him* to inherit Chateau Swansea? He was neck deep in gambling debts. Always begging poor Mr. Turner for funds. The bloody fool would've gambled the Turner fortune away within a year. Then where would we all be? I have worked here more than two decades. I'll not be turned out of a job in my old age, lose my pension. The master was in no position to stop his cousin. Dr. Sanders had declared him incompetent. Better that Mr. Dunn inherit than Mr. Young."

How could the older woman possibly have killed Mr. Young? He was far taller and stronger than her. But not her son. Had he done his mama's bidding again?

"Your son tried to shoot me earlier today," Maribeth said, her voice trembling.

The housekeeper's jaw tightened. "No, *I* did."

That was a barefaced lie. Mrs. Hawkins couldn't shoot a riffle and escape an entire police force. She was a mother protecting her child from imprisonment should he ever be caught.

"Will you kill my father?" Maribeth asked, her head jerking to where he lay, helpless.

"He's harmless that way. There is no need to kill him so long as you don't wake him. Open the balcony doors!" the housekeeper said, shaking the gun. "Enough talk."

Maribeth freed the latch and they swung traitorously wide. Her body trembled. Mrs. Hawkins wasn't much taller than her, but she was stout, sly, and held a loaded gun. And she was as skittish as a cat drowning in a rapid stream.

"Onto the ledge," the woman said. "You don't even have to look. Just fall backward and in a few seconds this will all be over. The coroner said Mrs. Turner died on impact."

"But you love my father," Maribeth pleaded as she stepped onto the ledge. "He wouldn't want this. Put the gun down and we can talk. Mr. Young deserved what he got. I won't turn you into the authorities. You've been a faithful servant all your life. I will speak with Arthur. He'll set you up in retirement immediately."

"Lies, lies. Your father already believes you're dead." Mrs. Hawkins stepped closer, waving the gun frantically now. "If he wakes, I'll say you took your life when you couldn't get through to him. Now, jump!"

Maribeth glanced over her shoulder and swayed from the dizzying height. Moonlight sparkled on the otherwise black surface of the pond. She'd jumped from the ship's railing many times in her youth, but never while wearing a nightgown and wrapper, and never in the dark. How deep was the pond?

"Jump!" the housekeeper hissed again, inching closer.

Taking a deep breath, Maribeth offered up a prayer and hurled herself at the housekeeper instead. Mrs. Hawkins's eyes widened, and she pulled the trigger.

Chapter Twenty-Three

The door shut behind Chief Inspector Marsh with a resounding thud, and Arthur leaned his hands against it, bowing his head. Laying a trap had been for naught. They were no closer to finding the killer. At least Maribeth would be on a train headed for London come sunrise.

God, he was exhausted. He trudged up the stairs. Tonight he would sleep on the chaise longue in Stanley's bedchamber. He wasn't taking any more chances. Upon reaching the second floor, his soul felt drawn toward Maribeth's bedroom like a magnet. He should've made love to her, told her the truth from the onset, and claimed her for himself like the selfish bastard he was.

A gunshot reverberated through the quiet house, and his heart leapt into his throat. That came from the east wing. Stanley! He raced down the corridor. Where in the hell were the guards? Skidding to a stop at the bedchamber door, he grabbed the handle and shoved.

Locked!

"Guards! Open this goddamned door," he shouted. He rattled the handle, screaming for entry, but no one answered. Muffled voices permeated the door, and he pressed his ear to it. Women's voices. *Maribeth?* He backed up to the other side of the hall and charged the door with his shoulder.

Another gunshot rang out the second he burst into the room. He looked frantically around, searching for Maribeth.

"On the balcony," came a weak voice.

"Oh my God," Arthur said, staring at the bed. "Stanley?"

"On the balcony!" his employer said, stronger this time. "Careful, she has a gun."

Crouching, Arthur snuck along the wall and peered outside through the open doors. Mrs. Hawkins straddled Maribeth's legs and fought for control of a gun. A red splotch grew on Maribeth's shoulder, spreading across her white wrapper.

"Mrs. Hawkins!" he shouted, leaping onto her back. Within seconds, he wrestled the gun out of her hands. "What in the dickens is going on here?"

"She tried to kill me," both women said simultaneously.

His head spun as he looked from one to the other. This didn't make any sense. Why would either woman want to hurt the other?

"Mrs. Hawkins killed Gabriel," Maribeth said, scrambling away from the other woman. "She planned to kill me as well."

"Utter nonsense," the housekeeper said.

"Stay there and don't move!" he ordered Mrs. Hawkins. Arthur strode to Maribeth and knelt by her side. "You're hurt. Let me help you stand." He looped her arm around his neck and stood, supporting her weight.

"Bella," Stanley said, leaning against the doorframe. "Bella, is it truly you?"

She nodded and a tentative smile spread over her lips. "I can hardly believe it myself, but yes, Papa, it's me."

"She lies," the housekeeper screamed. "There is no proof. I caught her in here with a gun pointed at you, Mr. Turner. She wanted to kill you for leaving her home alone with your vindictive wife."

Stanley lifted his hand, cutting her off. "Save your breath, Emily. I heard everything. And you're wrong. <u>There is proof." Turning to Maribeth, he said, "Give me your left hand."</u>

<u>She held it out, and her eyebrows knitted when Stanley flipped her hand palm up. He traced a scar on the fleshy part of her palm and tears fell from his eyes.</u>

<u>"You got this—"</u>

<u>"Jumping off the swing. The momentum was too much, and I fell forward on my palms. A rock sliced through my skin. I cried because blood dripped onto my pretty dress."</u>

"Not because you were hurt." Stanley tugged Maribeth into his arms and sobbed.

Maribeth is Bella. Arthur's gut instincts had been dead on. Ten years of scouring England for the young woman had finally borne fruit. Though, in reality, his efforts had nothing to do with the end result. She had found them, entirely by chance.

"Welcome home, Bella," he whispered, unwilling to ruin the reunion of father and daughter after sixteen years apart. The muscles in his throat tightened as he watched them hug.

Something moved in Arthur's peripheral vision. He turned and caught his breath. The housekeeper stood on the ledge of the balcony, peering below at the pond. She raised her arms on each side of her body as though preparing to fly.

"Please, don't!" he said to Mrs. Hawkins. He didn't dare move an inch, lest he startle the woman.

Stanley shoved Maribeth behind him and held his hands out. "Come off the ledge, Emily," he said, his voice shaking. "You don't have to do this."

Looking over her shoulder, the older woman nodded. "You know I must. After all I've done, they'll send me to Newgate. It's better this way. I pray you'll forgive me."

Stanley stepped closer. "For what?"

She faced him fully, blew out a breath. <u>"For kidnapping your daughter at your wife's behest,</u> for killing your cousin, and for almost killing your daughter after she finally came home to you." She spread out her arms and fell backward. Two seconds later, the sickening slap of her body against the water's surface rent the air. Arthur ran to the perimeter of the balcony and peered over the edge. Her body floated on the surface, her eyes open and vacant.

He stared, slack-jawed, unable to digest her confession. All these years, the housekeeper had known Bella's fate, and held her tongue. Mrs. Hawkins had been the greatest deceiver of them all, and he hadn't once suspected her.

"Are you all right?" Maribeth asked, squeezing his arm.

He met her gaze. "I should be asking you that question. You're wounded."

"I'll be fine. The bullet only grazed my skin. It looks worse than it really is. See, the blood isn't spreading anymore." She rubbed his cheek. "Will you be okay? This all must come as a terrible shock. I know you were fond of Mrs. Hawkins."

"I thought Caroline's lover had abducted you," he said in a daze.

Stanley shook his head. "That was simply another footman. I can't even recall his name. He quit before I returned from America."

Unbelievable. Arthur stared into the dark night. "Why did she do these horrible things? She killed Mr. Young. I cannot wrap my brain around the truth."

Maribeth chewed on her bottom lip and her gaze met Stanley's. He nodded. "Her livelihood was at stake if the truth came out. She wanted to keep her pension, feared Mr. Young would gamble away the Turner wealth. If you inherited everything, her future would be secure, and my father would never learn of her part in my abduction."

Oh, God. He should've been able to see through her masquerade.

Stanley clasped Arthur on the shoulder. "I know you're replaying years of interactions in your mind and wondering what clues you missed. Please, stop. Evil comes in many shapes and forms. But good triumphs in the end. Bella is home, and you kept her safe. Thank you!"

Arthur scrubbed his face. "We have to send word to the chief inspector after we tend to Maribeth's wounds."

"There's no need," Chief Inspector Marsh said from the doorway. "I heard the gunshot and came as quickly as I could. I'll send for my men soon. This entire time, it was Mrs. Hawkins." He shook his head and sighed. "I wouldn't have believed you had I not heard her confession myself."

Arthur tucked Maribeth under his arm and kissed the top of her head. "Let me tend to your wound. Then you can explain why you were so foolish as to leave your bedroom alone. Will you ever do as you're told?"

Her grin was instantaneous. "I'm afraid not, but as I recall, you love my stubborn bits, too."

"You love my daughter?" Stanley asked, his arms folded.

Arthur met his employer's stern gaze. "I believe the term I used was adore, not love. Don't look at me that way, Stanley. I've already told her we won't suit. I'm well aware of my station in life. She has a coming out ball soon and will find an appropriate suitor."

Maribeth's mouth gaped. "You cannot—"

He covered her lips with his own, and her protest ceased as she melted in his embrace. Thank God she was alive and this nightmare was over. He cradled her face, gazed into her dazed eyes. "Whatever you wish to say can wait until the morning, Maribeth. The house-keeper is dead, you've been shot, Stanley is out of his comma, and I'm exhausted. Let's tend to your wound and get a peaceful night of sleep, for once."

She nodded. "Fine, we'll talk first thing in the morning."

Stanley grinned. "Yes, that's my Bella. She always was a stubborn one. Come, daughter, and tell me who is holding the ball on your behalf. I should very much like to meet him."

As would Arthur, in order to arrange for Maribeth's hand in marriage, but that could never be. In the bright light of a new morning, their future paths would be plain to see.

Chapter Twenty-Four

At precisely nine o'clock the next morning, Maribeth knocked on the study door. Breakfast with her father had been a mite awkward without Arthur there. However, her time under Lord Covington's guardianship made for interesting conversation. Her father hung on her every word. With time, their bond would strengthen, no doubt.

"Please, enter."

Maribeth grinned at Arthur's lovely baritone. She felt as light as a feather and, if not careful, would drift away on the slightest breeze. He adored her! Smoothing the front of her gown once more, she tempered her exuberance and entered. Mrs. Hawkins had been a dear friend of Arthur's, and she didn't wish to be disrespectful while he was grieving.

"Good morning, Arthur." She approached his desk with a tentative smile. "I trust you slept well?"

He stood behind his desk upon her entering and offered a brief bow. "Good morning, Miss Turner. Thank you for inquiring. I'm quite well."

Her heart skipped a beat. He sounded as far away and as formal as the gentry greeting her in Hyde Park. Maybe he simply loved her new name, having searched for Bella Turner for so long. She narrowed her gaze on him.

"Perhaps still a little in shock from last evening's events," he added under her scrutiny.

Shock. Yes, that was it. Her shoulders relaxed a touch. "We missed you at breakfast this morning, but I forgive you. This has been a trying week."

"Quite so," he said, clearing his throat. He stared down at the desk, his gaze focused on an envelope. "I appreciate the invitation to dine with you and your father, but I thought it best that you two enjoy time alone, to become reacquainted. Besides, my duties as steward of the estate call. I've set them aside for too long."

He couldn't even look at her when he spoke. The coffee in her stomach churned. Where was the man with a quick wit that she knew and loved?

"Why so formal, Arthur? We're partners, friends. Please, call me Maribeth or Bella if you prefer. Bella feels awkward, but I suppose I'll get used to it again."

He gestured to one of the wing-backed chairs and she sat on the edge.

"You're very kind," he said, taking the seat opposite her, "but you're the heiress of the Turner estate, and I am your father's steward. We shouldn't speak on a first-name basis. Someday, I will serve you in that capacity. So, please, call me Mr. Dunn."

Heat flooded her cheeks. *Damn and blast!* Did he truly think she would let him hide under his shell like a turtle? He adored her! That didn't change simply because she would inherit a fortune. *Stubborn man.*

"You called my father Stanley last night, so you can use my given name, too."

Arthur's jaw tightened. "Only in private. I always refer to him as Mr. Turner in public, as is appropriate."

She rolled her eyes. "Fine, address me as Miss Turner in front of others if you must, though I find the notion ridiculous. I mean, really, Arthur. We'll be married soon. You don't plan to call me Mrs. Dunn, do you?" A smile sprang to her lips. "Actually, I would like that. Mrs. Dunn has a lovely ring to it."

He choked and his face grew pale. "Please don't jest with me. You will forever be Miss Bella Turner, until you take a proper husband. Heiresses do not marry stewards. As the ward of a former pirate, perhaps we could have... No, what am I saying? It simply isn't done."

"Poppycock!" Maribeth waved away his concern. "An heiress may choose whomever she prefers. And I want you, Arthur Dunn."

"You can't have me!" he growled.

She folded her hands over her stomach and glared back. "I most certainly can! You see, *I* solved the mystery of the Chateau Swansea killer, albeit a bit by chance, I grant you. Still, Lord Covington is an honorable man, and he'll sign over my dowry when I present him with the letter of recommendation you owe me." She leaned forward, piercing him with her gaze. "Do you know what that means?"

"You'll have a bevy of rich and titled suitors." His lips pressed together as he grabbed an envelope from the desk and handed it to her. "I've taken the liberty of writing your reference letter and a bank draft for fifty pounds. You earned every penny."

She yanked the envelope out of his hand. "Why are you deliberately being obtuse? My dowry is twenty thousand pounds, Arthur. Don't you see? We will be independently wealthy. I can choose my own husband, and I choose you!"

The blood drained from his face, and he shook his head. "Stop and listen to me for one minute, Maribeth. You are Miss Bella Turner, heiress of an estate worth more than three hundred thousand pounds. Your family belongs in a class of its own. I am your family's steward. We cannot marry."

She swayed in her seat, and Arthur leapt forward, grabbing her arms. *Three hundred thousand pounds.* She inhaled and exhaled, gulping for air. Surely, she had heard him wrong.

"Excuse me, but did you say thirty thousand pounds?"

His lips twitched, and he tucked a loose curl behind her ear. "You aren't hallucinating, Maribeth. I said three hundred thousand pounds. Should I fetch the smelling salts?"

Her hand trembled as she covered her gaping mouth. "I can't even … I've never heard of…" She searched Arthur's steady gaze. "How? Where does the money come from?"

Standing, he retreated to the desk and sat on the edge. He rubbed the back of his neck. "You should ask your father that question."

"Tell me! Whatever you have to say cannot be worse than ten lashings at the hands of a bloodthirsty pirate."

Turning, he flipped through a stack of papers on his desk and retrieved a discolored news article. His shoulders slumped as he blew out a breath, handing her the clipping. "Coal mining. Stanley sold the rest of his mines shortly after this incident and invested in steel."

She read the headline: No survivors found after Wheal Turner explosion.

"Caroline's ghost did not lie," he said, folding his arms. "She truly believed you were dead, and so did your father. They couldn't have known you were sold by the foreman into slavery."

The date on the newspaper registered in her brain. Had Mama ... Had Mrs. Hawkins's sister reported Bella Turner missing after the incident? The timing could be right. If not for the foreman's greed, Maribeth might be dead. Folding the article carefully, she tucked it into her pocket.

Words abandoned her. She stared at Arthur in silence. Her father grew rich on the backs of poor men and their children. *Oh, goodness.* She rubbed her temples where an ache grew with persistence. Her thoughts exploded in her head in a jumbled mess. Had she toiled in her family's coal mine as a child? Arthur had the news article handy. When had he pieced everything together?

"How long have you known I am Bella?"

"With certainty?" He cleared his throat. "Ever since I saw the portrait of your mother. There could be no denying the truth after that. But I suspected who you were when I asked you to accompany me to the playhouse."

Her eyes widened. "Why didn't you tell me?"

He hesitated, licking his lips. "At the time, I told myself you needed to come to the realization yourself, that you wouldn't believe me otherwise. But that was a lie." His eyes glistened as they met hers. "You want the truth?"

She nodded, even as her insides quaked.

"Because I didn't want to believe the truth myself." He knelt in front of her, taking her hands in his. "I wanted desperately for you to be Miss Maribeth Sommerset, ward of a notorious pirate, private psychic investigator, a beautifully independent woman who turned her nose up at society's dictates, someone who might one day fall in love with a steward and be truly happy. In my heart, I knew Bella Turner could never marry me."

Choking back a sob, she wrapped her arms around his neck, squeezing until he croaked. "But I do love you, Arthur Dunn. Maribeth, Bella. My name doesn't matter. I'm still the same person. I *can* marry you. All you need to do is ask for my hand."

"No," he murmured, nuzzling his cheek against her hair. "Both of your families would be social outcasts if we marry. I will not repay your father's generosity that way. You might not care what others think, but he does! I'd wager Lord Covington does as well."

Maribeth pushed him away as a swell of energy vibrated through her body. "My guardian was known as 'the Devil' and sailed a pirate ship for a decade. Do you honestly think he cares what society thinks of him?"

"Those days are long past," Arthur said. "He invited half of the *ton* to your coming out ball. That alone speaks volumes."

Her lips pinched and she stood, folding her arms. "My father married a famous clairvoyant. He didn't care what society thought of him. Why would he care who I choose as my husband?"

"<u>Stanley labored over that decision for two years.</u>" Arthur shoved his hands through his hair. "<u>They married in secret and, in the end, he never had to admit the truth to anyone.</u> Besides, men are afforded more leeway than women. Society will not welcome a woman who marries beneath her into their bosom. I am not a prince rescuing a fair maiden."

"Do you believe my father would've kept his marriage a secret if my mother had lived?"

"I don't know." Arthur rubbed his eyes and sighed. "The point is moot. In the ten years I've worked for Stanley, he's always observed societal norms."

Maribeth couldn't contain her derisive snort. "He didn't object to Caroline's outrageous behavior. I want to marry a respectable man. She tupped all the male servants in this household!" Arthur's brow lifted, and she amended with, "Except you, of course."

"Affairs in marriages among the wealthy are commonplace, so long as the parties are discreet," Arthur countered. "Until her most recent indiscretion, she met that requirement."

"That is the type of marriage you would condemn me to?" Maribeth growled and threw up her hands. "This is a ridiculous conversation. I'll speak with my father and my guardian. If they give their blessings, will you stop this nonsense?"

"Your future happiness is at stake. You'll regret marrying me. Maybe not in a month or year but, eventually, the outside pressure will be too much."

She poked him dead center in the chest, directly in the heart. "You cannot make that decision for me."

"No, I can't." He caught her hand and pressed it to his lips. "But I can decide for myself. Please, understand. I'm only thinking of your happiness."

She wanted to scream, stomp her feet, and maybe even slap him on the face. He needed something to bring him to his senses. What would it take to get through to him?

"If we're through here," he said, assuming a formal tone once more. "I have a pile of work begging for my attention."

He was discarding her like an old newspaper. She gritted her teeth, but her anger spilled out. "You are a coward!"

His eyes closed briefly before he met her glare. "I'm sorry you think so, but perhaps you're right. Another reason why we don't suit. You're the bravest woman I've ever met." He turned his attention to the paperwork on his desk, and then suddenly handed her another note. "Ah, I almost forgot. This came earlier from Chief Inspector Marsh. His wife refuses to believe her sister fell accidently to her death. He begs for you to speak with her."

Maribeth snatched the letter and confirmed the contents. "Why would she believe me?"

The corner of his mouth lifted. "Because you are Bella Turner, daughter of the infamous Madame Brown. That fact alone lends you more credibility than any reference on your résumé."

She stormed to the door then paused. If he saw himself as her servant, then perhaps she ought to treat him as such. "Have the coach ready for me at eleven o'clock, Mr. Dunn."

He nodded. "I'll inform Webber of your request, Miss Turner. Is there anything else I can do for you this morning?"

"As if stabbing me through the heart wasn't enough?" His lips parted, and she fled the room before the first tear rolled down her cheek. All her life, she'd dreamed of unraveling the secrets of her childhood. In doing so, she had gained a loving father but lost the love of her life.

Chapter Twenty-Five

Maribeth ran down the corridor, swiping at her cheeks. *Oh, the bloody fool.* All she needed to be happy was him. How could he be so blind? She would seek out her father, ask him to intervene. Arthur respected Stanley as a mentor, employer, and friend.

She came to a halt and took a deep breath. Maybe Arthur was overreacting under the shock of last night's events. All he needed was a little time to adjust to the idea of managing the Turner estate as her husband. Had she died, he would've inherited everything. What was the difference?

"Hello, Arabella?" The whispered words drifted through a door, left slightly ajar, on her left. She crept closer and peered inside. Her father stood at the throne of the séance chamber, his gaze darting around the room. She entered through the crack.

"Would you like me to speak with her on your behalf?" Maribeth said, pausing just inside the room. His eyebrows lifted, and she grinned. "I am a medium, after all. What good are my talents if I can't use them for my own selfish reasons?"

He waved her inside and gripped the back of the throne. "I haven't been in here since your mother died."

"Why not?" she asked.

"Too painful, I suppose." His hand trailed over the smooth surface of the table. "This was her domain, the essence of her soul. Do you feel Arabella's presence?"

She homed in on the room's energy, letting it wash over her senses. Unlike her last visit, this time a warm tranquility pulsed through her. *Hello, Mama, it's me. I'm home.*

"Hello, my sweet Bella."

A pure and radiant joy permeated her body, and she grinned. "She's here with us, Papa. Close your eyes, breathe deep. Feel her essence pulsing in your veins. The rush of tingles down your spine. Can you feel her, too?"

Her father stood still as a statue, his eyes shut in deep concentration. When they fluttered open, a sheen of moisture glinted in them. "Yes, I think I can. Arabella, what do you think of our daughter? She is something special, I think."

"She has the look of me but your stubborn nature."

Maribeth giggled and shook her head. "I can't tell him that."

"Tell me what?" her father said, tilting his head. "I can't hear her, but I feel her. Please, what did she say?"

Rich laughter filled Maribeth's head. *"He will smile if you do. Go on, tell him."*

"Mama says I inherited her beauty but your stubborn nature."

He laughed out loud, even as tears pooled in his eyes. "Oh, my Arabella. She would say that. I was a stubborn fool, waited far too long to make her mine. That is my life's biggest regret." He took Maribeth's hands in his. "Next to leaving you home alone in the care of my second wife. Can you ever forgive me, Bella?"

"Hush." She squeezed his hands. "You couldn't have known I was in danger. No more than your steward should've guessed Mrs. Hawkins was involved. I'm here now; that's all that matters."

"If only my conscience could accept that so easily." He studied her face and frowned. "You've been crying. Why?"

She nibbled on her lip. How should she approach the matter with him? Was it better to ease into the topic or take a more direct route? She didn't know the man standing before her well enough to judge.

Oh, Mama. What should I do? I love Arthur, but he won't marry me without Papa's blessing. Even then, he might refuse in order to save my reputation. Headstrong man!

Arabella crystalized before her. She sat on the throne and crossed one leg over the other. *"Ease into the conversation, my sweet. Your father will come around eventually, but remember, he is stubborn."*

Nodding, Maribeth took a seat at her mother's right and patted the empty chair beside her. "Sit here, Papa. Mama wishes to hear what I have to say as well. She's sitting just there, on the throne."

Her father almost missed the seat and tumbled to the floor, his gaze riveted on the spot where Arabella lounged. Maribeth cleared her throat, and he glanced at her sheepishly.

"I'm sorry, Bella." He rubbed his neck as his cheeks flushed with color. "Can you truly see her, talk with her? I want to believe ... I struggle to believe what I cannot see."

Arabella chuckled softly. *"You must relay a message word for word."*

Maribeth placed her hand over her father's. "Mama wants you to listen closely to this story she wishes to tell me." She closed her eyes and repeated her mother's words aloud: *"Minutes after you were born, I cradled you in my arms. I was so weak, but you were precious, and I could not leave without holding you once. You had the most darling rosy cheeks. I begged Stanley to give you something to always remember me by. He couldn't accept that I was dying. He promised me a ruby ring for bringing such a gem into the world and said I would give it to you one day. That day is today."*

The ring Arthur had searched for and failed to locate? He had said it was a wedding ring. Maribeth felt the love vibrating between her parents and smiled. Her father's lips parted, and he fished in his waistcoat pocket.

"I never told anyone that story," he whispered, his voice quivering. "By God, Arabella, you're truly here with us." He laid a ruby ring on the table in front of Maribeth. "I'm a man of my word. I planned to give this to you when you were older. Please, take this as a token of our love."

She slipped the oval-cut ruby ring on her left hand, and a tear trickled down her face. The gesture was beautiful. "Thank you."

"Why are you crying, Bella?" her father asked.

"Now tell him, my dear child, what is in your heart."

She sniffled and met his gaze. "I'm in love with an incredible man, but he won't ask you for my hand because he thinks you won't approve."

Her father's eyes widened. "You're speaking of Arthur Dunn, are you not? I saw the way you two interacted last evening. He cares for you and you him. But he's justified in his concerns, Bella. Our neighbors will not embrace you as a couple."

"I don't care."

"But he does," her father said, rubbing her hand gently. "He is a proud and stubborn man who doesn't understand his own worth."

"Please, talk to him. He'll listen to you."

Her father sighed. "I will try, but I cannot make any promises. Arthur has to come to terms with the idea himself. A man's pride is a powerful thing. I've known him many years. Do not get your hopes up."

Maribeth stood and breathed in slowly. "All I ask is that you speak with him and invite him to my coming out ball. He is the best of men, and I want him by my side. I'll reserve the first set for him, and every one thereafter if he wishes it. All he must do is come. For now, I must prepare to meet with Mrs. Marsh."

"Whatever for?" her parents asked in unison.

"The chief inspector begs for my assistance. His wife refuses to believe that her sister fell off the balcony by accident. I must go convince her of the truth."

"Absolutely not," her father said, pounding his fist on the table. "Her husband stood as witness to Mrs. Hawkins's confession."

Maribeth sighed. "But the housekeeper didn't confess to killing Caroline. I must go or the woman will hound you the rest of your days."

"Bring the letters from the parlor with you."

"But they're useless," Maribeth said.

"What's useless?" her father asked.

"Read them again and take note of the dates. 'The package' they speak of is you, my sweet."

All the blood drained from her head. She held onto the back of a chair and turned to her father. "What was the exact date of my abduction?"

"May 5, 1873." Her father's eyebrows gathered at the crook of his nose. "Why?"

"I'm sorry, but I must go now." Maribeth all but ran to the door. "Mama agrees that I must go. We'll talk more when I return. Don't worry, Papa. All will be well."

She gathered her cloak and stopped by the parlor for the letters. The grandfather clock chimed the eleven o'clock hour. She ran down the corridor and out the front door. Scurrying into the coach, Maribeth sat and tore open the first letter, reading with a new lens.

May 5, 1873
Chateau Swansea

My dearest sister Helen,

I must thank you again for your visit this afternoon. These have been trying times, but a weight is lifted. I am forever grateful for your support and love. Do tell your cook how much I adore her apple cobbler. She must share her recipe, or I will fall into another fit of depression.

May I inquire about the package you so graciously delivered to Rhondda on my behalf? Please write and assure me that the delivery was completed without incident.

Your loving sister,
Caroline Turner

Yes, of course. The Rhondda Valley was rich in coal and filled with mines. Caroline's sister had assisted in the kidnapping by transporting Bella out of Chateau Swansea unseen. As the lady of the house's sibling, no one would question Mrs. Marsh visiting at any hour.

Maribeth made short work of the second letter.

April 10, 1874
Beecher House, Swansea

My dearest sister Caroline,

Please accept my sincere condolences. You must be devastated with so many lives lost, not to mention the financial burden the disaster may have caused. You're in my prayers.

I'm sorry to inform you that the package you ordered never arrived. The postmaster believes it was lost in the rubble.

Your loving sister,
Helen Marsh[45]

The letters were dated nearly a year apart. If Bella was the package … Maribeth sucked in a breath and fished for the news article in her pocket. That was it! The disaster referred to the explosion at Wheal Turner on April 4, 1874. Mrs. Marsh kept in touch with the housekeeper's sister and informed Caroline that Bella had gone missing.

What a horrid, rotten egg Mrs. Marsh was! The carriage came to a halt, and Maribeth tucked the notes into her reticule along with the news article. She alighted from the carriage and shook out her skirt as she took in the three-story row houses lining the street. The Marshes lived comfortably but not in luxury.

She knocked on the door and was promptly greeted by the butler.

"Miss Bella Turner to see Mrs. Marsh," she said. "I only have a few minutes to spare, so please inform her of my arrival immediately."

"Good day." He waved her in and accepted her bonnet and coat. "My apologies, but the lady of the house isn't expecting you."

"Perhaps not, but her husband is," she said, digging through her purse for the chief's letter.

The hallow click of heels echoed on the wood floors, and Maribeth glanced up. Chief Investigator Marsh strode toward her.

"That'll be all, Cartwright. I'll see to our guest." The butler bowed and disappeared down the hallway. "Miss Turner, thank you

---

[45] Notice how late in the story this background information is revealed. When the housekeeper confessed to arranging to kidnap Bella, she never implicated Mrs. Marsh. But Arthur said in chapter two that Caroline's sister would never rest until Stanley was charged, so I had to close the loop on that thread. Besides, Maribeth should have the satisfaction of a bit of revenge on those who hurt her so deeply. We are in the aftermath section of the book, so now is the time to tie off all the loose threads for the reader. This backstory is the past influencing the present, which causes the heroine to act in a certain way to deal with Mrs. Marsh.

for coming. I apologize for the inconvenience, but I do believe you have a vested interest in convincing my wife that her poor sister died in a tragic accident."

She nodded. "Of course, sir. I'm sure I won't inconvenience your wife for more than a quarter hour."

He scratched his head. "My wife can be a mite stubborn, so you might find your visit a little longer. She may resist listening to you at first, but I beg you to have patience. Allow me to show you to the parlor and make the introductions. This way, please."

Maribeth lifted her brow. So the chief had invited her without his wife's knowledge. Well, this ought to be an interesting conversation.

He led her down a narrow corridor and entered the first door on the left. "Dearest," he said to his wife in an overtly sweet voice. "We have a visitor. Miss Bella Turner, this is my wife, Helen Marsh."

Mrs. Marsh glanced up from her needlework, and her eyes narrowed on her husband. Her auburn tresses were a slightly darker hue than that of her sister's, but the relation was obvious. "What is the meaning of this? I told you, I have no interest in meeting Stanley's bastard daughter."

"Now, Helen," the chief said with an apologetic glance at Maribeth. "We all know she is the legitimate heir of the Turner estate. All I ask is that you listen to her for a few minutes. She is Arabella's daughter, after all, and can reassure you that her mother means you no harm."

Maribeth strode inside and eyed the gaudy furniture, upholstered in pink and white striped silk. The chief nodded encouragingly and promptly exited the room, abandoning the lamb to the tiger. Only *she* was the tiger and Mrs. Marsh the lamb.

"Do not imagine that I am anxious to make your acquaintance either," Maribeth said, folding her arms. "I need only two minutes of your time and then I'll be off, and we will never have to see one another in the whole of our lives."

Mrs. Marsh blanched, and Maribeth grinned, inviting herself to sit on the settee.

"How dare you enter my house un—"

"Listen to me," Maribeth said, lifting her hand to halt the viperous bitch. "And listen well, for I will not repeat myself. My father did not kill your sister. After being presented with divorce papers, Caroline attacked Stanley, lost her footing, and fell to her death in an unfortunate accident."

"Lies, lies," the woman declared. "He killed her, and you cannot convince me otherwise."

"Oh, I believe I can. You see, I have proof that after William Hawkins kidnapped me when I was a child, your coach delivered me to Mrs. Hawkins's sister's house in Rhondda."

Mrs. Marsh's mouth gaped and she sputtered, "What a ridiculous notion. I don't know what you're talking about."

"Is that why your voice trembles?" Maribeth pulled the letters from her purse. She held the notes in one hand and tapped them on the other, like a death knell. "I think you're surprised that I know of William's involvement. How could I when he placed a sack over my head? Even your husband doesn't know the full truth of what happened that day."

The older woman's gaze was locked on the letters in Maribeth's hands. "No one will believe you. Mrs. Hawkins admitted her sins."

"Then you won't mind if I share these letters with the authorities? The ones in which you and your sister corresponded about a certain package being delivered on the day of my disappearance. Or the one shortly after the explosion at Wheal Turner when you confirm the package was lost in the rubble?"

"Let me see those." Mrs. Marsh leaned over and attempted to snatch them out of Maribeth's hands.

"I think not." Maribeth leapt to her feet and showed herself to the door. "Unfortunately for you, your sister was fond of keepsakes. I'll keep these as insurance. In the meanwhile, I suggest you inform your husband that you believe your sister's death was a terrible accident."

Mrs. Marsh pinched her lips but nodded.

"One more thing…" Maribeth paused for dramatic effect. "You need not fear my mother's wrath. But if you persist in seeking revenge against my father, you should fear mine. Do you know why I didn't die in the coal mine explosion?"

"I don't care," the other woman said with a stubborn lift of her chin.

"But you should. I was sold into slavery and raised by pirates, so I know how to carve out your tongue." She lifted the hem of her skirt, revealing the hilt of her blade. "And I always carry a knife."

Raising a hand to her throat, Mrs. Marsh gagged.

Maribeth dipped in a curtsey. "I'll see myself out."

The click of the door behind her had a beautiful ring of finality to it. She could've sent the woman to jail but instilling raw terror in her soul was infinitely better.

Chapter Twenty-Six

Standing on the back terrace of his house, Arthur stared at the wide expanse of the ocean. Waves crashed into the cliffs, one after another. While he usually found the sound soothing, today everything rattled his nerves. He consulted his pocket watch. Eight o'clock on a Saturday morning. The carriage would depart for London within the hour, taking Stanley and his daughter far away from Chateau Swansea for weeks, perhaps months.

"Good morning, Arthur."

He swiveled and smiled at his old friend. "Good morning, Stanley. This is an unexpected visit."

"Why unexpected?" Stanley assumed the same stance, hands in his pockets and his gaze riveted on the water. "We always talk the morning before I travel. I didn't find you in your study, so I figured you must be here. As far away from the departing coach as possible."

Arthur's lips twitched. His employer and mentor knew him too well. "I promised not to pursue your daughter, but I never said that decision would be easy. Forgive me for being weak. I cannot watch her leave."

Stanley clasped Arthur's shoulder and squeezed. "I never asked for your promise in that regard."

"Please, don't."

His mentor lifted his hands in defense. "I'm a wise old man who wishes to offer parting advice to an old friend before I leave for London. What you choose to do with this sage wisdom is entirely up to you, young man."

Arthur blinked hard and nodded.

"A man's true value isn't measured by his wealth but rather his character. Are you worthy of the woman you love by virtue of who you are inside? That's for you to decide. <u>Arabella struggled with the</u> <u>divide between our classes for two years before I finally convinced</u> <u>her that *she* made me happy, not my wealth or status in the neigh-</u> <u>borhood."</u>

"Excuse me," Arthur said, rubbing his forehead. "What do you mean 'she' struggled? You told me you regretted not marrying her earlier."

"True, but you assumed the reason was my decision. <u>Arabella</u> <u>was convinced I would regret marrying her because of the stigma of</u> <u>her trade. I would've given up everything for her."</u>

His throat tightened, and Arthur shook his head. "But you ob- serve societal dictates."

"Out of respect for Caroline's wishes." Stanley tilted his head. "<u>*I* suggested we speak on a first-name basis.</u> How many stewards in Swansea are so familiar with their master? Or housekeepers?"

None that he was aware of, yet who knew what happened be- hind closed doors? <u>"But only in private."</u>

<u>Stanley smiled. "At your insistence, not mine.</u> I welcome a friendship. But I don't want you to feel uncomfortable. I know you feel 'less than' others. Being the son of fortune-tellers does not diminish your self-worth. However, I cannot force you to see your value. That ability lies within you."

A cold breeze coursed through Arthur, raising gooseflesh on his arms. His mentor stepped in front of him and their gazes locked.

"Do you doubt my daughter's love for you?" Stanley asked. "When you've lived the life she has, money holds little sway. You say you're afraid society will reject my daughter, but I think you fear they won't accept you. Do not delude yourself into believing you made this decision for her benefit. So I ask you this: Is your love sincere, or are you just another fraud?"

Stanley handed Arthur an envelope and walked away.

He glanced down and sucked in a breath. An invitation to Mari- beth's coming out ball. Half of London's elite would be there in their finest clothes. All the gentlemen would laugh behind his back if he found the ballocks to claim what he so desperately wanted. That was a given.

All of London will spurn me. I cannot wear the latest fashions without exposing ... my past.

And yet Maribeth would mingle all evening with her head held high, because in the end, she didn't care what society thought of her. But she did care about her guardians' feelings. She would do this for them out of love.

You're a coward.

He wanted to be brave. Could he shed a lifetime of beliefs and become the man Maribeth deserved? He had one week to decide.

Chapter Twenty-Seven

"He isn't coming," Maribeth said, staring at the entrance of the crowded ballroom. She fidgeted with her dance card. The first two sets were blank, on reserve for Mr. Arthur Dunn. If he weren't so bloody stubborn, this night could be their engagement party instead of her coming out ball.

Edith stood on her tip-toes and scoured the ballroom floor. "You're certain he isn't already here among the guests? One can scarce move a single step without bumping into another person. I cannot believe he would decline an invitation from your father. No, he will come, I assure you."

Tears clogged Maribeth's throat. "How can he give me up so easily to another? The stubborn, wretched man! Papa has already given his blessing, and I don't care one wit about titles or blood lines."

"Nor does your former guardian," Edith said with a gentle smile. She nodded in the direction where Lord Covington stood beside Mr. Turner, introducing him to yet another elite member of London society. "I do believe the two men are well on their way to a lasting friendship. Just look at the line of ladies and gentlemen anxious to make your father's acquaintance. I still can't quite believe you are the daughter of Madame Brown."

"Yes, that makes for interesting small talk." A contented sigh passed through Maribeth's lips. The last week spent in Lord Covington's Piccadilly townhouse had, undoubtedly, surpassed all her expectations. With Dominick and Eveline acting as gracious host and hostess, there were no awkward moments while reacquainting herself with her father. He was a delightful man, both intelligent and charming.

"Chin up, Maribeth," her friend said, squeezing her hand. "This is your evening to shine. Your gown is stunning, and your dance card is full. If Mr. Dunn cannot see what a gem you are, he isn't worthy of your good opinion."

The deep gold ball gown was truly a masterpiece with delicate flowers stitched in burgundy thread and trimmed with leaves crafted from fine beads. The square neck décolletage was far more revealing than Maribeth was accustomed to but entirely appropriate for a woman of nearly twenty-one.

A waiter approached with a tray of champagne, and Maribeth swiped one glass. She offered another to her friend and took a sip. The sweet bouquet bloomed in her mouth, and she groaned. "Kill me now. The first set is about to begin, and I don't have a dance partner." She flicked open her fan and pumped the apparatus vigorously. "I'm a fool to have left the spot available."

A gracious smile spread over Edith's lips. Her friend nodded at someone behind Maribeth before raising her own fan to her lips. "Do *not* turn around, but I believe Lord Bolton is headed in our direction. He does you a great honor in asking for your hand in the first set."

Oh, goodness. Better that the floor cracked open and swallowed her whole. All eyes would be upon them throughout the dance. She sought out Dominick's gaze across the ballroom. He smiled and nodded. This was most certainly his fault, or that of his lady.

The first strains of a waltz started, announcing the beginning of the set. Maribeth swallowed and drew in air. She had practiced countless dances with her father all week. *Everyone will be watching Lord Bolton, not me.* At least there was that small consolation.

She turned, facing the dance floor, just as Lord Bolton bowed. His burgundy vest was adorned with fine gold stitching and complemented her dress to near perfection. She curtseyed and offered him a genuine smile.

"Good evening, Miss Sommerset." His sandy-brown hair was styled to perfection. He was incredibly tall, and she wondered whether she could reach his shoulders for the dance. "Would you do me the honor of dancing the first set with me?"

Her mouth felt unbearably dry. All she must do was nod, and yet she hesitated. *Arthur isn't coming. Accept the gentleman's offer.*

"Lord Bolton, thank you, that's very kind—"

"But Miss Sommerset already promised this set to me," a gentleman said from behind her. "And every single one thereafter."

She pressed her hands to her fluttering stomach but resisted the urge to squeal aloud. *Arthur came to claim her!* Still, the scoundrel ought to squirm a moment for waiting until the last possible second to appear. She whirled around and nearly melted from his dazzling smile.

★★★

"Excuse me, but you are rather bold," the impeccably dressed dandy standing beside Maribeth said. "The first two slots on Miss Sommerset's dance card are free, and I claimed them first."

Arthur met Lord Bolton's imperious glare head on. His stomach roiled as every single guest turned their focus on the three of them. Given his recent behavior, Maribeth ought to cut him to the quick. A bead of sweat trickled down the center of his back.

The orchestra grew louder, and couples began to line the dance floor, awaiting the guest of honor. Lord Bolton held out his arm to Maribeth with an easy air of confidence. The pompous ass could go hang himself if he thought Arthur would give up so easily.

Maribeth was the woman of his dreams. He captured her dazzling green eyes, and a warm smile spread over his lips. Propriety demanded she chose Lord Bolton, but she didn't fold under the rules of conduct.

He held out his arm. "Maribeth, who do you choose?"

She licked her lips and glanced between them. Her fingers hovered in midair, then she placed her hand on Lord Bolton's arm. Arthur's stomach clenched and he couldn't draw a breath as his world crumbled around him, but he held his head high.

"Thank you, Lord Bolton," she said. "But I cannot accept your offer when my heart is so wholly engaged by another. May I introduce my fiancé, Mr. Arthur Dunn."

The little minx! He hadn't asked for her hand. Yet.

The gentleman's eyebrows lifted. "I wasn't aware of your engagement."

"Well"—a blush stained her cheeks, and she smiled at Arthur—"we planned to announce the news tonight. You caught us by surprise."

Lord Bolton tipped his head in acknowledgment. "My congratulations."

Placing her gloved hand on Arthur's forearm, she let him escort her to the middle of the dance floor. His heart pounded in his breast, and his feet walked on air. He wrapped one arm around her waist and led her into the waltz.

"You are radiant tonight." He leaned in and said, "Forgive me for being tardy. I am the worst kind of jackal and deserved a set down in front of all your guests. For a moment, I thought Lord Bolton might call me out. Are you furious with me?"

Maribeth grinned. "Furious? No, I'm soaring like an eagle among the clouds. Did I not make myself plain? I want you and no one else. You are caught in my sticky web, never to escape again." Her eyes sparkled. "How do you feel about our engagement?"

"I cannot wrap my meager brain around that fact. Even after I was cruel," he said, his eyes hooded, "and deceived you, you still want me."

"You had cause for skepticism." She squeezed his hand. "I cannot fault you for that, given your childhood experiences. But in the end, you came around. The love and devotion you showed my father was admirable. Are you furious with me for entrapping you?"

"I'm not trapped," he said, pulling her closer. "I love you, Maribeth. But don't you know that the man is supposed to propose to the woman?"

She laughed, and the sound was sweeter than any melody the orchestra could play. "I don't need a grand gesture, Arthur. You're here with me. That's all I ever wished for. Tonight and forever. Together, we make a wonderful investigative team."

He raised an eyebrow. "You're planning to pursue your dream of becoming a psychic investigator? I rather thought you wished to become my wife."

"I'm a greedy sort of wench," she said with a smirk. "I want both. But I promise only to assist on cases in the vicinity of Chateau Swansea. Rumor has it, the town is haunted by many ghosts."

The music ended, and the guests clapped politely. Arthur guided her onto the balcony, away from prying eyes.

"You may have anything in my power to give," he said, kissing her hands, "so long as you stay by my side. All I've ever dreamed of is a home and family. Will you be my wife, Maribeth? Bella." He chuckled. "Whatever first name you choose, I want your surname to be Dunn."

She wrapped her arms around his neck and kissed him square on the lips. Propriety be damned. "Your wife, your partner, your best friend. Forever and always.

Thank you for reading *The Secrets of Chateau Swansea*. I hope this practical example from start to finish brought home all of the techniques you learned earlier in this book. In summary, I hope you noticed the following key messages:

- The majority of backstory was introduced in snippets of three sentences or less.
  - o Don't kill your story's pacing with long sections of backstory.
  - o Be vague to keep your reader's curiosity level high so they keep turning the pages.
- Longer passages revealed past events that impacted the heroine's GMC the most.
  - o Use the past to drive up the stakes of the character's GMC.
  - o These longer passages better pack a walloping punch.
- I used every method of incorporating backstory except a prologue (i.e. deep POV, dialogue, dreams, and flashbacks /memories), plus a few unique ideas such as suppressed memories, letters, and news articles.
  - o Variety is the spice of life and keeps the story fresh and interesting.
  - o Your readers will appreciate the creativity you bring to the story.
- Finally, twenty-two out of the twenty-seven chapters in the book include bits of backstory (i.e. all except twelve, fourteen, eighteen, twenty, and twenty-one).
  - o Weaving in backstory means bringing in bits and pieces throughout the current storyline, not dumping the information in the first few chapters.

I wish you the best of luck in your writing! Please drop me a line and let me know what wonderful and interesting methods you came up with to reveal backstory to your readers. I'd love to hear from you.